WITHD

MW01054539

Quality
N-1-98
29.95

70 Years
of Radio Tubes
and Valves

Second Edition

A Guide For
Electronic Engineers,
Historians and Collectors

by John W. Stokes

SONORAN
PUBLISHING, LLC
Chandler, Arizona

Sonoran Publishing, LLC., Chandler, Arizona 85226
© 1982, 1997 by John W. Stokes. All rights reserved
First edition published 1982
Second edition published 1997

Printed in the United States of America

Library of Congress Cataloging-in-Publication Data

Stokes, John W. (John Whitley)
    70 years of radio tubes and valves : a guide for electronic
engineers, historians and collectors / by John W. Stokes. -- 2nd ed.
        p.   cm.
    Includes bibliographical references and indexes.
    ISBN 1-886606-11-0 (pbk.)
    1. Vacuum-tubes--History. I. Title
    TK6565.V3S68   1997   97-13766
    621.384'132--dc21   CIP

Cover—*Known as a 'double-wing' Audion to distinguish it from earlier types, this De Forest Audion 1909 had two sets of plates and grids joined in parallel.*

Contents

Acknowledgements

I am indebted to the various individuals and organisations who have assisted, in one way or another, to complete this book. Chief amongst them are: Floyd Lyons of San Francisco, California, U.S.A., Fin Stewart of Sydney, N.S.W., and Lauren Peckham of Breesport, New York, U.S.A.

Others include: Thomas H. Briggs, Alan Douglas, Bro Patrick Dowd, Gerald F.J. Tyne, Dr. Henry E. Wenden (Ohio State University), all of U.S.A.

In Europe: A.J. Duivenstijn of The Evoluon and Franz Driesens, both of Philips, Holland, Chris Petsikoupolos of Athens, Greece, and George Jessop and John Ludlow, both of England.

Back here in New Zealand: George Askey, Stan Brehaut. Also Ian Thwaites, librarian, Auckland Museum.

George Weston assisted by reading through the typescript and spotting the errors.

A special thanks to my good friends Alan Douglas and Floyd Lyons (USA), Fin Stewart (Australia), and Stan Brehaut (New Zealand) who went to so much trouble to provide photographs of certain tubes in their collections.

Thanks are also due to the editors of *QST* (U.S.A.) and *Wireless World* (U.K.) for permission to use material from these publications. The General Electric Co., Schenectady, New York, gave permission to use material from a hitherto unpublished document entitled *The Development by the General Electric Company of Radio Receiving Tubes. March 1, 1929* (referred to in the text as 'GE Report').

Thanks are also due to others not mentioned by name who have helped in some way to complete this book.

And, last but not least, to my long-suffering wife who provided much needed encouragement and assistance—my special thanks.

J.W.S.

Nomenclature—Terminology

Throughout this book the term 'tube' has been used when speaking of all non-British developments and also when referring to vacuum tubes in general. In deference to Britishers, and this includes the residents of such English speaking countries as Australia and New Zealand, the term 'valve' has been used when referring to British developments. For English speaking people all other terminology, both in regard to tube structure and generic classification, is virtually identical. Those small variations which do occur are self explanatory.

Long before the first radio tube had appeared there had existed in the field of electro-chemistry a system of nomenclature which had arisen as a result of the special needs of the branch of electrical science concerned with the study of the flow of electric currents through liquids —electrolysis. The British scientist Michael Faraday was responsible for introducing these terms and it was Professor J.A. Fleming as convenor of a Nomenclature and Notation Committee of the Institution of Electrical Engineers who in 1886 put forward the terms for official adoption.

Some of these words were in turn later adopted in radio tube terminology, for example—anode, cathode, ion, and electrode. At the same time Fleming himself was responsible for other definitions used in connection with early types of discharge tubes, e.g., Geissler tubes and Crookes tubes, but only one of these is germane to radio:

'Vacuum Tube—A glass vessel containing air or other gas which has been rarified to a pressure at which the discharge ceases to be disruptive and takes the form of a glow or brush-like through the space, is called a vacuum tube'.[1]

This seems to be the earliest use of the term vacuum tube yet one cannot help wondering why at that time the more appropriate 'discharge tube' was not chosen, particularly as the presence of gas in the tube was an essential feature. In the event, discharge tubes continued to be referred to as 'tubes' and the device which was to become known as a 'vacuum tube' was not to appear until many years later.

Preface

Radio or 'wireless', used as a means of communication between the dwellers of this planet (whether earth-bound or astronautical) is of necessity a two-way affair, thus the basic requirements have always been a transmitter and a receiver. Because the radio tube was originally brought into being as a receiving device, and continued to be used exclusively in this role for over a decade, it follows that historically it must be accorded pride of place in any discussion of tube evolution. However, once the ability of the three-electrode tube to generate oscillations was discovered and put to use for the purpose of producing and transmitting continuous-wave radio signals, the transmitting tube quickly became equally important in the scheme of things and thus the peer of its receiving counterpart.

To many people and for many years the word tube meant only one thing—a 'radio' tube; that is, apart from its use as a scientific term for such earlier devices as Geissler tubes and X-ray tubes. To quote from the introduction to the RCA Transmitting Tube Manual TT3 of 1938:

> 'Vacuum tubes! The magic in these two words is best appreciated by the "Old Timers"—the amateurs, commercial and government operators who have followed the rapid progress of radio communication from its beginning'.

Radio was indeed a magic word and the aura of magic lingered for many years after broadcasting had become a part of everyday life. When in 1935 RCA marketed a novel form of electronic tuning indicator it was dubbed 'Magic Eye'. A year or so later the rather more staid Dutch firm of Philips was not above naming their version of the indicator 'Magic Star'.

In this book an attempt has been made to outline the evolution of radio receiving tubes and the part they played in the development of the domestic radio receiver. The information contained in the following pages is presented primarily for the benefit of tube collectors, particularly American tube collectors as there are more of them! At the same time it is hoped that the book will be of wider interest and will be a source of reference to all who are interested in the history and development of the vacuum tube.

Due to language difficulties no attempt has been made to fully document inventions and developments in countries other than England and U.S.A. Nevertheless, some information will be found on early work done in other countries, particularly when it has had a bearing on the course of tube development on a world-wide basis. To facilitate an understanding of the text it is suggested that the reader become familiar with the various terms mentioned in the following pages before plunging directly into the main body of the book.

Every effort has been made to ensure accuracy in the matter of dates and descriptions but the author welcomes any corrections or criticisms from any reader who feels inclined to write.

J. Whitley Stokes
Auckland, New Zealand.

Generic Vacuum Tube Terminology

Initially there was no need for any distinguishing nomenclature because as the three-electrode tube came into use the two-element type faded from the scene; thus for many years there was only one basic type of tube in use. Not until the advent of four-element tubes could any need have been felt for short simple names by which each basic type of tube could be referred to. Even the early four-element tubes played such an insignificant part in the scheme of things that the introduction of special generic names could hardly have been justified at the time. In fact it was not until the invention of the five-electrode tube in 1928 that the increasing complexity of tube development made it desirable, if not actually essential, to have a standardised system of terminology.

In 1919 Dr. W.H. Eccles, then of Manchester University, is credited with introducing the terms 'diode' and 'triode' to define two- and three-electrode tubes respectively. As in the case of other electrical borrowings the root words had the same honourable origins in classical Greek. However, Fleming would have none of this, at least as far as 'diode' was concerned. As the inventor of a two-electrode tube he seemed to consider it his prerogative to invent a name for it too. Fleming not only appeared to be quite upset to see his 'oscillation valve' referred to as a diode but also mistakenly assumes the objectionable word to have been of American origin as evidenced by the following:

'The importance of the invention is also shown by the determined attempts made by American wireless men to claim the invention for themselves and deprive the present writer of credit for it and remove his name from connection with it by re-christening identically the same invention by other strange names such as Audion, Kenotron, Tungar or Diode'.[2]

From the basic two-element tube, the diode, have sprung triode, tetrode, pentode, hexode, heptode (sexode), octode, and nonode. For the etymologically minded—a word of explanation. These composite words have been built up from the Greek word 'hodos', meaning a way or path, with the appropriate numerical index tacked on in front. In the case of a two-element tube the words di and hodos are united to become diode. It appears to be accepted practice when Anglicizing Greek words to drop the letter 'h' in the cause of euphony when it occurs between vowels.

However, if one stops to analyse the list there appear to be some inconsistencies. For example, in the case of tetrode, made up from tetra and hodos this could more properly have been rendered as tetra-ode or tet-hode. Similarly, in the case of pentode, pent-hode would have been better and indeed the five-element tube was for many years so referred to by its Dutch inventors. The only trouble here was that English speaking people habitually pronounce words in which the letters t and h are in conjunction with a 'th' sound, thus penthode was pronounced pen-thode, so making nonsense of the scheme.

Although this terminology has become accepted into all European languages it suffers from the drawback that its usefulness is limited solely to indicating the number of active electrodes operating in one electron stream, thus it fails to give any indication of the function of any particular tube. Furthermore, the original electrode terminology, anode and cathode, was inadequate for anything but two electrode tubes and as further electrodes, usually grids, were added new names had to be introduced to define them. Even the simple term grid was not always adequate once further grids were introduced—it became control grid. The additional grids were known as space-charge grids, screen-grids, suppressor grids, or velo grids depending on their particular functions.

REFERENCES

1. Quoted in *A Practical Elementary Manual of Electricity* by Andrew Jamieson, 8th edition 1914.

2. J.A. Fleming, The Thermionic Valve. Its Origin and Development, *Wireless World*, Sept. 30, 1925, pp. 417–422.

Chapter One

In the Beginning

The story of the thermionic valve or radio tube may be fairly said to have begun in 1880 with the discovery by Thomas Alva Edison that under certain conditions a current could be made to flow through a vacuum. This discovery was made in the following manner.

One of the difficulties Edison had encountered in connection with his carbon filament lamps was that after a period of use the inner surface of the glass bulb became progressively darkened and this had the effect of reducing the light output. In the course of investigating this problem Edison noticed two things: firstly that a thin clear line was visible on one side of any bulb that had become darkened and secondly this line, or slit as it could more accurately be described, was always in line with the plane of the filament. Furthermore, when the bulb finally burnt out the break always occurred at the negative end of the filament. In this respect it is important to realise that Edison was working exclusively with direct current (DC) and that these statements would only hold true if the polarity of the supply were not reversed during the lifetime of the bulb or, alternatively, if the bulb had not been reversed in its socket during this period.

During the course of his investigation Edison formed the idea that there might be some previously unsuspected current flowing in the bulb. How right he was! To test his theory he had an experimental bulb prepared, inside which a metal plate with a lead-out wire attached was mounted. With this bulb he discovered that when the lead from the plate was connected through an indicating meter to the positive side of the filament a current flow could be observed. This phenomenon was quite inexplicable at the time and indeed remained so for several years. And, as if to make things even more confusing, the 'carrying current', as Edison called it, could be made to flow in only one direction, that is with the meter connected as described. No current could be observed when the plate return lead was connected to the negative side of the filament. To put this in more modern terminology it may be simply said that the space current can be made to flow only when the plate is maintained at a positive potential with respect to the cathode. In Edison's case the positive side of the 110-volt DC line provided the necessary 'plate voltage' whilst the more negative portion of the filament constituted the 'cathode'.

Edison himself made no attempt to explain the phenomenon, which is not surprising as it defied explanation for several years. Nor does it seem likely that the uni-directional nature of the space current could have had any significance to him. After all, he was working solely with uni-directional current all his life. Nevertheless, Edison, being Edison, was canny enough to realise that perhaps somebody else might find a use for his discovery so took steps to invent a device embodying it whereby he could obtain a patent. To this end he devised an electrical indicator which could be used to indicate variations in the voltage of his electrical supply system. This device was patented on October 21, 1884 (U.S. Patent no. 307,031), and the patent is now generally recognised as being the world's first electronics patent.

No evidence has ever been forthcoming to show that the idea had any particular merit, nor was it ever developed any further.

As there has been some controversy as to just what the device was and what function it fulfilled it is worthwhile trying to set the record straight. After reading through the patent specifications and examining the accompanying sketches it seems evident that, although a workable device, it was in essence little more than a form of moving-iron voltmeter. An examination of the basic circuit (Fig. 1) shows that although variations in the filament temperature and plate voltage, caused by variations in the line voltage, obviously affected the space current through the bulb the resultant indication could just as easily have been obtained by operating the meter coil directly without the intervening bulb. Whilst it is possible that any element of non-linearity introduced into the circuit by the bulb would have affected the working, any such non-linearity would have been incidental and by no means essential to the operation of the device.

In practice the main effect of the bulb was to reduce the

1

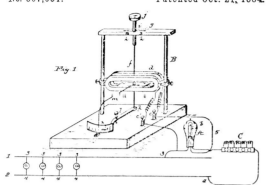

Drawing from the world's first electronics patent. Note lamp 'A' in circuit.

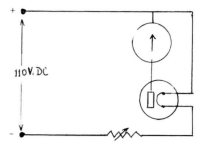

110 V. DC

Fig. 1
Basic circuit of Edison's 1884 patent for an electrical indicator. The galvanometer was mechanically pre-set to give a zero centre-scale indication under normal working conditions.

line voltage to a suitable value to operate the meter; a resistor could have done the job quite as effectively. So, although Edison did create a workable device incorporating his discovery, the device had little merit. All that can really be said for the idea was that it enabled him to obtain a valid patent, and that was probably all he ever had in mind.

In formulating an opinion as to whether the bulb was actually a rectifier, as has sometimes been claimed, it is only necessary to bear in mind the fact the patented device was designed solely for use on direct current. Furthermore, Edison himself was first and last a DC-only man and could have had no conception of the basic principle of rectification. He was utterly opposed to the very idea of an alternating current supply system and was always at loggerheads with his rival George Westinghouse, the chief protagonist of AC. This being the case the question of whether the bulb was a rectifier cannot arise; the fact that alternating current was not involved should make this self evident. If the bulb was never used on AC then its unilateral conductivity could never have had any significance. If Edison made no use of this one-way feature then he did not invent a rectifier.

The fact that the bulb was in essence a diode and *could* have been used as a rectifier is beside the point and does not, by any stretch of the imagination, constitute an invention.

In the same year that Edison had received his patent, 1884, a British 'electrician' John Ambrose Fleming (later Sir Ambrose Fleming) who had attended a meeting of the British Association held in Montreal that year also visited the United States. Fleming had a younger brother by the name of Howard living in New Jersey whom he visited on this occasion in addition to calling on Mr. Edison in July of the same year.

At this time Fleming was scientific adviser to the Edison & Swan Electric Light Co. of London and his visit to

Edison was in connection with problems of electric light distribution. It is not known whether Fleming was shown any of Edison's experimental bulbs on this occasion but it seems unlikely in view of subsequent events. Fleming himself makes no mention of it in any of his writings.

Another visitor calling on Edison that same year was William Henry Preece, Chief Engineer of the British Post Office. Preece, whose name was later to become well known in connection with wireless matters through his close association with the young Marconi, was in America to attend an International Electrical Exhibition being held in Philadelphia. In October 1884 Preece was given samples of Edison's mysterious bulbs which he in turn passed on to Fleming after carrying out experiments of his own. It is Preece who is credited with coining the term 'Edison effect' to describe the phenomenon of the space current in the bulbs.

Fleming, who in 1885 had been appointed Professor of Electrical Engineering at London University College, decided to carry out further investigations of the Edison effect. Accordingly, he had some experimental carbon-filament lamps made up for him by the Edison & Swan Co.'s factory. In each lamp a metal plate was incorporated and observations made on these bulbs enabled Fleming to confirm Edison's discovery of the unilateral conductivity of the space between filament and plate. Additionally, he also noticed the appearance of the thin clear line on one side of the inner surface of any bulb that had become darkened through use. Fleming gave the name 'molecular shadow' to this phenomenon. At that time he believed the darkening coupled with the appearance of the line to be solely due to the evaporation of the carbon filament and it was not until the discovery of the electron in 1897 by J.J. Thompson that further light was shed on the matter. In 1896 after completion of the experiments the lamps were put away in a cupboard of Fleming's laboratory where they were to lie forgotten for several years.

In addition to his professorship Fleming had in 1899 accepted a position as scientific adviser to the newly formed Marconi Company. In 1901 Marconi had decided to attempt to transmit wireless signals across the Atlantic and Fleming was requested to design the power generating equipment needed to supply the transmitter. On this historic occasion a coherer had been used as a detector at the receiving end. Disadvantages associated with such detectors had led Marconi to invent a practical form of Rutherford's magnetic detector some six months later. This new device whilst inherently stable in operation was somewhat insensitive but in the absence of anything better became the standard detector in Marconi equipment for many years. Meanwhile, the search for a better detector continued.

As is now generally known it was Fleming's search in this direction which gave him the inspiration to try one of his experimental lamps, which had previously been found capable of rectifying locally produced oscillations, as a detector of the weak signals present in a receiving aerial. What is not so well known is that Fleming had a personal motive which activated his search for a better, or, rather *different*, detector. Like his contemporary Edison he was hard of hearing and was unable to read signals aurally, thus he desired to find a detector which could be used to provide a visual indication of received signals. Fleming was later to write:

'Hence the author was desirous, if possible, of finding some method of working a sensitive relay by means of the feeble damped oscillations or intermittent telephone currents. Furthermore, having become the subject of a progressive deafness the writer desired to find some instrument to record radiotelegraphic signals which would appeal to the eye and not the ear'.[1]

Many years later, in a magazine article written in 1931 and entitled 'My Wireless Memories and Inventions', Fleming wrote:

'I was familiar with the use of the mirror galvanometer of Lord Kelvin, as used for submarine cable signalling, and wished to adapt it for wireless signalling. To do this it was necessary to rectify or convert into direct current the feeble alternating currents in the receiving aerial. After some ineffective experiments with electrolytic rectifiers, my old experiments in 1890 with vacuum tube rectifiers occurred to me and before long I asked my assistant to set up two large square coils which we had and to create electric oscillation in one coil and in the other coil circuit to include a mirror galvanometer and also one of the vacuum bulbs I had formerly made which contained a carbon loop filament and a metal plate. When the filament was made incandescent by a battery I knew that the space between filament and plate would convey negative electricity only in one direction.

Replica of an Edison 110-volt carbon-filament lamp compared with a commercial version of a Fleming diode.

Early unbased version of a Fleming Oscillation valve. Royal Ediswan c. 1905.

The matter to be ascertained was, however, whether this would hold true for very high frequency currents. A single experiment proved that it did. Therefore I asked the Edison & Swan Electric Light Company to make me a dozen 12-volt carbon filament lamps, and to place round each loop filament a metal cylinder connected to a wire sealed through the bulb.

If then a mirror galvanometer or telephone [earpiece] had one terminal attached to this cylinder, and the negative end of the filament (made incandescent by a local battery) was connected to another wire and the two placed as a shunt across the condenser of a wireless receiving circuit, this VALVE, as I called it, would rectify the alternating current and detect it. Hence was born into the radio world the first thermionic or Fleming valve'.*

*In view of an earlier patent by A. Wehnelt in January 1904 the reader is left to judge for himself whether Fleming was justified in claiming to have invented the world's first thermionic valve.

Thus it was twenty years after the start of his original experiments before Fleming found a practical use for his 'Oscillation Valve'. Now, however, the potentialities of this application caused him to lose no time in applying for British, German, and American patents.[2] These patents,

Photo courtesy Museum of Applied Arts & Sciences, N.S.W.
Two commercial versions of Fleming's 'Oscillation Valve' by 'Royal Ediswan.' The smaller has a 4-volt filament, the larger has a 12-volt filament c. 1905–06.

when granted, did not belong to Fleming personally as in the terms of his agreement with the Marconi Co. any patents were to become the property of that company. In later years this was to be the cause of some heartburning on Fleming's part for he once complained:

'As the original inventor of the thermionic valve I have never received a single penny for it, other than the retainer paid to me for years by the Marconi Company'.

The next step was to see if the oscillation detector valve could be of use in commercial equipment. Fleming sent some of the new valves to Marconi's and after tests they were duly put into service in two models of that firm's receivers. In one model a second (spare) valve was mounted on the panel alongside the one in use and wired to allow immediate changeover in the event of failure.

In spite of their proved abilities it should not be imagined that these new valves were an instant success which swept away all other existing detectors. For one thing they were no more reliable, stable, or sensitive than the carborundum mineral detector which was being used by Marconi's as an alternative to the magnetic detector and which remained in use until long after the end of World War I.

At much the same time on the other side of the Atlantic, the problem of finding a satisfactory detector was also occupying the mind of an American inventor, Dr. Lee de Forest. De Forest's need for a detector had been brought about through different circumstances from those which gave birth to the Fleming valve. As inventor of the De Forest 'system' of wireless telegraphy his pressing need at

that time was for a 'non-infringing' detector—a type of detector which he could use without running the risk of legal action by any competitors. In those days the owners of the various competing systems jealously guarded their respective patents and perhaps somewhat naturally refused to grant licenses to competitors.

De Forest had been using in his receivers a slightly modified form of an electrolytic detector invented by the owner of a rival wireless system, R.A. Fessenden. In 1905 after being prevented from further use of this detector by legal action De Forest cast about for a substitute and this led directly to his use of a two-element thermionic tube which was, in essence, a Fleming valve. In the matter of how he came to use the vacuum tube detector De Forest always maintained that it was an extension of earlier work with an experimental gas-flame detector. After all, he could hardly afford to say otherwise without acknowledging the validity of Fleming's American patent. In a magazine article written in 1940 De Forest wrote:

'By 1905 I had advanced to the point where I was using a carbon filament lamp to heat the attenuated gasses in a glass tube. In connection with this bulb I used, as I had always used in my gas flame experiments, a telephone receiver with a B battery connected between the plate and filament in the bulb. The device was not a rectifier but a genuine relay detector whereby the electric waves produced marked changes in the battery current which was flowing through the tube'.[3]

It was over the matter of the B battery that De Forest took his stand, for it was through its use that he claimed an essential difference from Fleming's valve. Nevertheless, the Marconi Co. thought otherwise and prosecution eventually ensued—but that is another and oft told story. We now know that both devices were diode rectifiers differing in that whereas Fleming's worked near the bottom of the characteristic curve, De Forest's, by the addition of a 22½-

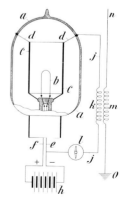

Drawing of an 'Oscillation Valve' and its associated circuit taken from British Patent Application No. 24850 dated Nov. 16, 1904.

volt battery, worked on the top portion of the curve where the tube was approaching saturation point.

De Forest's first commercial use of these 'Audions', as they had been named by his assistant C.D. Babcock, was in 1906 at a U.S. naval wireless station at Key West, Florida. In later years this led to the name 'Key West' Audions being applied to them. So it is a matter of record that although De Forest later became famous for his invention of the 'grid' Audion he did produce and use a diode detector at much the same time as had Fleming.

REFERENCES

1. J.A. Fleming, *The Thermionic Valve in Radiotelegraphy & Telephony,* p. 48.

2. British Patent Application 24850, Nov. 16, 1904; German Patent DRP 186,084 granted 1905; U.S. Patent 803,648 granted 1905.

3. Lee de Forest, The History of the Vacuum Tube, *Radio News,* Dec. 1940, p. 48.

Chapter Two

The Grid

Probably no other aspect of vacuum tube history has been more widely discussed than the invention of the triode by Lee de Forest. This invention represented the vital step whereby, in modern terminology, the vacuum tube underwent the transition from a passive to an active device. In spite of the fact that the creation of this completely new type of tube was to bring its inventor undying fame it was also to involve him in a great deal of strife, one way or another, but through it all his status as 'the man who put the grid in the vacuum tube' was never in question. It is only in De Forest's accounts of how he came to add the vital third electrode, wherein he denies that his Audion owed anything to Fleming's diode valve, that his word has been called into question.

In the previous chapter it was related how De Forest's search for a detector that did not infringe existing patents, particularly those of his rival Fessenden, led him to use a two-electrode tube for this purpose. It was the indifferent results obtained when using such a device which caused De Forest to experiment with various ways of connecting the tube into the tuned circuit. Initially it had been connected directly across the circuit and the resultant losses when so connected prompted him to try another approach. The next step was to connect the aerial to a piece of tinfoil wrapped around the outside of the bulb. Encouraged by the resultant improvement De Forest then hit upon the idea of inserting an additional electrode inside the bulb, and thus the triode was born.[1]

The acorn from which the mighty oak tree was to grow had been planted!

Originally the new 'control' electrode took the form of a metal plate, of the same size and shape as the existing anode, positioned on the opposite side of the filament. Further encouraged by the results obtained De Forest's next step was to insert a perforated metal plate in the space between the filament and anode, thereby inventing a rudimentary grid.

So far the development of the new tube had occurred during the short space of time following the use of the Key West Audions in October 1906 and December of the

Lee de Forest and his Audion.

same year. It was still only December when De Forest conceived the idea of forming the third electrode from a piece of wire bent into a zig-zag shape. Rather obviously it was the resemblance of the new electrode to a metal grid-iron that led to its being dubbed a 'grid'. In the event, its shape remained unaltered during the production lifetime of such tubes, a matter of some twenty years.

De Forest patented the earliest form of three-element tube, the one containing two plates, in 1906.[2] This is the now famous patent wherein the tube is described as: 'a device for amplifying feeble electrical currents', but without a proper grid it is difficult to envisage how such a tube could be capable of amplification. Shortly afterwards came another patent, this time for a tube with a grid interposed between filament and anode.[3] By comparison the specifications of this patent referred only to: 'Wireless telegraphy receivers or oscillation detectors'. In spite of the reference to amplifying properties in the original patent De Forest made no use of the tube for any other purpose than detection. In fact some six years were to elapse before he or anyone else recognised the amplifying possibilities of the Audion.

In its original form the 'grid' Audion was constructed along similar lines to its two-electrode predecessor; a tubular bulb of similar size and shape was used with the grid and plate leads sealed directly through the upper side walls. A little later a stem seal (press) was used at each end of the bulb and this style of construction was retained even after the use of tubular bulbs was discontinued. The filament connections were terminated to a standard American 'candelabra' lamp base (a screw base slightly larger than standard miniature Edison screw type) whilst the grid and plate connections were in the form of flying leads taken through the opposite end of the bulb.

This change was made purely as a matter of manufacturing convenience and no alteration was made to the size, shape, or spacing of the electrodes themselves.

A further change occurred in 1908 when two separate filaments were fitted, one of which was activated whilst the other was held in reserve as a spare. When the first filament burnt out the second could be brought into use by connecting up a wire lead provided. In 1909 a second plate and grid were placed on the unused side of the filament thus making better use of the available emission. The two sets of plates and grids were normally joined internally when the resultant tube became known as a double-wing Audion.

Up to about 1913 or 1914 tantalum had been used as a filament material but because it was softer than tungsten it had a tendency to warp in service. To overcome this drawback a change was made to tungsten but it was then found that the emission was lower than previously. In an attempt to improve matters a few turns of tantalum wire were wrapped around the central curved part of the filament and tubes so treated were described as having 'Hudson' filaments, the name being that of the inventor of the process. Because of manufacturing difficulties associated with

A McCandless motor-car lamp. The G-16½ bulb was also used for Audion manufacture.

Lamps or Audions McCandless made them both.

Single-wing Audion 1908, note spare filament lead.

Left: First commercial De Forest Audion c. 1908. Right: De Forest 'double' Audion c. 1914.

Because the tubes were made for De Forest by a manufacturer of electric lamps—the H.W. McCandless Co. of New York—it follows that lamp-making techniques were used in their construction. However, as tubular bulbs were not normally used in lamp manufacture McCandless early in 1907 suggested that the glass work could be simplified by using readily available stock-sized G-16½ automotive lamp bulbs. In American lamp-making parlance the letter G stood for globular (shape) and the following numerals indicated the diameter in eighths of an inch. The suggestion was accepted by De Forest and thereafter, apart from the tubular type T of 1916, spherical bulbs remained in use for as long as first generation tubes were in production.

wrapped filaments this technique was soon discarded in favour of coating the central portion of the filament with a paste made from finely ground tantalum.

Because McCandless was the sole source of supply for the De Forest Audions he was in effect the sole manufacturer of tubes in the U.S., at least up to 1915 when the first of the so-called 'independent' manufacturers entered the field. Details of this aspect of tube manufacture will be found in the section dealing with early U.S. independents.

During 1914 the McCandless Co. was taken over by Westinghouse[4] who carried on production of miniature lamps under the name McCandless Westinghouse until 1916. With the closure of the McCandless works De For-

7

est was left without a source of supply and consequently had to undertake tube manfacture himself. As it happened De Forest had recently set up a factory located in Sedgewick Ave. in the Bronx district of New York (sometimes referred to as the High Bridge factory) and by late 1914 or early 1915 was turning out spherical Audions as well as 'Oscillion' transmitting tubes.[5]

In addition to the spherical Audions a completely different tube, known as type 'T', was introduced early in 1916. This tube had a tubular bulb of small diameter and closely resembled the Cunningham AudioTron in appearance, though it differed in having only a single filament.

However, hardly had De Forest's High Bridge factory settled down to making tubes when the handing down of a Court decision in September 1916 on a legal action, earlier brought by American Marconi against De Forest for infringement of the Fleming patent, prevented further manufacture. This decision resulted in a stalemate situation whereby both parties were prevented from manufacturing triodes because in doing so each company infringed on the other's patents. By the same token no one else could make or sell triode tubes either. Thus the General Electric Co., who by then had done a considerable amount of research and experimental work, were also prevented from commercial manufacture. The Telephone Company on the other hand were free to make tubes for landline telephone work as these were not affected by the Court decision. Before the full effects of the decision had time to be felt America became embroiled in World War I when in April 1917 the U.S. declared war on Germany with the result that all amateur wireless stations were closed down and all commercial stations taken over by the U.S. Navy.

Single-wing Audion with Hudson filament c. 1914.

With the invention of the grid Audion De Forest had set in motion a train of events that was to lead to the vacuum tube becoming the key element around which for the next half century the future development of both receivers and transmitters would hinge. In spite of this De Forest himself played a very minor part in determining the

course of events, even though he had taken out no less than fourteen vacuum tube patents between the years 1906 and 1909.

It has been stated that when used as a detector the triode Audion performed little better than a plain diode, and in view of what must have been its extremely low efficiency this is not surprising. Once having achieved a workable device De Forest appeared content to leave things as they were, with the result that it was left to others to carry on the development of better tubes and their associated circuitry. Not that De Forest was by any means idle during this period for by 1949 he had over 200 patents to his credit in the field of electronics.

Because the so-called 'soft' tube, i.e., one containing a comparatively poor vacuum, had been found to be considerably more sensitive than a 'hard' tube when used as a detector this fact actually hindered its development as an amplifier. Not until the ability of a vacuum tube to oscillate in a controlled manner, as a regenerative detector or as a heterodyne oscillator for CW reception and finally as a transmitting oscillator, did tubes really come into their own. By this time (1914) Armstrong in the U.S., Franklin in England, and Meissner in Germany had all developed circuits using an oscillating tube. In the case of the regenerative detector the tube had to be operated at just below the point of oscillation so that it could more correctly be said to be operating as a positive feedback amplifier.

During this period the characteristics of the triode were being examined scientifically for the first time which for one thing led to an appreciation of the importance of a high degree of vacuum before stable amplification could be accomplished. Similarly, once the laboratories of such concerns as Western Electric and General Electric got to work on the audion (a generic name by then) it was not long before more efficient, more reliable, and more economical tubes appeared. Unfortunately, however, apart from tubes made by Western Electric for telephone use no others could legally be sold or used commercially in the U.S. due to patent restrictions. Even De Forest, it will be recalled, could no longer sell tubes after September 1916.

The development of the three-electrode receiving tube initially took place in two main areas—the improvement of its operating characteristics and economy of its operation, particularly filament-heating economy. When it is realised that bright emitter tubes required from 4 to 5 watts of heating power the practical difficulties of supplying these requirements, particularly when several tubes were in use, assumed considerable importance. Starting with an emissive efficiency of 1 mA per watt of filament power for plain tungsten this was by 1923 improved to 25 mA per watt for thoriated tungsten and by 1930 to 250 mA per watt for oxide-coated filaments—a quite dramatic increase within such a short period.

As for improvements in operating characteristics, particularly in the all important figure-of-merit, mutual conductance, these did not keep pace with improvements in emission, probably because an acceptable balance had to be maintained between performance and economy of operation. Nevertheless, certain British battery-operated output triodes had, by 1931, attained the remarkably high mutual conductance figure of 4 mA/V (4000 micromhos), a figure which represented a practical limit and which was not improved on in later years.

REFERENCES

1. Lee de Forest, *The Father of Radio*, p. 214.
2. U.S. Patent 841,387 applied for Oct. 25, 1906 issued Jan. 15, 1907.
3. U.S. Patent 879,532 applied for June 29, 1907 issued Feb. 18, 1908.
4. Lee de Forest, *The Father of Radio*, p. 332.
5. Ibid., p. 333.

Chapter Three

World War I

British Developments

Prior to the outbreak of World War I little developmental work on radio vaves had occurred in the U.K. apart from limited commercial use of Fleming's two-electrode detector by the Marconi Co. This was probably because of the monopolistic position enjoyed by Marconi with the consequent lack of competitors seeking improved detectors. Be that as it may, the triode remained largely a laboratory curiosity until called into use by the exigency of wartime demands. In later years even Fleming himself admitted to being 'too busy' at the time to develop his oscillation valve any further.

However, things were not entirely at a standstill in the pre-war years as between 1911 and 1914 some work had been done by H.J. Round of the Marconi Co. who was responsible for the design of several types of 'soft' valves intended for both transmitting and receiving use. By August 1914 Britain was at war with Germany so that subsequent developmental work on Round's original designs occurred during the war.

The Round valve was characterized by having a thin tubular extension on the top of the bulb which in English parlance was referred to as the 'pip'. This pip contained a pellet of asbestos which could be heated, usually with a match flame, in order to modify the degree of vacuum as required. The larger transmitting types had cylindrical anodes which were arranged to bear against the inner surface of the bulbs in order to facilitate cooling by oil immersion.

Round valves were used to a limited extent in certain models of Marconi equipment; for instance, the type N was used in the model 27 receiver and the types C and TN in the 'Short Distance' radio telephone. In addition to this the British Post Office made limited use of the valves for telephone repeater work. As with all soft valves they were somewhat erratic in operation and in this case also required expert operators handy with the match flame.

Another soft valve of different construction was known as the 'White' valve and made its appearance during the

war when it found limited application in Army radio equipment.

Undoubtedly the most successful European wartime tube was the so-called 'French' design attributed to Biquet and Peri working under the direction of General Ferrie of the French Military Telegraph Service. The standardised French design was manufactured by two companies under the brandnames Fotos and Métal and was known as type TM (Telegraphie Militaire). It was characterised by a high

French Metal 'TM' tube.

10

degree of vacuum and a horizontally mounted cylindrical (co-axial) electrode assembly. A spherical bulb fitted with a 4-pin base was used and it is interesting to note that this type of base eventually became the post-war European standard although not adopted by Germany until after 1925. The British rights to the Biquet and Peri patents were acquired by the Marconi Co. and formed the basis for most of the early British post-war designs. Similarly, the French design was also used in Holland and even crossed the Atlantic where it was used by Westinghouse in their WR21 tube.

The success of the French tube soon led to its becoming used as a standardised type by the Allied armies. Manufacture of a British version, which became known as the 'R' type, was first undertaken in 1916 by several electric lamp manufacturers including GEC-Osram, B.T-H Ediswan, and Met-Vick. Subsequent developmental work resulted in the production of several variants such as types R2, R2A, R3, R4, R4B, R4C, and R5. Of these the R2 and R4A made by Osram and the NR4C made by Mullard were fitted with American style candelabra-screw bases as used on the De Forest spherical Audions. The 'base' was cemented to the top of the bulb, covering the seal-off tip, and the filament leads connected to it were draped around the outer surface of the bulb. On viewing the resultant oddity one might be pardoned for imagining it to be a rather nightmarish version of a De Forest spherical Audion, and this is exactly what it was. The reason for its production was the obvious need for a British-made replacement for the originally used De Forest tubes which were by 1917 either difficult or impossible to procure due to wartime conditions. As Audions had been used in British naval and military receivers the availability of replacements was of some importance and so it was that the R valve was adapted for this purpose in the manner described.

Other variants of the R valve were the A, made by B.T-H and the B, made by B.T-H and Osram. In the case of the type R5 the electrode assembly was considerably smaller and at the same time a much smaller (tubular) bulb, measuring about one inch in diameter, was used. An unusual cup-shaped moulded base was fitted which enclosed part of the lower end of the bulb. The base was provided with three contact studs, the fourth connection being taken via a thin copper strip to another contact stud cemented to the top of the bulb. Two other valves of similar construction were the types C and D made for the Royal Flying Corps. Because of the symmetrical arrangement of the contacts used on these three valves it was possible to wrongly insert them into their mounting clips. To guard against this possibility the letters A and G were moulded in raised characters alongside the respective anode and grid contacts; in addition some valves have been sighted in which the word TOP appeared between the letters A and G.

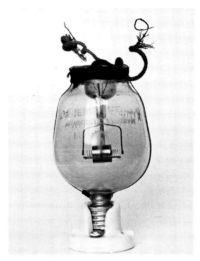

Mullard NR4C (Candelabra base).

OSRAM R.2 (Candelabra base).

Two of the most famous wartime valves were the Marconi types Q and V.24, the design of which was due to Capt. H.J. Round of the Marconi Co. These valves utilised a unique form of construction whereby all four lead-out wires were taken to widely-spaced contact points mounted on the surface of the bulb. This design resulted from circuit requirements calling for valves having very low inter-electrode capacitances for use in cascade stages of RF amplification where valves of conventional construction were unsuitable. The Q was intended for use as a detector and the V.24 for use as an amplifier.

It has proved difficult to obtain authoritative information regarding the date of introduction of these two valves. Some sources give 1919 but Round himself states 'issued in 1916'[1] and this is confirmed by the American E.H. Armstrong who, at that time, was a captain in the U.S. Army Signal Corps and who called on Round in London in 1917.[2]

Towards the end of World War I, or shortly afterwards, each of the three British Armed Services adopted its own system of type numbering. In the case of the Senior Service all type numbers commenced with the letter N, which

11

presumably stood for Navy. This was followed by one or more letters indicating very broadly the valve's function, while the following numerals indicated the sequence of issue. Thus NR indicated Naval receiving, NT indicated Naval transmitting, NS indicated Naval stabiliser or regulator, NU indicated Naval rectifier, and NGT indicated Naval gas-filled triode or thyratron.

Army Type Numbering System

British Army valves used a first letter A (for Army) and, as in the Navy system, the following letters indicated whether a particular type was intended for receiving or transmitting use. The Army system was distinguished by a more detailed classification of function which was expanded as the need arose; by World War II it included twelve different categories.

AR	= triode	ARTH	= triode-hexode
ARD	= diode	ARTP	= triode-pentode
ARDD	= duo-diode	AW	= stabiliser or tuning indicator
ARH	= hexode	AT	= transmitting triode
ARP	= pentode	ATS	= transmitting tetrode
ARS	= screen-grid	AU	= transmitting rectifier

Air Force Numbering System

Valves used by the Royal Air Force carried the initial letter V (indicating valve) followed by a second letter R or T which indicated whether a particular valve was a receiving or transmitting type. However, as some receiving valves bore VT numbers there is some uncertainty as to the application of this rule. As in the case of the Army system further letters were included as different classes of valves came into use and by World War II there were seven different categories.

VCR	= cathode-ray tube	VT	= transmitting valve
VG	= gas triode	VI	= tuning indicator
VR	= receiving valve	VU	= rectifier
VS	= stabiliser or regulator		

Marconi V24. Low-capacitance triode.

Towards the end of World War II a new common system of type numbering was adopted by the three armed services in which all valves were identified by the prefix CV (Common Valve). This was in line with American practice where the formerly separate Army and Navy numbering systems were replaced by the single 'JAN' (Joint Army Navy) system.

American Developments

America's entry into World War I in 1917 was the signal for a revolution in tube-making techniques, techniques which were to have far-reaching effects after the end of the war. By the time the U.S. entered the war radio was playing an increasingly important part in naval and military communications and this was reflected in the growing demands for radio tubes. While pre-war demands had easily been met by the De Forest Co. and the Western Electric Co. these two companies could not cope with the greatly increased wartime demands.

Although the De Forest Co.'s High Bridge factory supplied many thousands of tubes to the U.S. government during the war production facilities were inadequate to supply all America's wartime needs. The Western Electric Co., on the other hand, were geared solely to the production of telephone repeater tubes, the design of which was quite unsuited to military applications, and in any case the factory production techniques could not be adapted to large-scale production. Because of this situation it became necessary to turn to the lamp manufacturers who were the only people with sufficient expertise in mass production techniques to handle the problem. This is where the General Electric and Westinghouse companies, both of whom had extensive lamp-making experience and the necessary facilities, entered the picture.

For the duration of the war any company able to do so could make tubes for military use under government-granted freedom from patent infringement proceedings and thus the stage was set for large-scale production. However, before production could get under way it was necessary to decide on standardised designs and basing arrangements. Many difficulties were encountered but they were eventually overcome and in December 1917, nine months after America had entered the war, the first order was received from the U.S. Navy for 1000 tubes.[3] These tubes were designated CG-886 and were fitted with a base made from a black composition material. Three contact pins were fitted to the bottom while the side locking pin also served as the fourth contact. Another Navy tube using the same contact arrangement was the Western Electric 201-A but in this case a metal shell base was used.

The U.S. Army Signal Corps, on the other hand, had been using tubes specially made for military use by Western Electric but the company was unable to meet wartime demands. After consultations between the Signal Corps and Western Electric it was decided that the WE designs were not adaptable to being made on lamp-making machinery and it was left to GE to develop their own designs which were required to have the same electrical characteristics as the WE tubes.

First production was GE's version of the type VT-1, which in its original WE form had an oxide-coated filament and a grid punched from sheet metal—the so-called 'ladder' grid. Because the GE version, which was known as VT-11, had a 4-volt filament rating as compared to the 2-volt rating of the VT-1 it was necessary to make provision in the receiver to enable the use of either type of tube without the need for any wiring changes. This was done incorporating individual dropping resistors wired to each tube socket which were automatically shorted out when using the GE tubes.[4] The VT-11 tubes had one side of the filament connected to the metal base shell in addition to its being connected to the appropriate base pin in the normal way. In the receiver all the metal shells of the tube sockets were wired to one side of the battery so that when using GE tubes the resistors were shorted out.

Some idea of the GE undertaking can be obtained when it is known that the initial Signal Corps order was for 80,000 tubes, beginning at the rate of 500 a week and increasing to 6000 a week within six months.[5] A further

General Electric VT11.

order for 20,000 tubes was received in June 1918 and the Navy placed an order for 10,000 tubes of the same type (Naval designation was CG-890). Production of transmitting tubes for both services had also commenced at about this time.

Apart from GE and WE the only other American wartime tube manufacturers were De Forest and Moorhead. Moorhead tubes were made by Otis B. Moorhead of San Francisco who secured contracts to supply both the American and British governments. For the British orders the tubes supplied were almost identical to the standard French and British wartime designs which makes it obvious that the Moorhead tubes had to be completely interchangeable with them. Two versions were made, one marked 'R' which had a spherical bulb and a vertically mounted electrode assembly, while the other had a stubby tubular bulb and a horizontal electrode assembly and was marked V.T.32. Both types were fitted with the standard Franco-British type 4-pin bases, the bases themselves being made by Shaw using that company's patent moulding process. Moorhead tubes made for the U.S. Navy were of similar construction to those made for the British government but were fitted with a Shaw 4-prong Navy type

Western Electric 201A. Note 3-pin 'Navy' base c. 1917.

base. These tubes were designated SE1444 by the Navy and it is interesting to note that the prefix 'SE' stood for the Bureau of Steam Engineering!

Amongst wartime tubes made by De Forest were the types VT 21 made for the Signal Corps and the CF 185 made for the Navy. The VT 21 is notable as being the first De Forest tube to employ a welded grid which was fabricated in a unique 'chevron' formation, The CF 185 is interesting because it embodies two features otherwise unique to Western Electric tubes—the use of an oxide-coated filament and the use of a glass arbour to support

De Forest
CF185   VT21

Moorhead
VT32   R

Western Electric VT1 and VT2.

the top of the elements. Where the CF 185 tube differed was that the vertical sections of the glass arbour were used as lateral supports to wind the grid on. A 3-pin base made of a black composition material was used on this tube, the side locking pin being used for the fourth connection. This was the original so-called 'Navy' base.

As mentioned earlier, the style of construction used in Western Electric tubes was not adaptable to mass production methods and in any case the use of a glass support rod with its resulting fragility rendered the tubes far from ideal for military use. True, in the case of the type VT 1 the construction was modified by eliminating the glass rod entirely and the resultant tube was very rugged indeed.

REFERENCES

1. H.J. Round, *The Shielded Four Electrode Valve*, Cassel, 1927.

2. E.H. Armstrong speaking at 50th anniversary of the Radio Club of America, New York, 1964 (recorded on an LP record).

3. *GE Report*, p. 18.

4. *Proc. I.R.E.*, Vol. 18, No. 3, p. 385.

5. *GE Report*, p. 20.

Chapter Four

U.S.A. After World War I

The Radio Group

In 1919 with some encouragement from the U.S. government the Radio Corporation of America (RCA) was formed to take over the Marconi Wireless Telegraph Co. of America. Behind that short sentence is a long story but it is sufficient to say here that the American government desired to see what was virtually a monopoly in American wireless communication removed from foreign ownership.

Under the earlier mentioned tripartite agreement American Marconi continued to advertise and sell Marconi 'VT' tubes until the middle of 1920. This they were able to do because the agreement contained a clause requiring six-months notice by any party before it could be cancelled. Such cancellation if given soon after the formation of RCA would thus have become effective about the middle of 1920.

July 1920 is an important date in the history of American tube patents as during this month a far-reaching cross-licensing agreement was concluded between the major patent owners—AT&T, GE, and RCA. Westinghouse joined the group a year later. De Forest was not in the running as he had earlier sold his Audion patents to AT&T. This agreement had the effect of clearing the air and it permitted tube manufacture by the parties concerned free of the threat of legal action for patent infringement. At the same time it also had the effect of a cartel, for independent tube makers were denied manufacturing licenses for many years to come.

The stage was now set for the production of standardised types of tubes by GE and Westinghouse who were to supply such tubes to RCA for distribution. This arrangement remained in force until 1930 when an anti-trust action by the U.S. government resulted in a splitting up of the combine. After nearly two years of intensive negotiations between the three companies the suit was finally settled out of court in 1932 by what is known in legal terms as 'consent decree'. Before this had happened RCA had, in 1930, formed a new company known as the RCA Radiotron Co. which took over GE's Harrison Works in

February, 1920   ELECTRICAL EXPERIMENTER   1073

A WARNING

to Manufacturers
Importers
Dealers
Jobbers
Agents
Amateurs
Purchasers
Users of

Vacuum Tubes

The Marconi V. T. Patent is Basic

United States Letters Patent to Fleming, No. 803,684, November 7, 1905, has been held to be valid by Judge Mayer of the United States District Court for the Southern District of New York, and by the United States Circuit Court of Appeals for the Second Circuit.

Fleming Pat. No. 803684
De Forest Pat. Nos. 841387-879513

It is a basic patent and controls broadly all vacuum tubes used as detectors, amplifiers or oscillions in radio work.

No one is authorized to make, sell, import or use such tubes for radio purposes, other than the owners of the patent and licensees thereunder. Any others making, selling, importing or using them alone or in combination with other devices, infringe upon the Fleming patent and are liable to a suit for injunction, damages and profits. And they will be prosecuted.

THE AUDIOTRON AND THE LIBERTY VALVE ARE NOT LICENSED UNDER THE FLEMING PATENT

The price of the genuine Marconi V. T. delivered is $7.00 each. The standardized socket is $1.50 additional. The standard resistance, complete, costs $1.00 and is made in the following sizes: ½ megohm, 1 megohm, 2 megohms, 4 megohms, 6 megohms.

Do not take chances by making, importing, selling, purchasing or using vacuum tubes for radio purposes not licensed under the Fleming patent. By selling, purchasing or using licensed tubes for radio purposes you secure protection under the Fleming patent and avoid the risk of litigation for infringement thereof.

This warning is given so that the trade and public may know the facts and be governed accordingly.

Send all remittances with order to COMMERCIAL DEPARTMENT

MARCONI WIRELESS TELEGRAPH CO. OF AMERICA
RADIO CORPORATION OF AMERICA
235 Broadway   New York

Sole Distributors for De Forest Radio Telephone & Telegraph Co.

Retail Office and Exhibition Rooms, 25 Elm St., New York

Schofield Bldg., Cleveland, Ohio   Insurance Exch. Bldg., San Francisco, Cal.   301 Commercial Bank Annex, New Orleans, La.
American Bldg., Baltimore, Md.   136 Federal St., Boston, Mass.   109 South 2nd St., Philadelphia, Pa.

which to commence production of receiving tubes. Under the new agreement RCA was given until 1935 to establish its own receiver and tube-making facilities after which time GE and Westinghouse were free to re-enter these fields. Meanwhile, these two companies were to refrain from the production of receiving tubes.

To return to 1920, the first receiving tubes marketed by RCA were the types UV-200 and UV-201, these being first advertised for sale in December 1920 under the

15

brandname 'Radiotron'. At the same time identical tubes were marketed by the firm of E.T. Cunningham under the type numbers C-300 and C-301. Before proceeding further it will be as well to explain how the name Cunningham came into the picture. The origin of tubes labelled Cunningham was the outcome of an agreement reached between RCA and a San Francisco tube maker by the name of Elmer T. Cunningham which was concluded early in 1920. In the terms of this agreement Cunningham, who had previously made tubes under his brandname Audio-Tron, agreed to cease manufacture and become a distributor for RCA. This he agreed to do on the understanding that the tubes supplied to him were to be branded with his own name.

The strength of Cunningham's bargaining position has never been revealed and remains a matter for speculation to this day, but in any event he became an extremely active distributor with depots in New York, Chicago, and San Francisco. It is not known how long this agreement with RCA remained in force but the use of Cunningham as a separate brandname continued to at least 1932. In 1931 the firm of E.T. Cunningham Inc. was taken over by RCA and Cunningham himself entered their employ. By 1933 Cunningham had become president of the RCA Radiotron Co.[1] and from this time until 1935 all tubes made by RCA were marked RCA Cunningham Radiotron. After 1940 the use of the name Cunningham ceased entirely.

The first Radiotron/Cunningham tubes differed markedly from GE's wartime designs and represented a complete break with the European influence which had hitherto been apparent. The peacetime tubes had planar electrodes, a type of construction which was to become an industry standard for all types of storage battery tubes. Plain tungsten filaments arranged in the form of an inverted vee

Radiotron UV-201-A tubes 1923–1925.

were used, the rating being 5 volts, 1 amp. This voltage rating allowed extended operation from a 6-volt battery as it became discharged in use. When using a fully charged battery it was necessary to adjust the filament current by means of a rheostat and in the absence of a suitable meter this could be done by making a visual comparison between the lighted filament and that of a household tungsten-filament lamp; for this purpose viewing ports were provided in the front panels of most receivers of the period.

The tubes were fitted with the same type of base as had been used on the wartime VT-11. This base had four short contact pins set into a porcelain disc held in position at the bottom of the brass base shell. A small guide pin on the side of the base served to locate the tube in its socket and at the same time lock it in position. A tapered straight-sided (S-14) bulb was used, the dimensions of which had previously been standardised for use in 10-watt sign lamps.

The UV-200 was a 'soft' detector containing a small amount of argon gas which had been found to greatly increase the sensitivity of tubes used as detectors. The UV-201 was a 'hard' or high vacuum tube designed for use as an amplifier and in later form, as the 201-A, was to become the most widely used tube of its day.

At the time of their introduction there existed but a small demand for tubes because broadcasting had hardly commenced and the only listeners were experimenters and ham radio operators. Even to the enthusiast, as all such early listeners must have been, the heavy filament consumption of the UV-200 and UV-201 meant that even with a receiver using no more than two or three tubes the A battery would last for only a matter of hours before needing recharging. A more economical tube would obviously be welcomed with open arms.

In spite of this need the development of tubes with reduced filament consumption was not the direct result of research in this direction but came about largely because of an accident. Because the GE tubes were made in a lamp factory some of the laboratory work was common to both

Radiotron UV-199 dry-cell tubes.

lamps and tubes. In the making of tungsten-filament lamps it had become standard practice to add a minute amount of the so-called 'rare earth', thoria, during manufacture of the tungsten wire for reasons connected solely with lamp making. Some of this wire was once accidentally used for the filaments of vacuum tubes and it was subsequently found that any such tubes exhibited a greater than normal emission on test.[2]

Research into this phenomenon by Dr. Irving Langmuir, coupled with much developmental work, led in 1921 to the invention of a completely new type of filament having distinct advantages over plain tungsten. During the course of the development of the 'thoriated' filament, as it had come to be called, it had been found that tubes using the new filament required a much higher degree of vacuum than had previously been the case and this in itself led to the development of new manufacturing techniques which were to form an important part of all future tube manufacture.

It is outside the scope of this work to relate the full story of the development of the thoriated filament but one aspect must be mentioned. It had been found that the slightest trace of oxygen remaining inside the bulb after evacuation had an extremely deleterious effect on the emission from thoriated filaments. Before the new tubes could become a practical reality it was imperative to find a way of clearing up any residual gas left after evacuation, as well as any occluded gas which might subsequently be released during the life of the tube. A solution to the problem was achieved by including a small pellet of magnesium which was attached to the anode during assembly and which was subsequently 'fired' or vaporised during evacuation. The vaporised magnesium then condensed on the inner walls of the bulb giving it a characteristic silvery appearance.

Magnesium has the ability to readily absorb oxygen, so that as well as contributing to the process of evacuation when it is vaporised during firing it continues to absorb any subsequently released oxygen during the life of the tube. In the former case it is known as a 'getter' and in the latter as a 'keeper'. This important step in tube manufacturing, although improved by the later use of mixed getters, remained a basic feature thereafter.

For a short period in the early days of thoriated-filament tubes a mixed getter containing red phosphorous was sometimes used which resulted in such tubes exhibiting a multi-hued appearance and being referred to as 'rainbow' gettered. It has been stated that in the case of the earliest GE tubes those made at the Harrison factory used magnesium gettering while those made at the Cleveland factory used a mixed getter containing phosphorous.[3]

The first thoriated-filament tubes were the types UV-199 and UV-201A; they were produced by GE late in 1922 but were not available for general sale until well into 1923.[4] The 201A was identical in appearance to the 201 as it used the same size electrodes, base, and bulb but was

distinguishable at a glance because of the silvery appearance of the bulb. The new tube as well as being considerably more economical of filament power also had a greatly increased emission resulting in an improved performance. At 0.25 amps the filament consumption was only a quarter of that of its predecessor. For the next six years the 201A was to reign supreme and, apart from a minor modification made during 1923 which resulted in a slightly increased mutual conductance, its characteristics remained unchanged throughout its production lifetime.

March 1924[5] saw the introduction of tipless (stem exhausted) bulbs and in October of the same year bakelite bases were used for the first time to supersede the earlier brass bases. Next came the 'UX' style base in August 1925 bringing with it a change in the type number to UX-201A. Finally, after the introduction of the 'ST' style bulbs in 1932 the bulb shape was changed from S-14 to ST-14 and at the same time the type number officially became 01A.

At the time this was going on similar changes were taking place in the case of the UV-200 which became the UX-200 in 1925 and the UX-200A in 1926. The final version differed in being filled with caesium vapour instead of argon gas but even so was definitely obsolescent at the time of its release and the tube was never used commercially except as a replacement for the earlier types.

Coinciding with the release of the UV-201A was the arrival of the first dry-cell tube made by GE, the type UV-199. This tube was intended for use in portable receivers as well as in home receivers using dry batteries. Like its bigger brother the 199 used the same type of thoriated filament which in this case carried a rating of 3 volts, 0.06 amps, making it suited for running on three series-connected 1.5-volt dry cells. The rather large difference between battery voltage can be explained by the desire to have something in hand as the battery voltage dropped off during use. Even so it was found desirable to increase the filament rating to 3.3 volts about a year after the initial release.

Physically the 199 was much smaller than any previous GE tubes (it used a T-8 tubular bulb) which was in keeping with its intended application in portable receivers. Cylindrical electrodes were used together with an axial filament inherent to this type of construction. Initially a brass base was used which, because of the smaller diameter bulb, was of appropriately smaller dimensions than the standard UV style. This special small UV base was unique to the 199 and was never used on any other type of tube.

Tipless bulbs were introduced early in 1924 and bakelite bases came into use during October of the same year. August 1925 saw a change to a UX style base which, although fitting the standard UX socket, was of much smaller diameter and in addition had a characteristic reverse taper shape. Because of this the UX-199 could not fit the earlier UV style socket and it was thus necessary to continue production of UV-199s for replacement use.

From about 1932 the two types became known as V99 and X99 respectively.

In October 1925 a companion to the UX-199 in the form of a 'power' output tube, type UX-120, was issued.[6] The inverted commas around the word *power* are deliberate as at its maximum plate voltage of 135 volts the 120 was capable of only 110 milliwatts output, a figure only slightly higher than obtainable from the general-purpose 201A.

The first power tube capable of an output in excess of a watt was introduced in October 1925 under the type number UX-210.[7] An earlier version, type UV-210, is known to have been made but was not available for general sale. The UX-210 was a successor to the UV-202 and had a thoriated filament rated at 7.5 V, 1.25 A. It was widely used as an oscillator by amateur transmitters of the day in addition to being used in its intended application as an output tube in early all-electric radios and electric phonographs. At the maximum plate voltage of 450 volts the UX-210 was capable of an output of 1.5 watts, a

performance that was soon to be eclipsed by the development of more efficient tubes with oxide-coated filaments.

Following the introduction of thoriated-filament storage battery tubes RCA's policy was to issue new types only where a proven need existed. Two exceptions were the UX-200A a gaseous detector whose arrival in 1926 was a non-event, and the UX-240[8] a high-mu triode intended for use in resistance coupled circuits. Neither tube was ever used in commercially built receivers.

The next significant advance in the design of storage battery tubes was made when Westinghouse introduced output tubes using oxide-coated filaments. The release of such tubes early in 1926 marked a turning point in the history of battery-operated tubes as thereafter no new types of thoriated-filament tubes were produced.

A Radiotron tube, rare in he U.S. because it was apparently made only for export, was the type RCA-221. This tube had similar characteristics to the 201A but differed in requiring only 0.06 amps of filament current. Obviously such a low drain could only have been achieved by the use

MODEL	USE	BASE	GRID CONDENSER MFD	GRID LEAK (See Note 6)	DETECTOR GRID RETURN LEAD	"A" BATTERY VOLTS (SUPPLY)	FILAMENT TERMINAL VOLTS	"A" BATTERY CURRENT AMPERES	"B" BATTERY VOLTS DETECTOR	"B" BATTERY VOLTS AMPLIFIER	NEGATIVE "C" BATTERY VOLTS	PLATE CURRENT MILLIAMPERES NORMAL OPERATING (See Notes 1 & 5)	OUTPUT RESISTANCE OHMS (See Note 1)	MUTUAL CONDUCTANCE MICRO - MHOS (See Note 1)	VOLTAGE AMPLIFICATION FACTOR (See Note 1)	MAXIMUM DIAMETER OVERALL	MAXIMUM HEIGHT OVERALL
RADIOTRON UV-199	Detector Amplifier	UV-199 Base	.00025	2 to 9	+ F	4.5	3.0	.06	45	90	4.5	2.5	15,000	415	6.25	$1\frac{1}{16}$"	$3\frac{1}{2}$"
RADIOTRON UX-199	Detector Amplifier	RCA Small Standard UX Base	.00025	2 to 9	+ F	4.5	3.0	.06	45	90	4.5	2.5	15,000	415	6.25	$1\frac{1}{16}$"	$4\frac{5}{8}$"
RADIOTRON UV-200	Detector Only	Navy Base	.00025	$\frac{1}{2}$ to 2	- F	6	5	1.0	15 to 25	—	—	—	—	—	—	$1\frac{3}{4}$"	$4\frac{5}{16}$"
RADIOTRON UX-200	Detector Only	RCA Large Standard UX Base	.00025	$\frac{1}{2}$ to 2	- F	6	5	1.0	15 to 25	—	—	—	—	—	—	$1\frac{13}{16}$"	$4\frac{7}{16}$"
RADIOTRON UV-201-A	Detector Amplifier	Navy Base	.00025	2 to 9	+ F	6	5	.25	45	90 / 135	4.5 / 9.0	3 / -4	12,000 / 11,000	675 / 725	8 / 8	$1\frac{13}{16}$"	$4\frac{5}{16}$"
RADIOTRON UX-201-A	Detector Amplifier	RCA Large Standard UX Base	.00025	2 to 9	+ F	6	5	.25	45	90 / 135	4.5 / 9.0	3 / 4	12,000 / 11,000	675 / 725	8 / 8	$1\frac{13}{16}$"	$4\frac{7}{16}$"
RADIOTRON WD-11	Detector Amplifier	WD-11 Base	.00025	3 to 5	+ F	1.5	1.1	.25	$22\frac{1}{2}$	90	4.5	2.8	14,000	400	5.6	$1\frac{5}{32}$"	$3\frac{3}{4}$"
RADIOTRON WD-12	Detector Amplifier	Navy Base	.00025	3 to 5	+ F	1.5	1.1	.25	$22\frac{1}{2}$	90	4.5	2.8	14,000	400	5.6	$1\frac{7}{16}$"	$4\frac{7}{16}$"
RADIOTRON WX-12	Detector Amplifier	RCA Large Standard UX Base	.00025	3 to 5	+ F	1.5	1.1	.25	$22\frac{1}{2}$	90	4.5	2.8	14,000	400	5.6	$1\frac{7}{16}$"	$4\frac{7}{16}$"
RADIOTRON UX-112	Detector Amplifier	RCA Large Standard UX Base	.00025	3 to 5	+ F	6	5	0.5	$22\frac{1}{2}$ to 45	157.5 (Max) (See Note 2) 135 112.5 90	10.5 9. 7.5 6.	7.9 5.8 2.5 2.4	4800 5500 8400 8800	1670 1435 940 890	8.0 7.9 7.9 7.9	$1\frac{13}{16}$"	$4\frac{11}{16}$"
RADIOTRON UX-120	Audio Amplifier Last Stage Only	RCA Small Standard UX Base	—	—	•	4.5	3.0	.125	—	135	22.5	6.5	6,600	500	3.3	$1\frac{13}{16}$"	$4\frac{1}{8}$"
RADIOTRON UX-210	Amplifier Oscillator	RCA Large Standard UX Base	—	—	◄	8 8 8 6 6 6	7.5 7.5 7.5 6.0 6.0 6.0	1.25 1.25 1.4 1.1 1.1 1.1	—	425 (Max) 350 250 157.5 135 112.5 90	35 27 18 10.5 9 7.5 4.5	22 18 12 4.5 3.	5000 5100 5600 7400 8000 9700 9700	1550 1500 1330 1020 940 775 775	7.75 7.65 7.5 7.5 7.5 7.5 7.5	$2\frac{3}{16}$"	$5\frac{5}{8}$"
RADIOTRON UX-874	Voltage Regulator Tube	RCA Large Standard UX Base				Rated Voltage: 90 Volts D. C. Starting Voltage: 125 Volts D. C. Maximum D. C. Current: 50 Milliamperes *(Continuous)*											$2\frac{3}{16}$"	$5\frac{5}{8}$"
RADIOTRON UV-876	Ballast Tube	Standard Mogul Type Screw Base				Current Rating: 1.7 Amperes Voltage Range: 40 to 60 Volts											$2\frac{1}{16}$"	8"
RADIOTRON UV-877 (See Note 4)	Protective Tube	Double Contact Bayonet Automobile Type				Voltage Drop Across Half Filament / Entire Filament 2.5 / 5 At 20 Milliamperes D. C. 45.0 At 90 Milliamperes D. C.											$1\frac{7}{16}$"	$2\frac{1}{2}$"
RECTRON UX-213	Full Wave Rectifier	RCA Large Standard UX Base			•	Filament Terminal Voltage: 5.0 Volts Filament Current : 2.0 Amperes Max. A. C. Input Voltage per Anode: 220 A. C. (R. M. S.) or 440 across both Anodes. (See Note 5) Max. D. C. Load Current : 65 Milliamperes											$2\frac{3}{16}$"	$5\frac{5}{8}$"
RECTRON UX-216-B	Half Wave Rectifier	RCA Large Standard UX Base				Filament Terminal Voltage: 7.5 Volts Filament Current : 1.25 Amperes Max. A. C. Input Voltage : 550 A. C. (R. M. S.) (See Note 5) Max. D. C. Load Current : 65 Milliamperes					—						$2\frac{3}{16}$"	$5\frac{5}{8}$"

NOTE 1 At normal operating grid voltage. (Not at zero grid)
NOTE 2 Plate voltage for average use is 90 to 135 volts.
NOTE 3 R. M. S. Indicates "Root Mean Square" as indicated on an A. C. voltmeter.
NOTE 4 Connection to shell of base for third terminal which is the lead to mid - point of filament.
NOTE 5 The plate current values given are less than those obtained with zero grid, but are the currents actually obtained when the tube is operated at indicated values of plate voltage and grid bias voltage.

NOTE 6 The symbol ═◯═ = megohms.
NOTE 7 When 6 volt supply is used, no rheostat is required.

The entire total of all receiving tubes listed by RCA in 1925 was 17. Eight years later in 1933, it had grown to 74.

of an oxide-coated filament though confirmation of this assumption is lacking as published information on the 221 is almost non-existent. The 221 was intended for use as a low-drain replacement for the 201A though, as mentioned, it was not marketed in the U.S. The author believes that the 221 was produced specifically for export to areas where the sales of Radiotron tubes were being affected by competing low-drain tubes made in England and Holland. However, because the 221 was not marketed until early in 1930 it came rather too late to have much effect on the situation as by that time the demand for battery tubes was shrinking.

The first tubes produced after the establishment of RCA's own factory were types RCA-230, RCA-231, and RCA-232.[9] They were the first American 2-volt battery-operated tubes and their arrival, in June 1930, signalled the end of the era of 5-volt tubes. Incidentally, it may be mentioned that 2-volt valves had been available in the U.K. since 1925 so by comparison the American tubes were comparative latecomers. Shortly after the introduction of the American 2-volt tubes a special air-depolariser battery known as the Eveready 'Air Cell' was developed for use with battery-operated receivers and because of this the tubes were sometimes referred to as Air Cell types.

In their original form the 30 and 31 were fitted with T-8 tubular bulbs which in 1931 were changed to S-12 size and then, in 1933, to ST-12. Other early types in the same series were the type 33 O/P pentode, type 34 vari-mu pentode, type 49 O/P tetrode, and type 19 Class B twin O/P triode.

Westinghouse

The other old established electrical manufacturer who also entered the radio field and a little later became the

RCA-221. The 'export only' tube. Filament rating was 5V, 0.06A.

third member of the Radio Group, was the Westinghouse Electric & Mfg. Co. Westinghouse had done comparatively little radio work prior to or during World War I but following the establishment of what has been called the world's first broadcasting station, KDKA Pittsburgh, late in 1920 their products became better known. The story of this pioneering effort has become an oft told tale which has no place in a work of this nature; sufficient to say that it was, perhaps more than anything else, responsible for the early and rapid growth of broadcasting in the United States.

Once people knew there were voices and music in the air a demand soon sprang up for receivers capable of reproducing these sounds in the home. To help satisfy this

The '0I-A story—the final issue had an oxide-coated filament.

demand Westinghouse commenced to manufacture a line of receivers under the name 'Aeriola'. While they were not strictly the first made by Westinghouse they were the first produced specifically to cater to the demands created by the growing numbers of radio listeners.

Tubes to equip these receivers were also made by Westinghouse and in this connection it is interesting to compare the different approach to tube manufacture adopted, bearing in mind that both Westinghouse and GE were lamp makers too. The Westinghouse tubes bore a marked resemblance to wartime British and French types as they used the same style of cylindrical anode and spiral grid together with an axial filament. Additionally, the same 4-volt filament rating and the same style of 4-prong base were used; in fact the only difference lay in the use of a tubular bulb in place of a spherical style.

The first production was of a tube known as the WR21 which was made in two versions known as WR21A and WR21D,[10] the letter A indicated Amplifier while the letter D indicated Detector. These tubes were known as Aeriotrons and were intended solely for use in a Westinghouse receiver produced in 1922 known as the Aeriola Grand.

Meanwhile, also in 1922, a new Aeriotron type WD-11 was introduced.[11] This tube was almost identical in appearance to the WR21 but differed in having an oxide-coated filament rated at 1.1 V, 0.2 A designed for operation from a single dry cell. It was the world's first such tube intended for use in household receivers and in this connection remained unique for many years.

In its original form the WD-11 had no gettering but soon after a chemical getter in the form of a whitish paste applied to both sides of the press was used. This was the so-called Sutherlin lime getter and its use continued for some years after magnesium gettering had come into general use. The WD-11 was fitted with a modified version of the type of base used on the WR-21. It differed in having a larger diameter pin for the plate connection, a device

Radiotron UV-201-A made by Westinghouse.

intended to prevent the accidental insertion into a socket wired for a 4-volt tube.

After joining the Radio Group in July 1921 Westinghouse, like GE, supplied receivers and tubes to RCA who were the sole selling agent. This setup resulted in the names Aeriola and Aeriotron being phased out and after about 1923 Westinghouse's radio products were sold under the brandnames Radiola and Radiotron respectively. Special-purpose and transmitting tubes which were not subject to the agreement could be sold directly under the company's own name.

Under the Radiotron brandname WD-11 tubes were first used as initial equipment in Radiola receivers but by the middle of 1923 these tubes were being offered for general sale. Production continued without change until September 1924 when the bulb size was reduced to T-8 and a bakelite base superseded the former brass type. A final change occurred in February 1925 when a tipless bulb and magnesium gettering were introduced.

A variation of the WD-11, known as the WD-12, was introduced in 1923 to allow the conversion of certain Radiola and Westinghouse storage-battery receivers to dry-cell operation. The WD-12 was fitted with a standard UV style brass base and used the same T-10 bulb. A reduction in overall height occurred due to the lower portion of the bulb being 'buried' in the base shell.

From January 1925 the WD-12 presented a much-changed appearance due to a reduction in the bulb size to T-8, coupled with the use of a bakelite base of unique shape. Because the reduced bulb diameter could not con-

Aeriotron WD-11 (left) Radiotron WD-11 (centre and right).

veniently be matched to the diameter of a standard UV base it was necessary to design a new base which, while small enough internally to match the T-8 bulb, had an outside diameter of standard dimensions. Instead of using a thick-walled base the effective outer diameter was increased by the use of four raised flutes moulded onto the surface. Because this prevented the type number from being hot-branded on the side of the base it was consequently moulded in raised lettering on the underside.

Westinghouse also made a limited quantity of UV-201 bright emitter tubes which differed in several respects from those made by GE. These tubes used cylindrical elements and an axial filament rated at 4-volts, 0.8 amps and were fitted with a tubular bulb. All these features, it will be recalled, correspond with those of the WR-21. The question now arises as to whether the Westinghouse UV-201 could have actually been a WR-21 fitted with a UV base. By slightly over-running the filament by applying 5 volts to it the resultant current would have been close to 1 ampere, whilst the use of a cylindrical electrode structure would not in itself result in a tube having different characteristics.

It was in the area of power output tubes that Westinghouse did much pioneering work. For example, the first tube to have an output in excess of 100 milliwatts, type UX-112, and the first to have an output of over 400 milliwatts, type UX-171, were both from the Westinghouse stables. In order to obtain a larger emission an oxide-coated 'M' shaped filament was used for the first time; it consumed 0.5 amps at 5 volts. The UX-112 was released towards the end of 1925[12] while the UX-171 although produced at the same time was not advertised until well into 1926. Only a year later further improvements in filament efficiency led to the production of the types UX-112A and UX-171A both of which had quarter amp filaments. But because these tubes arrived on the eve of the all-electric era the 171A became more widely used in AC-operated receivers than in battery sets.

In 1928 there appeared a new power tube capable of what was then a phenomenal output of 4.6 watts, or over 10 watts when used as a push-pull pair.[13] This tube was Westinghouse's UX-250, the 'big daddy' of power tubes which remained supreme until superseded by RCA's 2A3 in 1933. The S-21 bulb as originally fitted was the largest ever used for a receiving tube and gave the 250 an impressive appearance commensurate with its power handling ability. From 1933 replacement types were issued fitted with ST-19 bulbs.

The final output tube of the period was the UX-245, the production of which represented a decisive step away from the use of high plate voltages in the output stages of radio receivers. At its maximum plate voltage of 250 V, the 245 was capable of 0.8 watts output, a figure which was twice that of the 210 when operating at the same voltage. However, the 245 was most commonly used in Class A push-

pull service when a pair of tubes could provide about 5 watts output. When first announced early in 1929 the 245 was fitted with an S-17 bulb which was later changed to ST-14 for replacement types issued after 1933.

'The Telephone Company'

An important step in the early days of vacuum tube development was the work done by the American Tele-

Radiotrons WD12 and WX12.

Radiotrons UX-171-A and UX-112-A.

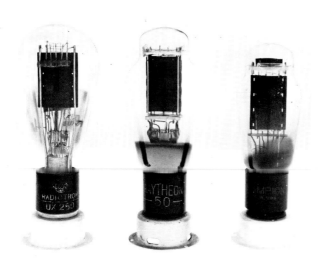

Radiotron UX-250 (1.) made by Westinghouse. Centre and right—later type 50 tubes showing bulb shape development.

The first Radiotron power amplifiers (1925).

phone & Telegraph Company in adapting De Forest's triode Audion for use as an amplifier in line telephony. Where previously Audions had been produced by a small lamp manufacturer merely as a side-line made without any direct supervision and with no understanding of the functioning of the device, once AT&T became involved a turning point in vacuum tube history was reached. As a result of work done by the company's Bell Labs the Audion was transformed into a stable, reliable product of workmanlike construction.

AT&T's interest in the Audion had arisen as a direct result of an approach made by De Forest in 1912 when he demonstrated an audio amplifier to officials of the company. Prior to this time, and indeed to several years later, the only way of overcoming losses occurring on long-distance lines was by the use of electro-mechanical relays, or 'repeaters' as they were known in telephone parlance. Whilst these were quite satisfactory for Morse telegraphy they were unsuitable for telephony so that at the time a very real need existed for a better repeater. Following De Forest's demonstration of the amplifying capabilities of his Audion bulb engineers of the Telephone Company's manufacturing subsidiary, the Western Electric Co. (WE), were sufficiently impressed by its possibilities to recommend that the company enter into negotiations to enable it to manufacture vacuum tubes for telephone use.

In 1913 De Forest, short of money as usual, was driven to accepting the sum of $50,000 from AT&T for the exclusive wire rights of several of his patents. De Forest later claimed that the Telephone Company had been prepared to go as high as half a million dollars and that a smart lawyer, aware of his financial straits, had tricked him into accepting one tenth of that amount.[14] Following the acquisition of these first patents AT&T later, in 1914, next acquired a license to use other Audion patents for wireless telegraphy and telephony, this action obviously presaging

the company's moves in these fields. Finally, in 1917, De Forest disposed of his remaining tube patents to AT&T, though retaining certain non-transferable personal rights.

Now, fully secure in the possession of the necessary patents Western Electric could proceed to develop and use vacuum tubes for any purpose they desired. This they proceeded to do with but one exception; apart from a very limited activity in the earliest days the company never entered the field of domestic radio production with either receivers or receiving tubes. On the other hand, Western Electric became well known as a manufacturer of broadcast transmitters, motion picture sound systems, and aviation radio, to name but three of their non-telephone activities.

The development of tubes for telephone work is a story in itself, outside the scope of this book, though it is interesting to compare one aspect of it with the entirely different approach adopted by the manufacturers of tubes intended for non-telephone use. Because any telephone system is regarded as a public utility and because it is not affected by the same sort of cut-throat competition encountered within the radio industry, vastly different equipment requirements resulted. This, coupled with the fact that telephone equipment is normally leased, not sold, to subscribers made the development of reliable long-lasting equipment of paramount importance. Apart from the desire to avoid breakdowns in an essential medium of communication there is the commercial aspect that the more reliable and long-lived the equipment is the more money it makes for its owners.

The vacuum tubes which became an essential part of long-distance telephone equipment were of course no exception to the above requirements. In fact as the weakest links in the chain special precautions had to be taken to ensure their reliability in service. These factors, coupled with the comparatively small quantities required, resulted in the development of a special breed of tube which was largely handmade in comparison with ordinary radio tubes which had to compete in the marketplace and which were later turned out by the millions.

In 1915 Western Electric's growing interest in the possibilities of the future long-distance transmission of speech by wireless telephony was demonstrated by the now famous occasion when the human voice was carried across the Atlantic by radio for the first time.

Following America's entry into World War I in 1917 WE, in common with other tube makers, became active in developing tubes for military applications and brief mention of their work will be found in the chapter dealing with wartime developments.

After the war AT&T entered into agreements with the so-called 'Radio Group' (RCA, GE, Westinghouse) intended to delineate the trading activities of the respective companies. In essence this was a cartel agreement but

in the event it led to much squabbling between the Telephone Co. and the Radio Group over their respective rights. Amongst other things AT&T had agreed not to compete in the manufacture and sale of broadcast receiving equipment but in spite of this were soon offering such items as loudspeakers, headphones, and even tubes for general sale.

In 1925 after prolonged discussion and arbitration AT&T was permitted to manufacture and sell on a restricted basis broadcast receiving devices, including tubes. By this time, however, the company appeared to have lost interest in continuing with this side of their business and eventually retired from this activity.

One of the best known of the early WE receiving tubes was the so-called 'peanut' tube, identified as type 215A. It was at the time the smallest tube in existence and not until 1938 were any tubes of comparable size produced by any other American manufacturer. The 215A is also historically interesting because, like Westinghouse's WD11, it boasted an oxide-coated filament at a time when either plain or thoriated filaments were the rule. Indeed oxide-coated filaments became the distinguishing feature of all WE battery-operated tubes, regardless of their application.

Readers interested in Western Electric tubes will find a detailed and authoritative account of their development in Gerald Tyne's *Saga of the Vacuum Tube*.

For the purpose of this narrative further mention of AT&T is confined to a brief account of Western Electric's overseas trading activities which were greatly affected by changes in the corporate structure of the company which took place shortly after the end of World War I. The Western Electric Co. was originally an independent manufacturer which was acquired by the Telephone Co. in 1882 and became its manufacturing subsidiary. Following this a company named the International Western Electric Co. was set up to handle overseas business. In the following year a British office was established which became the Western Electric Co. Ltd. (British WE).

Western Electric 201-A.

Western Electric 205-D.

In 1920 a newly formed company bearing the name International Telephone & Telegraph Co. (IT&T)* was registered in the state of New York by one Sosthenes Behn. Referring to IT&T *Time* magazine once commented on the adoption of such a name as 'an unabashed effort to trade on the reputation of the giant AT&T Co.'[15] Be that as it may, IT&T itself eventually grew to be one of the giants in the communications industry, becoming what is nowadays known as a multi-national.

By 1925 IT&T had been successful in purchasing from AT&T the International Western Electric Co. which was then renamed the International Standard Electric Co. (ISEC). This move gave IT&T control of all business formerly conducted outside the U.S. by Western Electric, with the exception of motion picture sound systems. In this field WE continued to trade both inside and outside the U.S. under their own name, though many years later the company name was changed to Western Electronics when the products brandname became Westrex. The effect of ISEC's formation on the British scene will be covered in the chapter dealing with Standard Telephones & Cables Ltd.

*In 1959 the company logo was altered to ITT.

Western Electric 'radio' tubes.

REFERENCES

1. News of Industry, *Radio Engineering*, April 1933, p. 23.
2. *GE Report*, p. 39.
3. Ibid., p. 39.
4. Ibid., p. 34.
5. Ibid., p. 39.
6. Ibid., p. 42.
7. Ibid., p. 42.
8. Announcement, *QST*, April 1927, p. 26.
9. News for Shop and Home, *Radio Craft*, July 1930, p. 27.
10. *GE Report*, p. 24.
11. Ibid., p. 24.
12. Ibid., p. 42.
13. Announcement, *QST*, April 1928, p. 36.
14. Lee de Forest, *The Father of Radio*, p. 310.
15. *Time* magazine, Sept. 8, 1967, p. 54.

Western Electric 264C, 221-D, 239-A. The 221-D was equivalent to RCA's 201-A.

Western Electric 'doorknob' tubes designed for VHF and UHF use.

Chapter Five

Some Early American Independents

Apart from De Forest only two manufacturers of any significance had marketed tubes before 1917 and this had been done openly and without benefit of patent licence from De Forest. Whether by coincidence or otherwise both these tube makers were located in San Francisco which may have been the reason why their respective products were so similar even though they differed radically in construction and appearance from De Forest's Audions.

The first and probably best known of the two independents was one Elmer T. Cunningham, whose name was

---

LICENSED BY DE FOREST
AUDIOTRON

The Original Tubular Vacuum Amplifier

The AudioTron Vacuum Tube is now manufactured and sold as a genuine audion licensed under DeForest Patents Nos. 841,387 and 879,532 to be used only for amplification in radio communication and only for experimental and amateur purposes and only in audio frequency circuits.

The AudioTron has a double filament of special thorium tungsten and the operating life is over 2,000 hours. No special socket is required. The electrical and mechanical dimensions result in a heavy plate current and corresponding signal strength. Plate voltage under 40. Our guarantee insures satisfaction.

PRICE $6.00 EACH

If your local dealer cannot supply you we will ship postpaid when cash accompanies order.

The AudioTron Exclusive Guaranty: Each and every AudioTron is guaranteed to arrive in good condition and to prove fully satisfactory. Replacement of unsatisfactory tubes will be made free of charge.

AudioTron Audio-Frequency Transformer $7.00
Laminated closed core, two coil type.

DEALERS:—Write for our attractive trade Proposition.

AUDIOTRON SALES CO.   **Lick Bldg.**   **SAN FRANCISCO, CALIF.**

You benefit by mentioning the "Electrical Experimenter" when writing to advertisers.   *April/1920*

In spite of the claim the Audiotron was not licensed by De Forest.

25

later to become well known for other reasons. Cunningham's tubes were sold under the name of AudioTron, or Audiotron, and were marketed by the AudioTron Sales Co. of San Francisco. For some reason Cunningham's name did not appear either on the tubes themselves nor in advertising during the five-year period in which they were made and sold. Just why this should have been so can possibly be explained by a desire on Cunningham's part as an unlicensed manufacturer to prudently conceal his identity.

The AudioTron tube was of unbased, tubular, double-ended construction having twin axial filaments. The cylindrical anode was of only slightly smaller diameter than the inside of the bulb and the grid consisted of a coarse spiral of thick wire supported at only one end. Both the long filament and wobbly grid could vibrate freely; a type of construction more prone to microphony would be difficult to imagine.

As an unlicensed manufacturer Cunningham was soon in trouble with De Forest over the matter of patent infringement and although a satisfactory settlement was reached similar trouble occurred later with RCA. This time a settlement between the two parties resulted in Cunningham agreeing to cease manufacture and become a distributor for RCA. Mention of Cunningham's later activities will be made in another chapter.

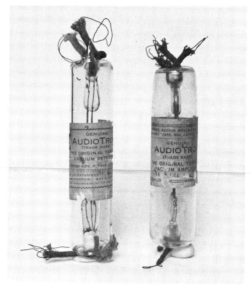

Cunningham Audiotron tubes of the 1916–1919 era.

It seems almost certain that Cunningham was quite happy to allow his tubes to be sold by others under various brandnames, judging by the identical appearance of several differently labelled tubes which appeared at the time. Only one will be mentioned here—the Roome 'Oscillaudion'. The enterprising promoter of the Oscillaudion was one Harry V. Roome of Los Angeles. In an advertising pamphlet (undated but apparently produced in 1916), Roome claims to have supplied his 'Super Sensitive Oscillaudions' to no less than thirteen American universities and colleges and two in Canada. Also included among his (satisfied?) customers were the U.S. Army Signal Corps, the Royal Australian Navy, and the Astronomical Observatory of New South Wales, Australia. No New Zealand customers are listed but someone must have been sufficiently interested to write for the leaflet now in the author's possession.

However, these claims are really not relevant to the matter under discussion which is the similarity of Roome's tube to Cunningham's AudioTron. Comparison between illustrations of the Oscillaudion and several samples of the AudioTron leaves no doubt in the author's mind that they were one and the same tube.

The second West Coast manufacturer was Otis B. Moorhead who originally made a tube of almost identical construction to the AudioTron which was sold under the name of Electron Relay by the Pacific Radio Laboratories Sales Co. Like Cunningham, Moorhead also became involved in patent infringements but was able to carry on until 'saved by the gong' following America's entry into World War I in 1917. During the war Moorhead, like anyone else, was free to manufacture tubes for military purposes without fear of incurring lawsuits, and this he proceeded to do. Notable amongst Moorhead's wartime productions were tubes made for the British government.

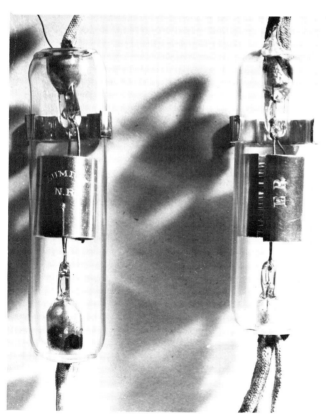

Right: Moorhead ER Electron Relay, 1917. Left: Lumion N.R. (maker unidentified).

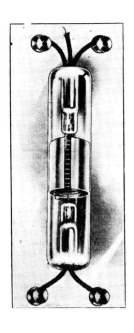
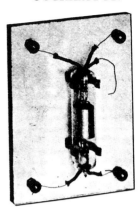
Roome Oscillaudion 1916.

Such tubes were based on a standard French military design which was also being used by British valve makers. Two versions were produced by Moorhead, the first of which had a vertically mounted electrode assembly and was fitted with a spherical bulb having the letter R ink stamped on the side. The second version had horizontally mounted electrodes and was fitted with a stubby tubular bulb bearing the marking V.T.32. In British military parlance of the day the letters V.T. stood for Valve, Transmitting, from which it is obvious that any tubes so marked must have had a sufficiently good vacuum to enable their use in this application. Both types were fitted with a Shaw-made version of the Franco-British 4-pin base.

Under a U.S. Supreme Court decision of 1916 the manufacture of tubes for general sale was again prohibited following the end of the war. For a short time Moorhead continued to make his double-ended Electron Relay and also offered a new type obviously based on the wartime R design. The new model, listed as type R, was a single-ended unbased tube about one inch in diameter, and a little over three inches in length. This tube was described in an undated sales leaflet, circa 1918, issued by the Pacific Laboratories Sales Dept. as being equivalent to the British R type. A higher vacuum version of the same tube was listed as type RH and was said to be suitable for low power transmitting use. A third type was also mentioned but no details were given apart from the fact that it could operate with 500 volts on the plate.

Moorhead was eventually successful in obtaining manufacturing licenses from De Forest and American Marconi but the arrangement under which the tubes were sold was unbelievably complicated. Firstly they were sold to De Forest personally who then sold them to American Marconi who sold them to the De Forest Radio Tel & Tel Co. Hardly had the agreement become effective when the take-over of American Marconi by the newly formed Radio Corporation of America resulted in its cancellation which became effective in July 1920. Meanwhile, however, production of tubes under the tripartite agreement continued. These were made in two versions which had a similar form of construction differing mainly in the relative diameters of the cylindrical plates and grids. Those marked V.T. on the bulb had a plate about 0.37 inches in diameter while the type marked E.R. had a plate nearly twice that size. Both types carried dual markings die-stamped into the base—Marconi VT on one side, De Forest Audion on the other.

After the expiration of the agreement Moorhead continued to make tubes which were sold under the name A-P (Atlantic-Pacific) for a short period but all production ceased in 1923.

A third name among early independents was that of Elman B. Myers. Originally Myers was employed by De Forest and in 1915 was put in charge of the Pacific Coast division of the Radio Telephone & Telegraph Co. It was in this same year that the Pan-Pacific International Exposition was held in San Francisco to mark the opening of the Panama Canal. De Forest secured a display booth at the Exposition at which he personally attended in company with 'Chief' Myers, as the latter was known to him.

Later in the year Myers left De Forest to commence making tubes on his own account. In a testimony given as a witness in a lawsuit several years later Myers claimed to have made tubes in 1915 under the name 'Radiotron' which he sold to Elmer T. Cunningham of the Haller-Cunningham Co., Market St., San Francisco. This was a short-lived venture for after a few months Myers was warned that he was infringing De Forest patents whereupon he ceased further manufacture.

Apparently there were no hard feelings as Myers returned to work for De Forest in 1916 where he remained until 1918. After leaving De Forest for the second time Myers worked first at GE and then at Western Electric before becoming associated with a company known as the Radio Lamp Corp. After being warned by RCA over patent infringement this company changed its name to the Radio Audion Co. and moved from New York to Jersey City. At this location a tube known as the Myers

RAC3 was produced. It was a compact, sturdily built tube of double-ended construction which differed from other duble-ended tubes of the day in being fitted with bakelite end caps carrying the contacts. A special holder was needed to mount the tubes and this was available from the company. Because both ends of the tube were the same they were coloured red and black to ensure correct placement in the holder which carried the markings RED at the upper end and BLACK at the lower end. The Radio Audion Co. continued to make tubes until 1922 when they were forced out of business by legal action instituted by patent holders.

Not to be outdone, Myers then hit on the idea of establishing a factory in some place where, presumably, he considered he would be safe from the threat of legal proceedings for patent infringement. Thus it was that E.B. Myers

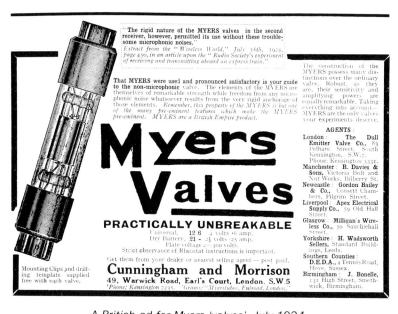

A British ad for Myers 'valves', July 1924.

Myers tube and cartons.

Seven Years of Superiority

KNOWN as the original HI-MU tubes before the days of BCL;

Preferred by amateurs and experts before the first popular receiving set was sold;

Progressively improved in construction and performance;

Made in the newest and best equipped plant in America.

Get the World on Your Dial With Myers Tubes

Low impedance, high amplification constant, high mutual conductance. Best results in any circuit —impedance, resistance or transformer coupled.

At Your Dealer's

Myers Radio Tube Corporation
Cleveland, Ohio

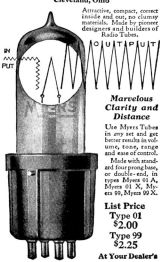

Last Myers ad (1926).

Co. Ltd. of Montreal came into existence. The Canadian factory continued making tubes of the same design but in two styles; the 'Universal' which had a filament rating of 4 V, 0.6 A, and the 'Dry Cell' which was rated at 2.5 V, 0.25 A. The tube cartons bore the legend 'Made in Canada Under Canadian Patent No. 229, 182–229, 183–229, 184.' The Canadian patent application dates were dated 14th January 1922.

During 1923–24 Myers tubes were exported to several countries including Britain, Australia, and New Zealand. In spite of the ban on their manufacture in the U.S. the Canadian tubes were advertised and sold by mail to customers in that country.

By 1925 Myers apparently considered it safe for him to return to the States and the Canadian operation was transferred to Cleveland, Ohio, where it was established as the Myers Radio Tube Corporation. In 1926 tubes of the original double-ended design were still being advertised though by this time were completely obsolete.[1] At the same time a range of four standard type tubes was offered which were described as being 'Made in the Newest and best equipped plant in America.' As nothing further was heard of the Cleveland factory after the middle of 1926 it is concluded that operations ceased at about that time.

Myers' name next appears in connection with the invention of a 'vacuumless' radio tube known as the 'Thermion'.[2] This tube can be politely described as being of unusual design and understandably was never developed beyond the laboratory stage. Nevertheless, it is interesting to note that it rated a mention in a British book published in 1928.[3]

In the few years that had elapsed between the end of World War I and the beginning of broadcasting what little demand there was for radio apparatus was provided by the small but growing number of experimenters and early amateur operators. However, once the idea of broadcasting had 'caught on', interest in the new medium grew like wildfire, and the demand for the necessary hardware, including tubes, mushroomed almost overnight. Whilst it was not too difficult for a large number of component manufacturers to establish themselves to cater for this demand such was not the case with tube makers. Here, the possession of patents by the big four—AT&T, GE, RCA, and Westinghouse, coupled with a policy of not granting manufacturing licenses to aspiring independent tube makers, effectively created a monopoly situation for the patent holders.

Inevitably this restrictive policy led to the production of 'bootleg' tubes, that is, tubes made without the benefit of patent license, by manufacturers who were prepared to face the risk of infringement proceedings. During the next few years the number of independents grew by leaps and bounds, reaching a peak around 1925 when it is estimated that over 80 were in existence. Of these the majority were small fly-by-night operators who came and went without a trace. It has been suggested some of these operations were

Myers tube holders Canadian (L.), USA (R.).

on such a small scale that in the event of threatened legal action the operators could move the entire plant under the cover of darkness and set it up elsewhere under a new name by the following day!

Because of the sheer weight of numbers of these offenders, coupled with their manner of operating, it was virtually impossible to stamp out their largely clandestine activities and bootlegging continued to flourish. It is only fair to emphasise that not all were bootleggers by choice and, given the opportunity, many would undoubtedly have been happy to legalise their status. Indeed, several of the largest eventually became licensed and well-respected independent manufacturers competing on more or less equal terms with RCA and even patenting their own improvements and developments as time went by. Before this could happen, however, nearly a decade was to elapse.

Because certain of the original tube patents were due to expire in the early 1920s some independents apparently thought that after this time they would be free to engage in unrestricted tube manufacture, but such was not to be. There were still numerous other patents which had longer to run and which were equally effective in preventing independent manufacture.

Fleming's original diode patent expired in 1922 and although this then allowed the unrestricted manufacture of diodes with bright-emitting filaments it was really of no help as signal diodes were as dead as the dodo and as yet there was no demand for power rectifiers. The first De Forest patent expired in January 1924 and this too gave fresh hope to many independents who then believed they would at last be free to legally follow their chosen avocation. That they were in error in their assumption is evidenced by the following announcement published by RCA late in 1923:[4]

'The expiration on Jan 15, 1924 of the vacuum tube patent No 841,387, will not permit the general manufacture, sale, importation or use of three element vacuum tubes as generally constructed, in which the grid

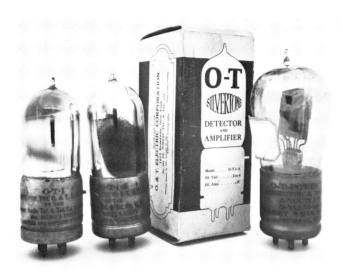

Typical 'bootleg' tubes of the early 1920s.

Magnavox A tube (1924), a gridless triode.

equivalent is interposed or located between the filament and plate.

This type of vacuum tube is still covered by U.S. Letters Patent No 879,532, under which Radiotrons are manufactured and sold to the public.

This latter patent has been sustained by the Courts, and unlicensed tubes have been held by the Courts to be infringements of this patent.'

Well, that was telling 'em, but what it didn't tell them was that the patent quoted had only about another year to run. After February 18, 1925 RCA would have lost another weapon in its armoury but the loss would by no means be sufficient to substantially weaken RCA's position. In 1925 there were still 22 patents operative. Judging by the increase in the number of independents, which reached a peak during 1925–26, this warning had little effect on their activities.

Because the existence of the De Forest 'interposed grid' patent was considered by some of the earliest tube manufacturers to be the main stumbling block in their path towards independent production this sometimes led to various peculiar 'odd ball' schemes to circumvent the patent, and one or two of these will be mentioned here.

Possibly the earliest of such tubes was the so-called 'Weagant Valve' invented by Roy A. Weagant, chief engineer of the American Marconi Co., and patented by him in 1918. This tube used an external control electrode clamped to the outside of the glass envelope in place of the normal grid. Because the Weagant valve was not produced commercially it will not be discussed further. Weagant himself later became vice-president and chief engineer of the De Forest Radio Co. in 1925.

Another of the early non-infringing tubes, known as the 'Sodion', deserves mention perhaps not so much because of its peculiarities but for the dogged determination displayed by its inventor in his long-standing attempts, ex-

tending over several years, to commercialise his invention. H.P. Donle of the Connecticut Telephone & Electric Co. started work on his first tubes in 1919 and continued to 1927. During this time Donle's tubes took many strange forms starting with an external anode type through to one using a liquid sodium anode (this tube could only be used with the bulb downwards) and thence to a type filled with sodium vapour maintained at a certain temperature by means of an external heating element.[5] Commercial versions of Donle's tubes were the Connecticut J117 and the Sodion types S10, S11, S13, S14, D21, followed by the Donle types B6, DR4, DP10, DP11, B8, the last five types being made by the Donle-Bristol Corp.

An unusual tube of somewhat surprising origin was made for a short period by an old established manufacturer of loudspeakers, the Magnavox Co. of Oakland, California.

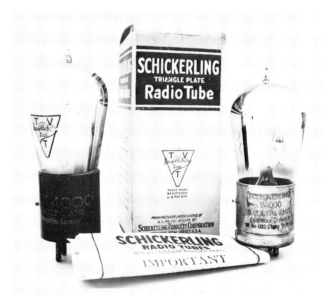

Schickerling SX400 and S-4000 typical 'bootleg' tubes of the 1920s.

Sodion S-13 and D-21.

Just how Magnavox came to be involved in making tubes is not known although the company had been producing amplifiers for use with their speakers. In 1924 Magnavox commenced production of radio receivers and it was at this time that the first tubes were made. Presumably these two ventures were complementary but as it happened they were both short-lived.

The Magnavox 'A' tube was first advertised for general sale in October 1924[6] and no further ads appeared after the end of 1926. In its original form the tube was fitted with a tip-sealed bulb and brass UV base but early in 1926 a change was made to the use of a tipless bulb and bakelite base. The notable feature of the Magnavox tube was the use of a special control electrode in place of a normal grid. This electrode was made of thin sheet metal punched into the form of an inverted vee having serrated edges.[7] This electrode was of the same contour as the filament and was positioned closely to it. In spite of being extensively advertised the tubes never became popular which, in view of what must have been an indifferent performance, is not surprising. Production of both tubes and receivers appears to have ceased at the same time though speaker manufacture was unaffected by this move. Incidentally, Magnavox re-entered the receiver field many years later with the production of high quality radio-phonograph combinations.

Apart from those manufacturers who attempted to produce non-infringing tubes the majority seemed content to follow established Radiotron designs fairly closely but as time went by examples of tubes with non-standard characteristics began to appear. One of the first of such tubes was Cleartron's type 101A, a high-mu type intended for use in resistance coupled audio circuits. It was announced towards the end of 1925,[8] some 18 months before RCA's UX-240. Other high-mu tubes were CeCo's type 'G' (May

1927) and an unidentified type by Ken Rad (December 1926). Also in 1926 one manufacturer, Sonatron, produced two different types of high-mu tubes and at the same time claimed to have '. . . the largest range of radio tubes in the world.' (No comments!) The De Forest Radio Co. also got in on the act with their range of 'Specialist Audions' produced in 1926–27; the word 'Specialist' in this connection indicated that the tubes had varying characteristics enabling their use in specialised applications.

Other innovations during the period were the use of an 'M' filament by Perryman in January 1926; the introduction of low-drain tubes, known as type 201B, by CeCo and Sonatron in 1928, and the use of oxide-coated filaments in 201A type tubes by Arcturus and National Union in 1933.

Further examples of non-standard productions were the so-called 'adaptor' tubes. These fell into two groups; the first consisted of a standard type tube fitted with a type of base normally used on a different tube. An example from this group is the Sonatron A199 which was a 199 tube fitted with a standard sized UX base. Such tubes could be

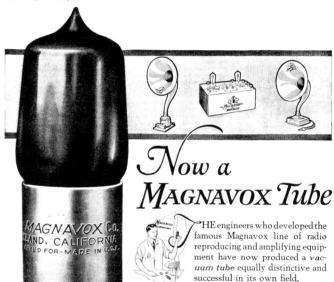
32

used to convert a wet-battery receiver to dry-cell operation. The second group consisted of tubes fitted with a modified type of UX base carrying four terminals mounted on a flange. These were power output tubes having interrupted grid and plate connections to enable the use of additional grid bias and plate voltage without disturbing the internal wiring of existing receivers. This was a rather clumsy expedient to enable the use of a power tube in the last stage of any receiver normally using a general purpose tube in this position. Examples of such tubes are Magnatron DC12, Sonatron 171, Van Horne 5VCX. Nowadays these tubes are of interest to collectors due to their comparative rarity coupled with their unusual appearance.

FOR THE LAST AUDIO SOCKET

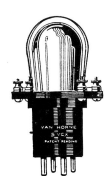

Van Horne Adapted Mogul 5 VCX Power Tube

The Mogul 5 VCX is a double capacity power tube—specially to carry all of the signal to the speaker without distortion or loss of signal quality.

Because it can be used in your set without a change in wiring it is an addition that you should make for that increase in volume and improvement in reception that is absent when an ordinary tube of unsufficient capacity is used.

Ask your dealer to demonstrate this remarkable tube to you.

THE VAN HORNE CO

FRANKLIN, OHIO (1926)

After 1928 the rapid growth of such large receiver manufacturers as Atwater Kent, Crosley, Majestic, and Philco, who required vast quantities of tubes to keep their production lines running, led to rapid changes in the tube industry. Henceforth, only those tube manufacturers capable of large-scale production would survive into the 1930s. Almost overnight the number of independents dropped dramatically, such were the changed conditions. Of those in existence in 1926 fewer than half remained by 1928 and the process of attrition continued until 1931 when only 19 remained. Few of the earliest independents successfully made the transition from battery tube manufacture to large-scale production of AC tubes, some of the better-known survivors being CeCo, De Forest, Ken-Rad, Raytheon, and Sylvania.

Although several new independents became established after 1927, examples being Arcturus (1927), Perryman (1929), Triad (1929), Champion (1930), and National Union (1930), only the last named survived World War II. In October 1929 an article in *Radio News* made refer-

ence to 'over 50' tube manufacturers of whom only about a dozen were RCA licensees and went on to suggest that tube manufacturing 'may conceivably be overdone'. It must be realised, however, that the small percentage of RCA licensees at that time was largely the result of RCA's former policy which until 1929 had denied licenses to the independents.

By 1930 the tube industry had become established on a firmer footing with about 15 licensed manufacturers, apart from RCA, in existence. This was a far cry from the chaotic days of 1926 but the number of independents continued to drop throughout the 1930s until by 1935 only 8 receiving tube manufacturers remained. Not all the casualties occurred as a result of the highly competitive conditions within the industry for it must be remembered that in the early thirties the prevailing economic depression was at its worst and this in itself was the cause of the demise of many smaller companies. Although by 1932 twenty companies had been successful in acquiring manufacturing licenses few of them survived long enough after that to obtain the benefit of their new status.

Between 1935 and the time of America's entry into World War II the number of independent tube manufacturers remained fairly constant and comprised the following: Arcturus, Champion, Hytron, Ken-Rad, National Union, Raytheon, Sylvania, and Tung Sol. Of these all but the first two remained in existence throughout the war and were active in producing tubes for military purposes. In some cases one company acted as a sub-contractor making specialised types of tubes which they did not normally produce. For example, Tung Sol made the Western Electric type 717A (VT-269) doorknob tube and Sylvania made the Philips-Mullard type EF50 for the British government. However, the important part played by all types of vacuum tubes during World War II is a story in itself which is outside the scope of this book.

REFERENCES

1. See, for example, advt. *QST*, April 1926, p. 71.
2. H.G. Silbersdorff, The Vacuumless Tube, *Radio News*, May 1925, p. 71.
3. G.G. Black, *History of Radio Telephony & Telephony* (1928), p. 259.
4. Quoted by John B. Brady in The Vacuum Tube Patent Situation, *Radio News*, May 1924, p. 1573.
5. John V.L. Hogan, A New and Ultra-Sensitive Detector, *Radio News*, December 1923, p. 686.
6. See advt. Magnavox Co., *Radio News*, October 1924, p. 359.
7. New Developments in Vacuum Tubes, *Radio News*, Feb. 1925, p. 74.
8. See advt. Cleartron Vacuum Tube Co., *Popular Radio*, December 1925, ads. 74.

Chapter Six

Another Grid

In order to trace the origin of the first four-element tube, or tetrode as it later came to be called, it is necessary to go back to a period in history during World War I. At that time the German Army was seeking a tube which could operate satisfactorily on a low plate voltage in portable field equipment where considerations of bulk and weight were of prime importance. Any tube that could fulfil this requirement would allow a much smaller and lighter HT battery to be used. This led to research on the part of Dr. Walter Schottky of the Siemens & Halske Co. which resulted in what came to be known as the Siemens-Schottky double-grid tube.

In this tube an additional grid, held at the same potential as (but not connected to) the plate was interposed between the filament and control grid. In practice the voltage applied to the inner grid and plate was often as low as 10 volts. The effect of this extra grid was to neutralise the so-called 'space charge' existing between the filament and grid, thus allowing a higher degree of amplification at quite low plate voltages.

Schottky patented two forms of this new tube in 1916[1] and 1917 and also produced a version in which the additional grid was placed between the control grid and plate. However, as this version proved less suitable for the particular application it was not developed beyond the laboratory stage.

Following the end of World War I manufacturers in other countries turned their attention to this new type of tube. Amongst the first in the field was the Dutch firm of Philips who had for many years been engaged in the manufacture of incandescent lamps. Their first double-grid tube, type Q, was marketed in May 1923.[2] In 1924 the type Q became type D-VI, following a change in Philips numbering system,[3] and at the same time another tube, type B-VI, was introduced. The two earlier productions were bright emitters with filament ratings of 3.5 V, 0.5 A, while the B-VI was a dull emitter requiring 1.8 V, 0.15 A for its filament. Plate and inner grid voltage for all types was 10 volts max.

Three different styles of base were used, depending on which country the tubes were sold in. For the European market the wartime Franco-British 4-pin base fitted with a side-mounted terminal was used, but in addition the French Radiola large 5-pin metal-shell base was also available. For markets outside Europe the American UV metal-shell base was used, modified by the addition of a cleverly designed contact strip to which was affixed a screw terminal. Such an arrangement was necessary due to the surface of the base shell being covered when the tube was inserted in its socket.

In 1926 a new version, available in four different voltages, was issued; the type A141, A241, A341, and A441 were rated at 1, 2, 3, and 4 volts respectively. These tubes were fitted with smaller tapered bulbs, the inner surface of which was obscured by a heavy getter deposit. Four-pin bases of the now standard European type, modified by the addition of a side terminal to which the inner grid was connected, were used.

Double-grid tubes 1924.

Although the double-grid tube originated in Germany it does not appear to have been widely used there. Examples are the Telefunken types RE82 and REO74d. The former was the earlier of the two being fitted with a special Telefunken 5-pin base, whilst the latter was fitted with a standard European 4-pin base modified by the addition of a side terminal.

France was really the home of the double-grid tube since a greater variety of types was produced and they remained in use longer than in any other country. Known as the Bigrille (or Bigril, depending upon the whims of the particular maker) the French tube was used mainly as a frequency changer in superheterodyne receivers. From about 1930 onwards this type of tube was also produced in an indirectly heated version which remained in use until finally ousted by the coming of the more modern heptode and triode-hexode tubes. Examples of the earlier French double-grid tubes are the Métal DG and the Radio Micro R43.

On the British scene the M-O. Valve Co. was in a unique position in that it could claim to have made four-electrode valves for longer than most European manufacturers. This was quite true but it should be pointed out that the valves referred to, such as the FE1 of 1920, were screen-grid, not space-charge grid types. The first British double-grid valves advertised for sale were the types FE.3 and DE.7,[4] the electrode structures of which were closely modelled on the ubiquitous R valve. Filament ratings were 4 V, 0.65 A and 1.8 V, 0.4 A respectively and both types had a recommended voltage of from 6 to 15 volts for the inner grid and anode.

Some idea of the insignificant part played by the space-charge tetrode can be gained from the fact that in 1925 only two manufacturers, Mullard and M-O.V., listed double-grid types. By 1932 there were three makers, Cossor, Mullard, and M-O.V- producing double-grid valves designed for use as frequency changers in battery operated superhets. Within two years, however, these were completely superseded by the coming of the heptode frequency changer.

Before leaving the space-charge tetrode mention must be made of an attempt during 1924 to revive interest in its use by the publicising of a circuit known as the 'Unidyne'. The Unidyne was the brainchild of G.V. Dowding and K.D. Rogers, of the London weekly publication *Popular Wireless*, who devised a circuit wherein the normal HT battery was dispensed with.

A four-electrode valve, originally known as the Thorpe K4 and later as the Unidyne valve, was specially produced by the Bower Electric Ltd., London, for use in the Unidyne circuit.[5] This valve bore a fairly close resemblance to the M-O FE.3 and carried a filament rating of 4 V, 0.42 A. Unlike the M-O. valves the Unidyne was fitted with a special 5-pin base requiring a matching 5-pin socket. Incidentally, this is the first known use of a 5-pin base by a British valve maker and in this respect the Bower Electric Co. was a pioneer even though their base did not become the one adopted as the industry standard some five years later.

The idea of attempting to operate a valve without using

Mullard PMIDG. 1929

Philips A141. 1926.

Two German double-grid tubes.
1927   1925

an HT battery may seem absurd yet an examination of the circuit reveals that although no separate battery was used the plate did receive a positive voltage, albeit a small one, due to the plate return being made to the positive side of the filament supply. By using a 1.8-volt valve, such as the M-O. DE.7, with the filament tapped across the most negative cell of a 6-volt LT battery the remaining four volts were then available to supply the plate and inner grid. The Unidyne used a 4-volt valve with only a 4-volt battery, however.

Not surprisingly, the idea of a receiver which could be operated without the need of the usual HT battery met with considerable skepticism and in June 1924 *Wireless World* published an editorial supported by letters from six 'eminent authorities' pointing out the futility of trying to obtain something for nothing.[6] A month later, however, probably in an attempt to show lack of bias, the same journal published an article on the construction of a receiver making use of a four-electrode valve operating without an HT battery.

In spite of the publicity given to the Unidyne little more was heard of it and by the end of the year it had passed into limbo. Before this had happened, however, the Unidyne had crossed the Atlantic where its cause was espoused by none other than Hugo Gernsback, then editor of *Radio News*. Writing editorially in the August 1924 issue Gernsback mentions having secured the American and Canadian publication rights to the Unidyne circuit, now renamed 'Solodyne', and also stated that the word had been registered as a trade-mark by *Radio News*.

The absence of any American double-grid tube was soon remedied by the production of one by the Nutron Mfg. Co. of New Jersey. Known as the Nutron Solodyne[7], this tube resembled the ubiquitous UV-201A in appearance but differed from its European counterparts in having no actual terminal for the inner grid connection. Because the UV type base did not readily lend itself to the addition of a side-mounted terminal the inner grid connection was made directly to the tube's metal base shell. Of course this meant that it was essential to use a socket which also had a metal shell in order that electrical contact could be made with the base of the tube.

In America as in Britain the B-batteryless circuit proved to be a flash in the pan and within a similar length of time both the circuit and the tube were completely forgotten.

Another form of tetrode, almost equally as old as the space-charge type, was one in which the additional grid was placed between the control grid and plate. Although no commercially produced tube ever resulted solely from the insertion of an extra grid in the way that occurred in the case of the space-charge tetrode, the idea eventually resulted in a completely new type of tube.

One of the first-encountered inadequacies of the triode was its inability to provide a satisfactory degree of ampli-

fication at radio frequencies without instability or feedback and oscillation occurring due to the internal plate-to-grid capacity. Developments of triodes having extremely small inter-electrode capacities had reached a practical limit with the production of Round's wartime type V.24 valve. Circuitwise, attempts were made to overcome the problem of attaining stable amplification by either of two different methods. The simplest and crudest of these was to add damping to the circuit by the inclusion of a resistor in series with the grid of the tube—the so-called 'losser' system.

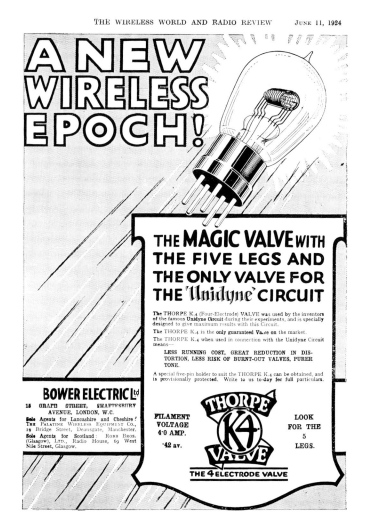

The second and more efficient method consisted in coupling an out-of-phase voltage from the plate circuit back to the grid, which had the effect of neutralising the plate-to-grid capacity of the tube allowing a reasonable degree of RF amplification to be obtained. The best and most widely known of such schemes was the so-called 'Neutrodyne' circuit developed by Professor L.A. Hazeltine of the Stevens Institute of Technology in New Jersey as far back as 1919. Later the Hazeltine Corporation was formed which licensed receiver manufacturers to use the patents.

As an RF amplifier for broadcast-band reception the neutralised triode reigned supreme for many years, both in battery and AC-operated receivers but on shorter wavelengths it was a different matter. Even with the best and most carefully adjusted neutralised circuits it was impossible to obtain appreciable amplification below wavelengths of 50 metres. A further practical difficulty was that neutralisation remained effective over only a very narrow band of frequencies in any particular tuned circuit and was thus impracticable where a wide tuning range was required.

One of the earliest attempts to improve on the radio-frequency performance of the triode was made as early as 1920 by H.J. Round of the Marconi Co. Taking as a basis his existing low-capacity V24 triode Round added a wire mesh screen between grid and plate in an attempt to reduce the grid-to-plate capacitance. The resulting valve was known as type FE1, the letters FE indicating Four Electrode.[8] That this design was only partially effective is admitted by the valve's inventor but nevertheless it must be regarded as the progenitor of all later British screen-grid valves. The FE1 valve is known to have been used in a Marconi shipboard receiver Type 91, circa 1923, but not in screen-grid mode.[9] A somewhat smaller version of the FE1 known as the FE2 is known to have been produced but no reliable information on its characteristics or use is available.

It must be borne in mind that at this period in history broadcasting had hardly begun and shortwave communication was very much in its infancy which meant that there was consequently no market for Round's valves and thus little incentive to make further improvements. By 1927, however, broadcasting was becoming well established in Britain and the growing number of both home constructors and receiver manufacturers was creating new demands for better valves. At this time, and indeed for several more years, the most popular receiver whether homemade or factory built, was a three-valve set consisting of a regenerative detector followed by two stages of AF amplification. As in America the problem of obtaining stable RF amplification remained and although neutralised triodes were by no means unknown they were not as widely used.

Doubtless this was partly due to the fact that the average British receiver used no more than three valves, and as stages of transformer coupled audio resulted in much higher overall gain a valve could not be spared as an RF amplifier. When RF amplification was used it was normally limited to one stage, and any additional selectivity needed obtained by the use of a bandpass filter to the grid of the RF valve. In order for it to be really worthwhile to spare a valve for RF amplification clearly that valve had to be able to 'pull its weight', but before that could happen a much more efficient type of valve was needed. The stage was set for the appearance of the screen-grid valve.

Captain Round's name now appears in connection with two new types of screen-grid valves patented by him in 1926.[10] The first of these and the one forming the basis for the first commercial development was a valve of unconventional design wherein a V-shaped filament was enclosed by a grid in the normal manner but only one side of this assembly was presented to the remaining two electrodes. The anode took the form of a flat metal disc positioned 'end on' to the filament and grid, while the screen completely enveloped the anode. The screening-grid extended crosswide to the walls of the bulb and in use the valve was positioned so that it protruded through a hole in a sheet-metal partition, the edges of which had to be aligned with the edge of the screen-grid to form an electrical extension of the latter.

Round's second design, although patented only two months after the first, differed substantially in construction as the plate and screen were arranged in the normal co-axial manner and all electrodes were mounted on a single pinch. As shown in the patent specification, the plate was taken through the side of the bulb but apart from this the design foreshadowed future developments.

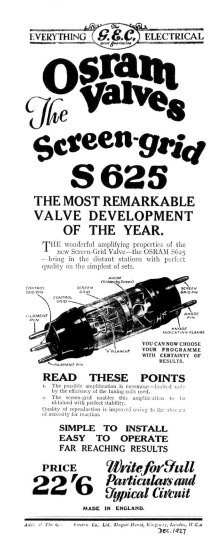

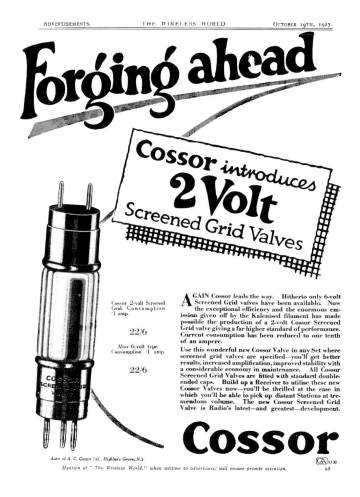
Somewhat surprisingly, however, the first commercial pro-
duction was of a valve closely resembling the one described
in the earlier patent.

In principle both these valves were identical to one of
American design due to A.W. Hull of GE. Hull's screen-
grid tube had been patented[11] in the U.K. at much the
same time as the two valves of Round's but it is not known
what influence, if any, the patent had on British developments.

The first commercial version of Round's valve was released in October 1927 under both Marconi and Osram
brandnames as type S.625. Marconi kitsets, models T.1
and T.2, using the new valve were on display at the 1927
Manchester Show held in October of that year. In December *Wireless World* described their first screen-grid receiver and during 1928 the first factory-built sets incorporating screen-grid valves were marketed.

Cossor was the only other valve maker to produce a
double-ended valve modelled on the S.625 and it was offered with a choice of either 6-volt or 2-volt filaments.[12] A
military version of the S.625 was made by Cossor and
MO-V under the Army type number ARS6.

Mullard had also announced screen-grid valves at the
1927 Manchester Show but these were not advertised for
sale until well into 1928. By the end of 1928 all valve

makers with the exception of Cosmos were marketing standard type valves with 4-pin bases and top-mounted anode
terminals.

The use of an insulated screw terminal on the top of the
bulb for the plate connection remained an industry standard, in both Britain and the continent, for all types of
SG valves throughout their production lifetime. This was
in direct contrast to American practice where the grid
connection was always taken to the top cap.

As in the U.S., vari-mu valves were first produced in
indirectly heated form, though as a matter of interest Cossor had marketed a battery version, type 220VS, in December 1931.

As a species the screen-grid valve had the shortest production of any generic type, being completely eclipsed
within the space of seven years by the radio-frequency
pentode.

As has so often happened in the history of mankind's
inventions, it will be found that similar work was going
on at much the same time in different countries and the
case of the screen-grid tube was no exception. In the
United States the first application of the screen-grid principle occurred in 1924 when Dr. A.W. Hull of GE was
seeking a high-gain RF amplifier for laboratory use in
investigating the problem of tube noise in the early Armstrong superheterodynes. The amplifier was required to
have an overall gain of at least 10,000 times and in order to
achieve this Hull had to design a special tube for the purpose. The outcome was the production of the first American screen-grid tube, a laboratory type which formed the
basis for the development of a future commercial type.

Marconi-Osram S625 screen-grid valve.

That the design was successful may be judged from the
fact that Hull was able to obtain a gain of over 4,000,000
at 400 metres from a four-stage amplifier. The higher
amplification of the tetrode was a welcome additional
characteristic in addition to its lower inter-electrode capacitance, assuring it of an important place once a commercial form had been developed.

In February 1927[13] GE started small-scale production of
an SG tube bearing the type number UX-222, and in October RCA announced its public release.[14] The 222 had an

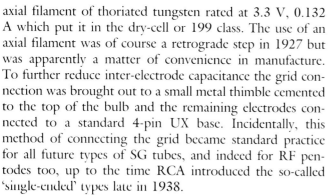

Radiotron UX-222. Note spiral wire screen in tube on right.

CeCo type RF22, equivalent to Radiotron UX-222.

axial filament of thoriated tungsten rated at 3.3 V, 0.132 A which put it in the dry-cell or 199 class. The use of an axial filament was of course a retrograde step in 1927 but was apparently a matter of convenience in manufacture. To further reduce inter-electrode capacitance the grid connection was brought out to a small metal thimble cemented to the top of the bulb and the remaining electrodes connected to a standard 4-pin UX base. Incidentally, this method of connecting the grid became standard practice for all future types of SG tubes, and indeed for RF pentodes too, up to the time RCA introduced the so-called 'single-ended' types late in 1938.

Amongst thoriated-filament tubes the 222 was unique in having the magnesium getter fired from an inverted cup thus confining the condensed deposit to the lower wall of the bulb, unlike other tubes which had their bulbs completely obscured. This procedure was obviously necessary in order to prevent the metallic condensate coming into contact with the internal grid lead to the top of the bulb. From about 1932 onwards replacement versions of the 222 exhibited constructional differences from the original type. The filament was changed from axial to inverted 'V' and was now oxide-coated while the remaining electrode structure was considerably enlarged, presumably to accommodate the larger filament area. At the same time the bulb shape was changed from S-14 to ST-14. In this form the 22 was made by all the larger independents, including Ken-Rad, N.U., Raytheon, Sylvania, and Tung Sol. By comparison, very few independent tube makers produced

the type UX-222, one of the earliest being the Shieldplate Tube Corp. of Chicago who advertised their type SP-22 in January 1928.[15] Another was the C.E. Mfg. Co. Inc. of Providence, R.I. who advertised their CeCo type RF-22 in May 1928.[16]

One reason for the lack of interest in the 222 was probably because at the time of its appearance in 1927–28 the attention of the industry was focussed on the development of AC-operated triodes and thus there was little incentive to develop new types of battery-operated tubes.

Compared with the position in Europe only a minimal number of different types of battery-operated SG tubes was produced. Apart from the dry-cell type 22 there was only one, type 232, in the original 2-volt Air Cell range. It was, of course, a sharp cut-off type as vari-mu tubes had not then been invented. By comparison with its predecessor the 232 had a considerably reduced filament consumption and at the same time required only half the plate current as well as having improved performance.

No remote cut-off tetrode was issued in the Air Cell range but later on some manufacturers produced tetrode versions of existing 2-volt pentodes. The tubes in question are types 1A4 and 1B4 which had dual generic identities depending on which company made them. In order to differentiate between them it became necessary to add distinguishing symbols to their type numbers—thus the 1A4 became 1A4T or 1A4P, depending on whether it was made in tetrode or pentode form, the same applied to the type 1B4.

40

REFERENCES

1. German Patent 300,617 of June 1, 1916. British Patent 145,421 of May 1916.

2. Information received from Ir. F.J.J. Driesens, Hapert, Holland.

3. See Philips catalogue dated June 15, 1924.

4. See advt. *Wireless World*, Oct. 1, 1924, p. xxxi.

5. See advt. *Wireless World*, June 11, 1924, p. 267.

6. See editorial *Wireless World*, June 4, 1924.

7. See advt. *Radio News*, Sept. 1924, p. 393.

8. H.J. Round, *The Shielded Four Electrode Valve*, pub. Cassell, 1924.

9. See *Harmsworth's Wireless Encyclopedia*, 1924, p. 960.

10. British Patent 275,535 appln. date May 5, 1926 and British Patent 279,171 appln. date July 22, 1926.

11. British Patent No. 255,441.

12. See advt. *Wireless World*, Oct. 19, 1926, p. ad. 12.

13. *GE Report*, p. 53.

14. Ibid.

15. See advt. Shieldplate Tube Corp., *Radio News*, Jan. 1928, p. 813.

16. See advt. C.E. Mfg. Co., *Radio News*, May 1928, p. 1279.

Radiotron 232 and 32 2-volt S.G. tubes (1930–31).

Chapter Seven

A Turning Point

American Developments

The production of receivers that could be operated directly from the household AC mains (the so-called 'all-electric', 'socket power', or 'batteryless' receivers) resulted from the inconvenience and expense attendant on the use of battery-powered sets. The appeal of such receivers was undeniable and, more than anything else, enabled the idea of 'a radio in every home' to become a reality.

Although the production of mains-operated receivers hinged largely on the development of special AC tubes, some receiver manufacturers initially found ways of making sets incorporating existing battery tubes. This was done because the new AC tubes were both expensive and hard to procure; for example, the bulk of Radiotron production was at this time being reserved for use in RCA Radiola receivers. Furthermore, many early AC tubes were often less than satisfactory in service.

As it was impossible to use 'raw' AC to supply the filaments of battery tubes, without the resultant audible hum spoiling the quality of reception, ways and means were sought to provide a supply of DC for the purpose. The simplest way to do this was to incorporate a built-in 'A' battery eliminator capable of supplying as many parallel-connected tubes as were used in the receiver. Due to the excessive cost and bulk of such a system it was seldom used commercially though at least one manufacturer resorted to it.[1] This particular model used five series-connected 201-A tubes fed from a pair of Tungar 0.6-A rectifiers used in a full-wave circuit.

A second, and more economical, method of feeding series-connected filaments was to make use of the existing high tension or 'B' supply to provide the filament current in addition to its normal function. Such a scheme was practicable only if the total filament drain did not exceed the capabilites of existing HT rectifiers. By using type UX-199 low-drain tubes the current needed was only 60 mA. Reasonably satisfactory operation of a multi-tube receiver could be obtained provided some other arrangement was made for supplying the output tube, which, of

necessity, needed more filament power. Fortunately it was found possible to run the filaments of directly-heated output tubes on AC without encountering problems with hum and, as a matter of interest, the use of directly-heated output tubes remained a common practice for many years after the universal use of indirectly-heated tubes in all other stages of a receiver.

Although 199 tubes were economical of filament power, the fragility of their filaments made it desirable to use the more rugged 201-A tubes in their place. However, this was not possible until a rectifier capable of handling the 250 mA required, plus the receiver's HT requirements, had become available. By the end of 1926, however, the production of a 350 mA gaseous rectifier by Raytheon solved this problem.

An indication of just how far receiver manufacturers were prepared to go in devising methods of using battery tubes in AC sets can be seen in the case of one model produced by the Balkite Mfg. Co. of Chicago in 1928. This company dreamed up a unique method of supplying five series-connected 201-A tubes by feeding the filaments with a 4 MHz current generated by a UX-210 tube functioning as an RF oscillator.[2] Of course the frequency chosen had to be not only supersonic but also outside the limits of the broadcast band in order to prevent heterodyne interference. Apparently the idea was quite practicable as well as being comparatively inexpensive as no filtering of the filament supply was needed.

Meanwhile, receiver engineers were awaiting the arrival of a new type of tube that could use AC directly on its filament. In September 1927 such a tube was introduced by RCA under the type number UX-226.[3] This tube closely resembled the 201-A, both in physical appearance and characteristics, the main difference being that it had an oxide-coated filament. Whilst this latter feature gave the tube a somewhat better performance it had no bearing on its suitability for use on an AC filament supply.

It had been found that there were two factors connected with the running of tube filaments on AC which caused modulation of the emission by the alternations of the sup-

Next Year's Radio Set Will Be Designed to Operate On House Electric Current!

ply. The first of these was the electro-static field produced by the voltage drop across the filament; whilst the second factor was the electro-magnetic field set up by the current. By carefully proportioning the ratio of voltage to current it was found possible to keep the resultant hum level to a minimum. In practice a one-to-one ratio of 1.5 volts at 1.5 amps was found to be the most effective. This, together with a centre-tapped resistor across the filament, or a centre-tapped winding on the supply transformer, reduced the hum to an acceptable level, enabling the 226 to be used in any stage except the detector. For use in the critical detector position it was necessary to develop a completely new type of AC tube. Surprisingly, in view of the Radio Group's efforts, such a tube had actually been marketed some two years earlier by an independent company.

In connection with the development of the AC tube it had quite early been recognised that if a tube's filament could be made to serve only as a source of heat without being the actual emitter of electrons, a way lay open to obtaining an electron stream unpolluted by an AC fila-

ment supply. The Westinghouse Co. were pioneers in the field of AC tube design and much of their work formed the basis for future developments. A tube wherein the filament was no longer the emitter but served solely to heat a separate emitting cylinder was patented by two Westinghouse workers, Freeman and Wade, as early as 1921.[4] In its original form this tube was of double-ended construction with the filament, or 'heater' as it was now called, taken out to separate contacts located at the top of the bulb. This type of construction was adopted in order to isolate the AC heater circuit from the signal carrying circuits. Although the double-ended design was not developed beyond the laboratory stage by Westinghouse, it did serve as a basis for the commercial production of similar tubes by at least three independent tube makers.

The first indirectly-heated AC tube was announced in 1925[5] and it was also first advertised for sale at this same time by a company named the McCullough Sales Co. of Pittsburgh. This tube was the brain-child of one F.S. McCullough, a former Westinghouse employee who had several patents to his credit.[6] Early in 1926 it was announced that the McCullough tubes were being made by the Kellogg Supply & Switchboard Co. of Chicago.

The double-ended construction of the McCullough tubes, apart from its intended hum reduction feature, also enabled the tube to be used for electrifying existing battery-operated receivers. The electrically isolated heater allowed any number of tubes to be supplied by means of a separate 'filament' transformer without the need for alterations to the wiring of such receivers. Furthermore, the tube's characteristics closely matched those of the ubiquitous 201-A and thus the receiver's performance was unaffected.

Just how a previously unknown independent was able to produce and market an indirectly-heated tube some two years ahead of RCA has never been satisfactorily explained, although it has been suggested that it was done with the tacit approval of the Radio Group in order to allow the McCullough tube to play a guinea pig role. Be that as it may, McCullough soon relinquished his control of production and marketing arrangements which, later in 1926, passed into the hands of the Kellogg Supply & Switchboard Co.

Tubes under the Kellogg brandname became available during the latter part of 1926, being used in Kellogg receivers as well as in several other commercially built receivers of the 1926–28 period. However, following the introduction of standard type tubes by RCA and other tube markers, late in 1927, Kellogg tubes soon waned in popularity leaving only the replacement market to be catered to.

For the information of tube collectors the following details are included. The earliest McCullough tubes were fitted with brass UV bases and had the bulbs obscured by a heavy getter deposit; identification was by means of an ink-stamp marking on the base—McCullough AC Tube. Second production used a Shaw bakelite UV base and had the wording McCULLOUGH PATENTED AC TUBE contained within a circle imprinted on the surface of the bulb. The cartons carried the marking TYPE 400. Published details on the characteristics and ratings of the earliest tubes are lacking but it is presumed that they were

similar to the later type 401. Final production used a Shaw bakelite UX base hot-branded McCULLOUGH TYPE 401 AC TUBE.

The first production under the Kellogg brandname differed only in having the word 'Kellogg' in place of 'McCullough' hot-branded on the base. The second, and probably final, production had a bakelite UX base marked on the underside with the letter 'K' in raised moulding, the same marking being applied to the top cap connector. In addition to the type 401 two power tubes, types 402 and 403, were later introduced. These were of similar construction to the 401, using the same style of base and top connector. The shape of the bulb differed in being tubular as compared with the distinctive 'reverse taper' or bullet-shaped bulbs of the general purpose McCullough-Kellogg. Heater rating of the power tubes was 3 volts at 1.5 amps. There is no record of either the 402 or 403 being used in commercially built receivers.

During these formative years several other independent tube makers, for example, Arcturus, Cardon, Marathon, and Sovereign, produced their own individual styles of indirectly-heated AC tubes. Of these the Sovereign most closely resembled the McCullough design in having its heater connections terminated at an insulated top cap. There was a slight difference in the actual style of connections which were in the form of screw terminals, and the bulb shape differed in being tubular instead of tapered. The Cardon and Marathon both had elongated UX bases with the heater connections taken to side-mounted terminals. The two makes were not interchangeable because, apart from a difference in heater voltages (6 volts for the Marathon and 3 volts for the Cardon), the style of side contacts were dissimilar. Cardon tubes were used extensively in Sparton receivers during 1927–28. Reference to Arcturus tubes will be found in a separate place.

To revert now to mainstream developments: the origi-

Kellogg 403 power output tube.

Final production type Kellogg 401 (L.). Unbranded 401 replacement (R.).

44

nal Westinghouse design, being of double-ended construction, had proved to be unsuited to mass production and was accordingly redesigned in single-ended form. Apart from the resultant benefit of simplified manufacture the receiver manufacture also benefitted in that the new design allowed the clumsy overhead wiring formerly needed to be dispensed with. In May 1927 a practical form of single-ended tube fitted with a 5-pin base was announced by RCA under the type number UY-227.[7] The 227 was a landmark tube as, apart from being the first standardised indirectly-heated tube, it ushered in the era of the mass-produced all-electric receiver.

The 227 was the first tube to use both a standardised heater voltage and a standardised 5-pin base. The figure of 2.5 volts chosen for the heater voltage was to remain an industry standard for all types of AC tubes produced over the next five years. All UY-227s used S-14 sized bulbs until 1932 when the type number was officially changed to 27. From then on a smaller, ST-12, bulb was used and the base diameter was reduced to match.

In its original form the 227 used a hairpin-shaped heater, insulated from the cathode by means of a twin-bore ceramic tube. A coating of metallic oxides was applied to the outer surface of the cathode tube which formed the electron emitter. This was in essence the principle of the indirectly-heated cathode. However, the actual form of construction was to undergo many changes and refinements during the next few years.

A practical disadvantage resulting from the original form of construction was the long time taken for the cathode to reach emitting temperature and in an effort to improve matters a new design was introduced in 1928. This later production used a tightly coiled spiral heater supported and centred with the cathode by a porcelain bush at each end. Although the absence of any solid insulation between heater and cathode dramatically reduced warm-up time, the use of a single-coil heater resulted in an increased hum level which necessitated a further change. A return was made to the earlier style of construction in a modified form which resulted in an acceptably short warm-up time coupled with a satisfactory hum level. For the next few years the twin-bore insulator remained in use on Radiotron tubes until finally ousted by the slip-coated heater which came into use from 1933 onwards. Whilst only the type UY-227 has been singled out for specific mention the foregoing remarks apply equally to the companion types UY-224, 224A, and 235.

During this transitional period of development several different designs of heater construction and methods of heater-cathode insulation were tried and discarded. One of the earliest attempts to dispense with a solid insulator was made by Eveready Raytheon who, in 1929, succeeded in producing a design in which a hairpin heater was insulated solely by means of a coating of kaolin (aluminium silicate) applied to it.[8] Although this design resulted in a reduced

National Union NY67 (6.3 volts). A landmark tube. April–May 1931.

Experimental AC tube, prototype of UR-227. Note heater connections at top of bulb.

45

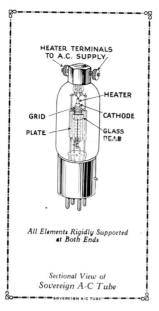

Sectional View of
Sovereign A-C Tube

All Elements Rigidly Supported
at Both Ends

UY-227. Note glass bead in earlier type on the left.

Marathon AC608R. Note heater connections on sides of base.

Farad—an early AC tube. Note twin heater-cathodes.

warm-up time it was not entirely successful due to cracking and flaking of the coating after a period of use, and further research continued. In 1931 Eveready Raytheon were using a coated heater made in the form of a reflexed helix centred under tension within the cathode; later in the same year the design was modified to include a central ceramic core or 'beanpole' around which the heater was twined.[9] Variations of this form of construction, which included a floating beanpole, were in general use up to about 1933.

Some tube makers, notably Ken-Rad, continued using ceramic heater insulators up to as late as 1933. In the case of 6.3-volt tubes the use of 4-bore insulators of incredibly small dimensions resulted in a cathode diameter no greater than that needed for a 2-bore type. Ken-Rad are known to have used a 6-bore insulator in the case of certain power output tubes having high-voltage heaters where a large cathode area was needed in order to secure adequate emission.

By the end of 1933 all previous styles of heater-cathode had been discarded in favour of the free-floating heater insulated by means of the slip-coating process originally invented in England in 1927. Depending largely on the voltage rating of the heater, it was made as a tightly-wound reflexed spiral or else in bundled zig-zag form.

By the standards of even a few years later the heater wattage of the 227 was high; 4.575 watts compared with 2.5 watts for its successor the type 56 introduced in 1932. Because AC power was so much cheaper than the battery variety there was no particular incentive to improve efficiency solely on the score of more economical running. From the point of view of performance, however, decreased heater wattage allowed cooler running which in turn permitted closer electrode spacing with resultant improvement in characteristics. Nevertheless, had it not been for the introduction of automobile receivers, with their quite different tube requirements, the 2.5-volt heater rating might have remained in use for another decade. In point of fact in European countries where the motor-car did not find such rapid acceptance, the originally used figure of 4 volts remained in current use for over ten years.

Once the idea of radios in motor-cars began to be taken seriously by the radio industry it was soon realised that existing tubes were quite unsuited to this application. Not only was the heater wattage excessive when viewed as a drain on the car's electrical system, but the 2.5-volt rating prevented parallel connection of tube heaters. Additionally, the restricted space available for mounting a radio in a car imposed limitations on the size of the set which in turn led to a demand for smaller tubes.

The obvious step was to design a series of tubes especially suited for use on the 6-volt electrical system then universally used in American vehicles. This, then, is how

the figure of 6.3 volts came to be selected as the heater voltage for these new tubes.

The heater voltage having been pre-determined by the voltage of the car battery it only remained to select a suitable current rating for the new tubes and here there was an initial lack of standardisation. In May 1931 National Union announced a range of 6.3-volt tubes having a current rating of 0.4 amps.[10] Incidentally, these were claimed to be the first 6.3-volt tubes to be marketed. The series consisted of four types—a sharp cut-off tetrode NY64, a vari-mu tetrode NY65, a triode NY67 and an output pentode NY68. Majestic also produced a similar range but minus the output pentode.

Following the release of the 0.4-amp series it was but a short time before the remaining tube makers came down heavily in favour of the figure of 0.3 amps for the heater rating. Amongst the first to use this rating were Arcturus, Raytheon, and Ken-Rad who marketed types 236, 237, 238, 239 during July.[11] At much the same time RCA and Sylvania also joined the ranks. As a result of the majority

Sparton AC tube with side connections for heater wiring. 1927.

Kellogg version of the standard type '27 tube.

decision in favour of the 0.3-amp rating the earlier 0.4-amp tubes quickly became obsolete.

Once the current rating had become standardised for car radio use it was found convenient to use the same rating, and indeed the same tubes, for 110-volt AC/DC application where the heaters were series-connected. This obviated the need for a separate range of special AC/DC type except in the case of output tubes and rectifiers which called for a greater emission than could be provided by the 6.3 V, 0.3 A rating.

By 1932 the use of 6.3-volt tubes was being extended into the field of AC-operated receivers, and by 1934 the figure of 6.3 volts had become the industry standard with no new 2.5-volt types being released from then onwards. Although the heater consumption of 1.89 watts was not appreciably lower than the figure of 2.5 watts applicable to the later 2.5-volt types, it represented a practical minimum as evidenced by the fact that 0.3 amps remained the standard for most types not requiring a greater emission than this rating could provide.

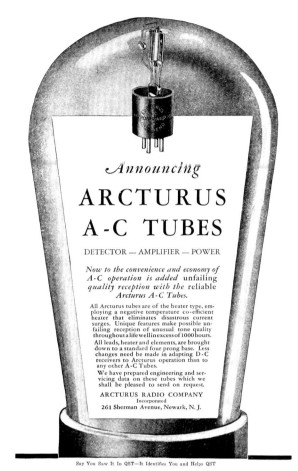
November 1927. A carbon heater was used but the illustration was deceptive.

British Developments

Production of AC valves in England commenced slightly later than in the U.S. which accounts for the seeming paradox that indirectly-heated types appeared before directly-heated ones. Strictly speaking, however, this statement applies only to the products of M-O.V. as this was the only firm to produce a range of directly-heated types.

The first Osram d.h. valves were marketed towards the end of 1928, nearly two years after their first i.h. types had appeared.[12] The design of these valves may be considered as being a development of the American UX-226 whereby the filament was made even thicker and the voltage and current ratings adjusted accordingly. Actual ratings were 0.8 amps at 0.8 volts from which the name of the series—'Point 8'—was derived. Included in the range were three triodes including a low-power output triode, a screen-grid and a special detector consuming no less than 1.6 amps at the same 0.8 volt rating.[13] The thinking behind this last named production appears to have been based on the idea that if point eight is good then double that figure should be even better; in other words an attempt was

Advertisements for " The Wireless World " are only accepted from firms we believe to be thoroughly reliable.

MORE POWER LESS HUM

WITH THE ...
AC/PI

The
MAZDA AC/PI

CHARACTERISTICS:

Filament Volts	4.0
Filament Amps (approx.)	1.0
Max. H.T. Voltage	200
Amplification Factor	5
Anode A.C. Resistance (ohms)	2,000
Mutual Conductance (mA/V)	2.5

PRICE 17/6

There is no need to use a directly heated output valve in your all-mains set — with consequent risk of hum and the additional inconvenience of having to provide a separate L.T. winding on your transformers. Use the AC/PI — the finest output valve ever developed for all-mains sets, a valve which gives a huge output at only 200 volt H.T.!

MAZDA RADIO VALVES

THE EDISON SWAN ELECTRIC CO., LTD.
Incorporating the Wiring Supplies, Lighting Engineering, Refrigeration and Radio Business of the British Thomson-Houston Co., Ltd.
Radio Division:
1a Newman Street, Oxford Street, W.1
Showrooms in all the Principal Towns
EDISWAN

A MULLARD A.C. MAINS
COMBINATION

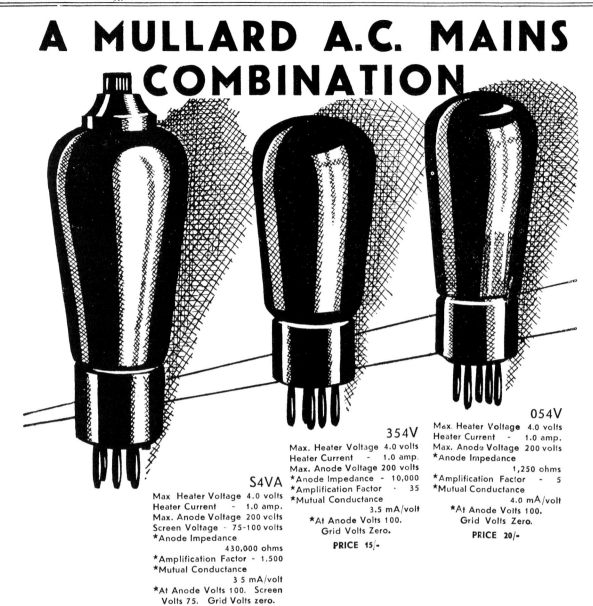

054V
Max. Heater Voltage 4.0 volts
Heater Current   -   1.0 amp.
Max. Anode Voltage 200 volts
*Anode Impedance
                    1,250 ohms
*Amplification Factor   -   5
*Mutual Conductance
                    4.0 mA/volt
   *At Anode Volts 100.
   Grid Volts Zero.

   PRICE 20/-

354V
Max. Heater Voltage 4.0 volts
Heater Current   -   1.0 amp.
Max. Anode Voltage 200 volts
*Anode Impedance - 10,000
*Amplification Factor   ·   35
*Mutual Conductance
                    3.5 mA/volt
   *At Anode Volts 100.
   Grid Volts Zero.

   PRICE 15/-

S4VA
Max Heater Voltage 4.0 volts
Heater Current   -   1.0 amp.
Max. Anode Voltage 200 volts
Screen Voltage - 75-100 volts
*Anode Impedance
                    430,000 ohms
*Amplification Factor - 1,500
*Mutual Conductance
                    3 5 mA/volt
*At Anode Volts 100. Screen
   Volts 75. Grid Volts zero.

   PRICE 22/6

The latest types of Mullard indirectly-heated A.C. mains valves in your new-season's receiver will ensure perfect reproduction. S4VA for the H.F. stage; 354V the improved super-detector; and 054V the new indirectly-heated output valve.

This combination will give you great sensitivity, perfect quality, and ample power for operating a large moving iron or moving coil speaker.

Mullard
THE · MASTER · VALVE

WE ARE EXHIBITING AT

BRITISH AND BEST   **THE NATIONAL**   SEPT. 18 TO 26
RADIO
EXHIBITION
SEPT. 18 TO 26   **OLYMPIA**   BRITISH AND BEST

Advt. The Mullard Wireless Service Co., Ltd., Mullard House, Charing Cross Road, London, W.C.2.

Advertisements for " The Wireless World " are only accepted from firms we believe to be thoroughly reliable.

made to further increase the thermal inertia of the emitter by using a still heavier filament.

The design of the Point 8 series does not appear to have been particularly successful even though one or two types had been incorporated in commercially made receivers. They appeared rather late in the day and by 1930 had been entirely superseded by a completely new M-O.V. range of standard 4-volt indirectly-heated types.

A somewhat similar occurrence took place in Germany at much the same period according to a report appearing in *Wireless World*, where it was stated that directly-heated tubes appeared after the introduction of indirectly-heated types.[14]

In spite of the lack of success of directly-heated valves in general, they continued to be used as output types in both triode and pentode form for several years after other indirectly-heated types had become firmly established. Particularly this was true in the case of triode output valves, although it must be borne in mind that after about 1932 triodes were seldom used in output stages by comparison with pentodes and this fact may account for less emphasis being placed on their development. In fact it may be said that such triodes were never developed to the extent that they superseded d.h. power output types. British power output triode development reached a peak with the production of highly efficient types having plate dissipations of up to 25 watts which became available from 1933 onwards. Some examples are: M-O.V. PX4, PX25; Cossor 620T, 660T; Mazda PP3/250, PP5/400; Mullard AC044, D024. Some of these had mutual conductances in the order of 6mA/V to 8mA/V, which represented a maximum for valves of this class.

British work on the development of the indirectly-heated cathode, although initially a little behind that which had occurred in the U.S., was in the event to have far-reaching effects. From a purely manufacturing point of view the change from filamentary to i.h. cathode was to create many problems which had hitherto been undreamed of. One of these problems was to find a satisfactory means of insulating the heater from the cathode. The insulating medium had to be capable of withstanding high temperatures and remain stable throughout the lifetime of the tube. The original American type of i.h. cathode had made use of a rigid ceramic tube as an insulator and this design formed the basis for nearly all subsequent designs for the next four or five years. During this period other materials such as silica or magnesia had been tried as insulators, with varying degrees of success, and the use of a solid insulator remained standard practice until 1932.

Because of its importance in the development of all later AC tubes and, as a corollary, the development of the mains-operated receiver itself, it is worth recording here something of the work which led to the universal adoption of the subsequent so-called 'slip-coated' heater design. Quite apart from the work done in America two completely different lines of approach had been followed in England during 1926. The first of these appears to have been based on earlier work done by H.J. Round of the Marconi Co. who had patented a form of i.h. cathode many years earlier although it was never used commercially. In June 1926 C.W. Stropford[15] of M-O.V. patented a unique design of i.h. valve in which no solid material was placed between heater and cathode; instead the heater was supported by being coiled around a silica rod which served solely to centralise it within the cathode tube. The first of such valves to be offered for sale was known as type KL1 and appeared in January 1927, and later in the same year a second valve, type KH1, was marketed.[16]

The second British approach was also unique but in a quite different way. Only twelve days after the Stropford patent E. Yeoman Robinson of Met-Vick lodged a patent for a valve of entirely different construction.[17] The Robinson valve made use of an extremely small-diameter cathode with the heater insulated solely by means of a special coating applied to its surface. Originally this coating had been applied by dipping the heater into a porcelain slurry but later a paste made from powdered alumina was used. This revolutionary method of insulating the heater eventually completely superseded all former methods and became universally adopted.

The many advantages of the slip-coating process, which include rapid warm-up time, lower heater temperature plus simplicity, and lower cost of manufacture, mark it as a vital invention in the development of the indirectly-heated tube. Additionally, the closely-spaced electrodes of the Cosmos Short Path design which resulted in a higher mutual conductance foreshadowed the course of development in the years to come. So it may be fairly said that E. Yeoman Robinson's name deserves to rank alongside other better-known ones that have rated mention in the annals of radio history.

By September 1927 two valves types AC/R and AC/G made by Met-Vick were offered for sale under the Cosmos brand. Both had heaters rated at 4V 1A, a figure that was to become an industry standard. The superiority of the Cosmos design was reflected in the high efficiency of these valves, the AC/R having a mutual conductance of 4.0 mA/V; a figure that was not attained by any other manufacturer for five years. Furthermore, the Cosmos design, unlike others, was completely successful right from the start.

Other early British i.h. valves were made by Cossor and Ediswan. Both these resembled the American McCullough-Kellogg design in being of double-ended construction with the heater connections brought out to contacts on top of the bulb. Valves in these two brands appeared towards the middle of 1928 but were superseded within the space of two years.

A type of i.h. small power output triode which may be regarded as being peculiarly British, in that its development continued until the end of 1931, was produced originally by Cosmos and Cossor in 1928 and later by Mazda and Mullard in 1931. Bearing in mind that somewhat similar tubes had become available in the U.S. in 1927–28 but had quickly become obsolete, the continued development of such valves in Britain is interesting particularly when the impressive performance figures are noted. The mutual conductance of the Mazda AC1/P1 was 2.5 mA/V while the figure for the Mullard 054V was no less than 4.0 mA/V. In spite of their high efficiencies none of these valves had a power output capability exceeding 1 watt, which in 1931 was low even by the standards of the day. Judging by the fact that such valves were seldom used in commercially built receivers they must have had little appeal to set makers. Furthermore, it seems to have been uneconomical to develop higher power versions though it may be mentioned that in 1937 American i.h. O/p triodes, types 2A3H and 6A5G, having outputs of 3.5 watts per single tube were successfully developed.

REFERENCES

1. See schematic Stromberg Carlson model 734 in *Rider's*, Vol. 1, p. 11.

2. See schematic Balkite Symphonium model B in *Rider's*, Vol. 1, p. 1.

3. *GE Report*, p. 44.

4. U.S. Patent No. 1,909,051 (filed 1922, granted 1933).

5. See, for example, *Radio News*, July 1925, p. 25.

6. See, for example, U.S. Patent No. 1,806,108, filed Jan. 6, 1926.

7. *GE Report*, p. 47.

8. H.W. Kadell, The Evolution of the Cathode, *QST*, June 1931, p. 31.

9. Ibid.

10. New Types of Receiving Tubes, *Radio Craft*, May 1931, p. 563.

11. Ibid.

12. The Trend of Progress, *Wireless World*, Oct. 3, 1928, p. 465.

13. Valves of To-day, *Wireless World*, October 2, 1929, p. 377.

14. The Berlin Show, *Wireless World*, September 12, 1928, p. 310.

15. British Patent 277,756, filed 1926.

16. See announcement *Wireless World*, January 26, 1927.

17. British Patent 278,787, lodged July 7, 1926.

Marconi-Osram KL1 (1927). A landmark British Valve.

Mazda AC/HL (1929). An early British AC Valve.

Chapter Eight

Penta-Hodos

Early Days

Quite early in the history of the tetrode it had been found that this class of tube was unsuited for use as an audio-frequency power amplifier. This was because under certain operating conditions encountered in this class of service the tetrode exhibited a negative-resistance characteristic caused by secondary emission from the anode being attracted to the positively charged screen. Although this peculiarity did not affect the tetrode's performance as an RF amplifier it did prevent its use as an output tube, at least for several years until certain specialised developments had occurred.

Meanwhile, it followed logically that if by some means the secondary emission could be prevented from reaching the screen grid, then presumably the full capabilities of the tube could be realised. So it was that the idea of placing an additional grid, held at cathode (filament) potential, between the anode and screen fulfilled this requirement and resulted in a tube having the inherently high efficiency of a tetrode but without its drawback.

The pentode was born! And its arrival must be regarded as one of the most important steps in the history of vacuum tube development.

Initially the third grid was sometimes referred to as the 'cathode' grid but later it became known as the 'suppressor' grid in obvious recognition of its role in suppressing the effects of the secondary emission. From this deceptively simple addition of an extra grid sprang a whole new family of tubes which before long were to render the screen-grid tube obsolete and to topple the triode from its position of supremacy in many applications. Indeed, so rapid was the development of this new five-element tube that within the space of two years of its American debut in 1931 an all-pentode receiver was not merely a possibility but a practical reality.

Credit for the invention of the pentode is due to two Dutch workers, Drs. Gilles Holst and Bernard Tellegen of Philips Research Laboratories who applied for a Dutch patent in December 1926.[1] Although Holst's name ap-

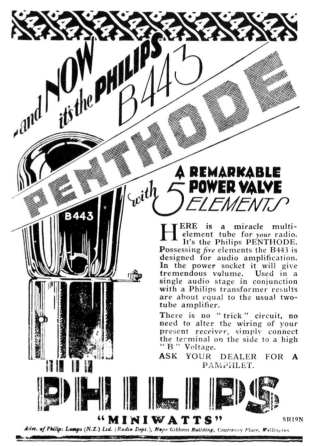

November 10, 1928

peared with Tellegen's on the patent application it was actually the latter who was responsible for the design of the pentode in its practical form. By an odd quirk of fate the patent application lapsed before the necessary formalities were completed and no Dutch patent was ever issued. Legally anyone was free to manufacture pentodes in Holland! Such was certainly not the case elsewhere for Philips quickly took steps to safeguard their new invention by taking out patents in no less than 18 other countries.[2,3,4]

54

In September 1927 the world's first pentode, Philips type B443, made its appearance. It was incorporated as an output tube in the firm's model 2502 receiver; an event which constituted both the first commercial production of a pentode and of a receiver using such a tube. Towards the end of 1928 Philips' pentodes were issued for general sale in several countries including Australia and New Zealand. Also at this time a British version, identical to the B443, was issued by Mullard under their type number PM24. On the American scene an existing marketing arrangement between RCA and Philips delayed the release of the pentode in that part of the world for a further three years, although the delay was partly due to the American desire for a higher power version which called for further developmental work.

Although the B443 was essentially a battery-operated tube its arrival on the eve of the era of mains-operated receivers resulted in its being pressed into service in this application as a stop-gap measure until more powerful versions could be developed. Larger power outputs were subsequently achieved by the production of tubes requiring plate voltages as high as 300 or 400 volts and this had the effect of delaying the general acceptance of the early Philips-designed tubes because such voltages were greatly in excess of those normally encountered in domestic receivers.

The first pentode designed for mains operation, type C443, appeared in 1929, its rated maximum output of just under 2 watts requiring the use of 300 volts on the plate. Also in 1929 the first pentode, type E443, to have an output of over 3 watts appeared but it required 400 volts on the plate to achieve this. To obtain an output of 3 watts without the need for a plate voltage of more than 250 volts it was obviously necessary to increase the tube's efficiency and in 1933 this was done by the production of the type E443H, a tube which had a mutual conductance of 3 mA/V. By this time the 'power pentode' had well and truly arrived.

Mullard's access to Philips' designs and production methods naturally resulted in their being the first British maker to market pentodes in the U.K. Furthermore, they were the first to offer a range of 2-, 4-, and 6-volt types known as PM22, PM24, and PM26 respectively.[5] There is also record of a 1-volt type known as PM21 which was the equivalent of the Philips D143. At the time of their first production Mullard introduced the tradename 'PENTONE' for all pentodes, a word which remained in use until the era of miniaturisation following World War II. Philips on the other hand used the word 'PENTHODE' for a somewhat shorter period—up to approximately 1936—at least as far as tube markings are concerned.

When pentodes were first released in the U.K. in 1928 the initial marketing policy was aimed by persuading the relatively large number of home constructors and owners of battery sets to 'try a pentode'. The manner in which

Philips Type B443. The world's first pentodes (1928).

these valves were constructed enabled them to be substituted for existing triodes with a minimum of bother as no wiring changes were needed in the receiver. In practice a pentode could simply be plugged into the output valve socket, a terminal on the side of the valve base allowing the necessary connection to the screen-grid to be made directly to the HT battery. The pentode's suppressor grid was internally connected to the centre point of the filament and this arrangement was to become standard practice throughout the world for all types of directly-heated pentodes.

Early in 1929 all the major British valve makers were offering at least one pentode in their respective ranges, examples being: Ediswan 5E225, Cossor 'Quintode' 230Q, Osram PT235. An unusual form of pentode produced by Mazda at this time (types 230 Pen and 425 Pen) had the suppressor grid connected to the screen instead of to the filament.[6] The reason for this unorthodox procedure was stated to be that in the event of a plate-to-suppressor short circuit occurring all the other valves in a receiver would not be burnt out as would have been the case had the normal method of connection been used.

With the increasing popularity of mains-driven receivers which, unlike their battery-operated counterparts, were not restricted in audio output by consideration of economy, more powerful versions of the pentode soon made their appearance. By 1933 the major British makers each had at least one valve in production capable of 3 watts or more output. Even so the use of a pentode output stage was by no means universal amongst receiver manufacturers at that time and the development of output triodes

Philips F443   Osram PT25
*Giant European pentodes of 25 watts anode dissip. There were
no American equivalents.*

continued for the next five years or so. Nevertheless, the pentode had come to stay, its high efficiency eventually resulting in its becoming the most commonly used type of output valve.

During 1934 in the U.K., a type of class B operation of output pentodes known as quiescent push-pull (QPP) attained a degree of popularity in battery sets as it offered increased output combined with reduced battery consumption. Some valve makers produced special two-in-one valves for this purpose, examples of which are: Cossor 240QP, Mazda QP240, Mullard QP22A, Osram QP21. These were the first double pentodes ever produced and British QPP valves remained unique in that no equivalent types were made elsewhere.

Touching briefly on European radio-frequency pentodes we find that battery-operated types did not appear until after the advent of mains types. First on the scene was the Marconi-Osram VP21, a vari-mu type released in June 1934, while by the end of the year other manufacturers had similar types on the market. For some reason, probably because of a lessening demand, M-O.V. did not produce a sharp cut-off type even though others makers were offered such valves.

American Pentodes

Following the marketing of pentodes in Europe during 1928–29 it was some two years before the first American versions became available and by that time mainstream tube development was centred around the production of AC tubes. Thus it was that although a 2-volt battery pentode (type 33) was available at much the same time as AC

types its arrival passed almost unnoticed and it remained for many years the sole representative of its class. On the other hand, the development of indirectly-heated types proceeded apace.

Just which manufacturer produced the first American pentode is open to question but it is a matter of record that as early as April 1930 one company had announced a radio-frequency type.[7] This tube was a product of the C.E. Mfg. Co. and was known as the CeCo type P-1. It was unique in being constructed to operate in the so-called 'space-charge' mode with the innermost grid connected to a potential of +10 volts.

The P-1 may be regarded as being a lineal descendant of the European space-charge tetrode which had created a brief flurry of interest some six years earlier and then quickly faded from the scene. Because of the known drawbacks associated with space-charge operation it is somewhat surprising that a tube such as the P-1 should have been introduced but, in the event, it remained the only one of its kind. Its brief moment of glory came when a receiver manufacturer, the Norden-Hauck Co., used the P-1 tube in the RF stage of their model 'Super DX-5' in 1930. It was the first and only known commercial use.

Throughout 1930 rumours of the impending release of power output pentodes was rife and in May of that year advance data on an Arcturus pentode was announced by the company under the somewhat unlikely title of 'The Pentode as a Service Problem'.[8] Imagine there being a service problem before any tubes had been released! Perhaps the article was prophetic because as it happened the early pentodes were responsible for quite a few headaches.

In January 1930 the Champion Radio Works Inc. produced and demonstrated an experimental power pentode and by June 1931 a production version of the same tube advertised for sale as type P-704.[9] Data on the first Arcturus pentode, known as type 'PZ', was contained in a fac-

Mullard PM21 and MP26. The first British pentodes.

56

British double pentodes

Marconi QP21 (L.)   *Ediswan QP230 (R.)*

tory bulletin dated March 1931. In June of the same year RCA announced their Radiotron type 247 and by July all other tube makers had pentodes in production so it can be seen that there was little difference in the matter of release dates.

The type 47, in keeping with other AC tubes of the period, used the industry standard 2.5-volt rating for its filament and used the standard 5-pin (UY) base. It was both the first and only directly-heated pentode in this voltage grouping as well as being the first commercially used output pentode. A landmark tube. In subsequent developments which include indirectly-heated types, the characteristics of the 47 formed the basis for the design of many future types, the figures of 16.5-volts bias and 7000-ohms load becoming synonymous with 'single pentode' output stages.

Following hard on the heels of the 47, so closely in fact that it arrived almost simultaneously, came the release of the first indirectly-heated pentode. In July 1931[11] the type 238 was announced at the RMA Trade Show by several tube makers although it had actually been in use as early as April of that year. The 38 was the first pentode in the newly introduced 6.3-volt automobile range and its 0.3-amp heater rating enabled to also be used in DC and AC/DC applications. In spite of its modest 1.89-watt heater rating the 38 could almost match the power output of its bigger brother the 47 when supplied with the same plate voltage. With its high efficiency and compact size (S-12 bulb) the 38 became the most widely used output tube in applications for which it was intended. By 1931 the prevailing economic conditions had resulted in the production of small low-priced receivers which were required to provide comparatively large power outputs. It was the timely arrival of the American pentode which enabled the production of such receivers to be successfully accomplished.

During 1932 several new i-h power pentodes appeared including the first in the 2.5-volt range (type 59),[12] and the first in the 6.3-volt AC range (type 42). In addition this year also saw the introduction of the first standard type radio-frequency pentode (type 39) which had the distinction of being the first vari-mu type. The 39 was announced in February 1932[13] and not long after a somewhat similar tube designated type 44 also appeared. The two types had much the same characteristics, the main difference being that the 44 had a more extended cut-off point. For a short while some manufacturers listed both types but by the middle of 1935 the two types had been combined under the dual number 39/44.

The first 2.5-volt RF pentodes announced were the types 57 and 58, advertised by Speed[14] and Arcturus in June 1932, though both types had been in commercial use for some time previously; in fact the 58 had been used in a standard production model receiver as early as August 1931.[15] This meant that American practice was some two years ahead of that in the U.K. at this time where the first RF pentodes were not announced until March 1933.

A novel feature of these two tubes was the bringing out of their suppressor grids to two separate base pins. The reason for this procedure has never been completely explained but in any event it became standard practice thereafter with all RF pentodes. Admittedly it is possible to vary a pentode's characteristics by the application of a voltage to the suppressor grid but this was seldom done in practice. In the vast majority of cases the tubes were simply used with the suppressor grid connected directly to the cathode at the socket. Only one manufacturer is known to have deviated from the norm. An examination of relevant Philco receiver schematics reveals that in some models the vari-mu RF pentodes had their suppressor grids connected via a tertiary winding on the associated IF transformer to a low negative voltage or else to earth (chassis). When connected in this manner it was possible to claim that a tube was not being used as a pentode but as a 'triple-grid amplifier'. Whether this procedure had any practical advantage is open to question but the thought occurs it could be used as a means of avoiding the payment of patent royalties which would otherwise have been incurred had the tube been used in the conventional manner.

Another feature of the 57 and 58 was the first use of the so-called 'ST' style domed bulbs which eventually became standard practice for all American tubes. This bulb shape was part of a new style of construction whereby the element assembly was braced at its upper edge by mica spacers bearing against the narrower top section of the bulb.

Champion

POWER PENTODE TUBE

||||| *Champion*

ENGINEERS' 1930 CREATION

PUBLIC 1931 ACCEPTANCE

ON January 15, 1930, Messrs. Briggs and MacLeod of Champion's engineering staff demonstrated before a distinguished gathering at Columbia University, the principles of a radically different radio tube—the POWER PENTODE. In the March 1930 issue of the "Proceedings of the Radio Club of America, Volume 7, No. 3," the following paragraph is noted. "Those who heard the demonstration of the Pentode Tube, which followed the presentation of the paper (demonstration of a Pentode by A. D. MacLeod and R. S. Briggs of the Champion Radio Works, Inc.) will recall that, etc., etc."

Then came months of study and experimenting . . . of laboratory tests . . . of intensive effort, day and night by the entire engineering staff of Champion to PROVE it's finding. Champion's new tube must meet the most rigid specifications of set manufacturers . . . it must be SUPERIOR in every way . . . greater in tone brilliance . . . more faithfully reproducing the high notes . . . duplicating every tonal inflection of the artist as though he stood before you!

Now the Power PENTODE Tube is ready! Ready for your most critical audition. Ready to demonstrate a depth of power, tonal beauty and brilliancy never before available in radio! Hear it. Decide for yourself! You'll admit—once more —Champion is FIRST.

•

CHAMPION
Radio Works, Inc.

DANVERS
Massachusettes

Columbia University, New York City

Here, over a year ago on January 15, 1930, the Power PENTODE tube was first demonstrated by Champion engineers.

Champion Laboratory, DANVERS, Massachusetts

Through the untiring efforts of Messrs. Briggs and MacLeod of Champion Engineering staff the Power PENTODE attained its present perfection.

Home of Champion Radio Tubes
DANVERS, Massachusetts

For more than a quarter-century, the name CHAMPION has stood for sterling worth and integrity.

The first indirectly-heated power pentode in the 2.5-volt range, type 59,[16] incorporated two unusual features—it was the first tube to be fitted with twin cathodes and the first to have its suppressor grid to be brought out to a separate base pin. The reason for using twin cathodes was that the tube had a planar electrode assembly of almost identical dimensions to that used on the type 47 filamentary pentode; with such a structure it was almost impossible to secure uniform distribution of the emission by using a conventional single cathode. Having said that it must now be admitted that another tube of somewhat similar construction, the type 48, used only a single cathode, albeit of modified dimensions.

While the presence of a suppressor grid obviously enabled the 59 to be classed as a true pentode, the fact that this third grid was not permanently tied to the cathode enabled the tube to be used in a plurality of ways resulting in its being referred to as a triple-grid power amplifier. One suggested way in which the 59 could be used was in Class B service with grids 1 and 2 tied and No. 3 grid connected to the plate, thus effectively making the tube a high-mu triode. Operated in this manner a pair of 59s with 300 volts on their plates were capable of an output of 20 watts.

The first AC-operated power pentode to use a cylindrical electrode configuration was the type 42 which came into use towards the end of 1932.[17] Early in 1933 it was joined by the first 2.5-volt version, the type 2A5. Some manufacturers made both these tubes in the large S-17 style bulbs but by the middle of 1933 the use of the smaller ST-14 bulb had become standard practice, though Philco went through an intermediate step of using S-16 bulbs for a short period. Another easily recognisable change occurring at this time was the addition of grid radiators, a feature which became the hallmark of all future output pentodes. Incidentally, one manufacturer, Arcturus, is known to have issued replacement type 47 tubes modified by the addition of grid radiators.

For a short period prior to the advent of the so-called universal or AC/DC receiver some manufacturers built sets designed to operate from 110-V DC power lines. The earliest of such receivers dates back to 1928 and used 1/4-amp battery tubes in all stages. However, after the release of 6.3-volt indirectly-heated tubes these quickly supplanted battery types except in the output stage. In spite of the availability of the type 38 pentode some set makers continued to use filamentary output triodes. One receiver produced by Fada used no less than six types 71A tubes in push-pull in order to obtain the desired power output. This company was also the first to use a filamentary power pentode, type TS-257, developed by Tung Sol especially for DC line operation.[18] However, this did not indicate a general trend; for one thing it was considerably more difficult to provide grid biassing when running d-h tubes in series-string circuits. In the case of the Fada receiver men-

Output pentodes

Type 38 (L.)   Type 33 (R.)

tioned bias for the output tubes was obtained by the use of a 22½-volt bias battery.

A tube of interest not because it was a pentode, but because it was unique at the time in having a dual-voltage heater, was the type 12A5 which was introduced by Raytheon in 1933. It was designed for use in either auto-radio or AC/DC applications, the tube having two distinct heater-cathode assemblies with the heaters being joined in series. The centre point or junction of the two heaters was brought out to a separate base pin thus allowing either series or parallel operation as required.

American Battery Pentodes

As suggested earlier, the development of American battery tubes tended to be of secondary importance in comparison with progress in other areas with the result that comparatively few types were produced. In the original 2-volt Air Cell range released between 1930 and 1932 only two pentodes—one RF and one output—were included.

The first of these, type 33 announced in mid-1931,[19] was able to provide nearly four times the output of its triode contemporary type 31 when operated at the same plate voltage. Apart from one non-standard type, the 950 of 1934, the 33 remained the sole representative of its class until 1937 when an improved and more economical ver-

59

·A·
POWER AMPLIFIER
PENTODE
NOW AVAILABLE

The RCA-247 has been designed for use in the audio power output stage of newly-designed AC receivers.

ONCE AGAIN the RCA Radiotron Company, Inc., gives the set designers a new tool to work with — the screen-grid power output pentode, RCA-247. Owing to the addition of a "suppressor" grid between the screen and plate, this Radiotron is capable of giving large audio power output for relatively small signal voltages impressed on the grid. The suppressor is connected to the cathode and is, therefore, operated at the cathode potential. Thus, the suppressor is effective in practically eliminating the secondary emission effects which limit the power output of four-electrode screen-grid types.

The preliminary ratings and characteristics are:

Filament Voltage	2.5 Volts	Plate Current	32 Milliamperes
Filament Current	1.5 Amperes	Screen Current	7.5 Milliamperes
Plate Voltage, Recommended	250 Volts	Plate Resistance	38,000 Ohms
Screen Voltage, Recommended and Maximum	250 Volts	Mutual Conductance	2,500 Micromhos
Grid Voltage	16.5 Volts	Load Resistance, Approximate	7,000 Ohms
	Power Output	2.5 Watts	

RCA RADIOTRON CO., INC. ~ HARRISON, N. J.
A Radio Corporation of America Subsidiary

RCA RADIOTRONS
« « THE HEART OF YOUR RADIO » »
Say You Saw It in *QST* — It Identifies You and Helps *QST*   June 1931

60

sion, type 1F4, made its appearance. In the same year the first and only double pentode, type 1E7G a tube designed for Class A push-pull service, was introduced. However, the 1E7G found little favour with receiver manufacturers who preferred to use twin-triode tubes in Class B.

The radio frequency pentode, type 34,[20] was a vari-mu type and it is interesting to note that no companion sharp cut-off pentode was included in the range. Where circuit requirements called for a tube with sharp cut-off characteristics receiver engineers had to be content with the type 32 tetrode. At least that was the position when Sylvania introduced their type 15 early in 1933.

The 15 was unique in being the only American 2-volt battery tube to have an indirectly-heated cathode, in spite of which the heater consumption was only 0.22 amps. The reason for the introduction of such an odd-ball tube was the result of circuit demands calling for a pentode capable of operating as an autodyne converter in superheterodyne receivers at a time when the first battery-operated pentagrid converter, type 1A6, was somewhat deficient in performance.

An early non-standard RF pentode, type 951, was produced by Ken-Rad and Raytheon during 1934–35 but as it had almost identical characteristics to the then standard type 1B4 production soon ceased in favour of the latter. For a short period thereafter some manufacturers issued the tube under the combined type number 1B4-951.

The first vari-mu RF pentodes

Type 39 (L.)   Type 58 (R.)

British Indirectly-Heated Pentodes

By mid-1930 the development of indirectly-heated valves had reached the stage where earlier defects had been overcome and efficient long-life valves, having considerably better characteristics than their battery-operated counterparts, were freely available. Furthermore, valve makers had by then established standards in the matters of heater voltage and basing which made their products more acceptable to receiver manufacturers who by now were turning increasingly to the production of all-mains receivers.

Power output valves, whether triode or pentode, remained directly heated for the same reason which applied in the U.S. at that time—it was impossible to design indirectly-heated valves capable of more than a few hundred milliwatts output without running into problems of grid emission. Because of this difficulty and because the hum level of directly-heated types had proved acceptable there was consequently not the same incentive to develop indirectly-heated output valves; in fact DH output pentodes remained in general use for the next five years or so.

It may therefore come as a surprise to some readers to learn that in spite of the foregoing one British valve maker had, by the middle of 1930, been successful in producing not only the world's first i-h output pentode but a very successful first in addition.[21]

Type 59. Triple-grid power amplifier.

61

The first..
INDIRECTLY
HEATED
PENTODE

EDISWAN LEADS AGAIN WITH THE
MAZDA AC/PEN

THIS new power output valve marks an important step in the history of Radio. The indirectly heated Cathode absolutely prevents hum, and the AC/Pen is the most sensitive pentode in existence.

With a grid swing of only ten volts it will give wonderful results when used with a good cone speaker, and is ideal for operating a moving coil speaker such as the R.K.

PRICE 30/-

The Amazing

CHARACTERISTICS

Filament volts	4.0
Filament amps (approx.)	1.0
Anode volts (max.)	250
Auxiliary Grid Volts (max.)	200
Mutual A.C. conductance (mA/V)	2.2

THE EDISON SWAN ELECTRIC CO., LTD.
Radio Division,
1a Newman Street, Oxford Street, W.1
Showrooms in all the Principal Towns

Vari-mu RF pentodes

Type 34 (L.)   Type 234 (R.)

In May 1930 a valve from the same stable as the earlier Cosmos 'Short Path' i-h series was announced—the Mazda AC/Pen. So successful was the design of this valve that it became the basis for subsequent Mazda productions and indeed foreshadowed the course of future events when some five years later all makes of d-h types had almost disappeared from the scene. The success of the AC/Pen was all the more remarkable when it is realised that the Cosmos factory had never previously made any pentodes at all and thus its designer, E. Yeoman Robinson, was starting from scratch.

Following the formation of A.E.I. in 1928 the Cosmos pentodes were issued under the Mazda label and it is interesting to note that, apart from battery-operated types, no directly-heated pentodes were ever issued by Mazda. It is a matter of history that Mazda's decision to stick to the production of i-h output pentodes at a time when d-h types were predominant, both within the U.K. and in other countries, was later vindicated.

Well over a year elapsed before other valve makers produced any indirectly-heated pentodes, some examples being Cossor MP/Pen, Osram MPT4, and Mullard PenA4. It might be thought strange that Mullards, who had introduced the pentode to the British market, were amongst the last to manufacture i-h types, but this was obviously because they were the last major manufacturer to market any type of indirectly-heated valve.

Indirectly-heated o/p pentodes were originally fitted with 5-pin bases having side-mounted terminals for the screen connection. When the standard British 7-pin base came into use in 1933 it was fitted to all i-h pentodes then in production, including older types. However, to cater for the replacement market it was necessary to continue producing earlier types in their original 5-pin form. Be-cause the same valve was then available with two different styles of base it was consequently essential to specify the type of base required when ordering.

Apart from pioneering the production of the i-h output pentode Mazda also originated a new breed in the species, the high-sensitivity type. This was a peculiarly British development which had no counterpart in the U.S. though tubes with somewhat similar characteristics were later produced by Philips. With a mutual conductance of 8 mA/V the Mazda AC/2Pen set a new standard of sensitivity in 1934,[22] enabling the output valve to be fed directly from a diode detector. This circuit feature became a characteristic of many smaller British receivers produced after 1934.

For nearly two years after its debut the AC/2Pen remained the sole representative of its class but by 1936 most other valve makers had similar valves on the market. Examples of these are: Cossor 42MP/Pen, Brimar 7A3, Mullard PenA4, and Osram N41. All these valves had power output capabilities of between 3 and 4 watts with a grid swing of less than 6 volts.

British radio frequency pentodes appeared about a year after corresponding types had been marketed in the U.S., though one firm had actually produced an example of the species as early as 1930.[23] This particular valve, the Cossor MS/PenA, remained the sole representative of its class for nearly three years until Mullard announced their SP4 and VP4 in March 1933.[24] Hard on their heels came Osram's MSP4 and VMS4 together with Brimar's 8A1 and 9A1. This time it was Mazda's turn to bring up the rear with their types ACS2Pen and AC/VP1, which did not appear until 1934.

Early American pentodes, c. 1931.

63

Mazda AC-Pen, the world's first indirectly-heated pentode.
Note grid radiator and carbonised anode in later valve shown
on right.

Mullard SP4 screened pentodes.
The earlier type is on the right.

REFERENCES

1. Dutch patent appln. date Dec. 14, 1926.
2. British Patent No. 287,958 appln. date Dec. 24, 1926, granted March 26, 1928.
3. French Patent No. 629,357 appln. June 25, 1927.
4. German Patent No. 527,449 appln. May 1930.
5. The Pentode, *Wireless World*, July 4, 1928, pp. 7, 9.
6. Olympia 1929, *Wireless World*, Sept. 25, 1929, p. 326.
7. The AC Screen Grid Pentode, *Radio Craft*, April 1930, p. 512.
8. George Lewis, The Pentode as a Service Problem, *Radio Craft*, May 1930, p. 578.
9. See advt. *Radio News*, June 1931, p. 1097.
10. See advt. *QST*, June 1931, p. 95.
11. See *Radio Craft*, July 1931, p. 41.
12. See Ken-Rad tube chart dated Aug. 4, 1932.
13. Louis Martin, New Tubes for Old, *Radio Craft*, Feb. 1932, p. 458.
14. See advt. inside front cover *Radio Craft*, June 1932.
15. See *Riders Perpetual Troubleshooters Manual*, Vol. 2, Insuline Corp. of America 'Super Conqueror', schematic dated Aug. 1931.
16. See Ken-Rad tube chart dated Aug. 4, 1932.
17. Progress in Tubes for Radio, *Radio Engineering*, Feb. 1933, p. 11.
18. See *Radio Craft*, Sept. 1932, p. 142.
19. See *Radio News*, July 1931, p. 56.
20. Tube Progress, *Radio Engineering*, March 1932, p. 39.
21. The First Indirectly Heated Pentode, *Wireless World*, May 8, 1930, p. 55.
22. See *Wireless World*, March 9, 1934, p. 116.
23. See *Cossor Wireless Book*, Sept. 1930, p. 4.
24. T.E. Goldup, The Screened HF Pentode, *Wireless World*, March 1933, pp. 221–222.

Chapter Nine

Developments in Tetrodes

Back in April 1928!

TYPE AC-22

CeCo Announced This Type AC-22 Screen Grid Tube

The five prong tube of the separate heater type operating directly on alternating current

—now recognized as the most outstandingly successful amplifying tube of the season.

CeCo pioneered—and did its pioneering without the fanfare of trumpets. But it is pleasing to know that an increasing number of radio engineers and experts look with confidence to the CeCo laboratories for each new development in the tube industry...a reward not measured in dollars and profits.

Do not miss CeCo's entertaining radio broadcast each Monday evening at 8:30 Eastern time (7:30 Central time) over the Columbia Broadcasting System.

CeCo Mfg. Co., Inc., Providence, R.I.

CeCo Radio Tubes

Screen Grid

Following the triode in generic sequence, as in the case of battery tube development, came the tetrode or screen-grid tube. In June 1928[1] the C.E. Mfg. Co. announced an AC-operated type having unspecified characteristics or type number. This tube was later identified as CeCo type AC-22 and it was stated to have similar characteristics to the battery-operated UX-222. The heater rating was 2.5 volts, 1.75 amps.

An announcement published in October 1928 by Arcturus claimed that their 15-volt SG tube, type A22, was 'the first shielded-grid tube on the market'. Though no date was mentioned this claim was obviously intended to apply only to AC tubes. Just which of the two companies was actually first in the field is open to question but their respective claims could probably be settled on the basis that CeCo marketed the first standard type having a 2.5-volt heater while Arcturus produced the first (and only) 15-volt type.

In spite of this early start the AC screen-grid tube did not really get off the ground until RCA announced the type UY-224 in May 1929.[2] This tube used the same heater-cathode structure and same 5-pin base as the existing type 227 triode. Its external appearance was quite similar to the battery-type UX-222 as it used the same S-14 bulb and top cap connector. As might be expected the 224 offered a considerably better performance by comparison with its battery counterpart.

By the end of the year all manufacturers of AC tubes had the type 224 in production with Arcturus claiming their type 124 to be the first quick-heating version. RCA's type UY-224A appeared some time later, the suffix 'A' in the type number indicating a quick-heating version. Other manufacturers quickly changed over to producing this type of tube and by 1931 the 24-A had completely superseded the earlier type. In 1932 the bulb shape was changed to the then new ST style.

In April 1929 the firm of C.R. Leutz Inc. claimed to be the first manufacturer to produce a receiver using AC screen-grid tubes; three Sonatron type AC222 were used in that company's 'Seven Seas' model. It was only by a slim margin that this claim could stand for by July of that year several of the largest receiver manufacturers such as Atwater Kent, Crosley, and Stewart Warner were marketing screen-grid models.

Within a remarkably short space of time the AC screen-grid tube rendered the triode obsolete as an RF amplifier and even as a detector, but in spite of its suitability for the purpose was never employed as a resistance-coupled voltage amplifier in AF circuits in commercially built receivers. The reason for this was probably because of the trans-

Early production model UY-224. Note fork-shaped screen assembly.

former coupled fixation on the part of engineers on both sides of the Atlantic at the time.

A solitary exception may be found in the case of a power amplifier marketed in 1930 in which a type 24 tetrode was used in the first stage and 'direct-coupled' to the output triode. Such amplifiers were sold under the name 'Loftin-White' by the Electrad Co. of New York. It was the only known commercial application of a screen-grid tube as an AF voltage amplifier. It must be emphasised here that although several small radio manufacturers incorporated the Loftin-White direct-coupled circuit in their receivers during 1930 the 24 tube was used as a biassed detector, not as an audio amplifier. Extravagant claims, based largely on the omission of the coupling condenser, were made for the performance of the Loftin-White circuit but history relates that it did not stand the test of time and after a little more than twelve months had passed quietly into oblivion.

Another application for the 24A was as a 'dynatron' oscillator. In this case the negative-resistance characteristic exhibited by the tube under certain operating conditions allows it to function as a specialised type of oscillator when the plate voltage is held lower than the screen voltage. Used in this mode the 24A found little practical application though a solitary manufacturer (Crosley) did incorporate a dynatron oscillator in certain early superheterodyne receivers made during 1931–32.

It is a matter of record, however, that as things turned out this particular application was largely unsuccessful though not because of the dynatron oscillator as such. It was found that later 24A tubes when used as replacements for earlier types would function erratically or not at all. This was because the dynatron principle depended for its

66

operation on the existence of secondary emission from the plate of the tube. Later versions of the 24A had plates that were carbonised or otherwise treated to reduce the normally unwanted secondary emission thus rendering them useless as dynatron oscillators!

The final development of the screen-grid tube was concerned with the production of a specialised type which became known as the 'variable-mu' or 'remote cut-off' type. This tube was invented to fill a specific need caused by reception conditions which had arisen in certain parts of the U.S. from the end of 1929 onwards. The rapid growth of broadcasting often resulted in numerous high-powered stations being concentrated in metropolitan areas which led to a peculiar difficulty in receivers using screen-grid tubes. In many cases it was found impossible to separate two stations operating on closely adjacent frequencies even though highly selective tuned circuits were used. Subsequent investigation of the problem revealed it to be caused by a phenomenon known as 'cross-modulation' which was brought about by non-linearity in the grid circuit of the first tube.

A solution to this difficulty was achieved by the development of a modified type of screen-grid tube which had a specially constructed grid. In practice this was achieved by winding the turns of the grid spiral with a non-uniform pitch; that is to say the turns were spaced further apart in the central section than they were at either end. This type of grid imparted a special characteristic to any tubes so constructed enabling them to handle large signal inputs without cross-modulation occurring. Furthermore, it also enabled the gain of a receiver to be controlled either manually or automatically by applying a variable control voltage to the grids of any such tubes. So it was that the invention of the vari-mu tube killed two birds with one stone as it greatly facilitated the development of the so-called automatic volume control (AVC) circuits which would otherwise have been severely limited in scope.

In May 1931 initial production of the new tubes, designated type 551, was commenced by Arcturus, Majestic, and Raytheon under license to the Bontoon Research Corp., the holders of the patent.[3] At the same time as this was going on RCA brought out their version which was known as type 235[4] and the remaining tube makers soon had one or the other of these two types on the market. Due to their similarity it was soon considered redundant to continue producing both types for replacement purposes and by 1935 the type 551 was discontinued. For a short time some manufacturers issued tubes under the combined marking 35/51.

As in the case of indirectly-heated triodes 6.3-volt versions of screen-grid tubes were not long in making their appearance. In July 1931 a sharp cut-off type, the 236, was announced; it had been in commercial use as early as April of that year.[6] A somewhat similar tube, National Union's type NY64 (incidentally claimed to be the first

6.3-volt tube of any kind) was announced in May.[7] Presumably because of the imminent introduction of RF pentodes a vari-mu SG tube was not included in the standard 6.3 V, 0.3 A range though there was one, type NY65, produced in the non-standard 0.4-amp range.

From the foregoing it can be seen that the development of the A.C. screen-grid tube was an important step forward which, particularly in America, led to the rapid development of the superheterodyne receiver. However, such was the pace of development during this period that no sooner had the SG tube become established than it was eclipsed by the coming of the radio frequency pentode.

British A.C. Screen-Grid Valves

The production of the first British indirectly-heated screen-grid valves occurred at much the same time as in the U.S. By September 1929 the four main manufacturers —Cossor, Mullard, Cosmos/Mazda, M-O.V.—all had 4-volt versions on the market. Similarly, in the case of vari-mu types these appeared within six months of their American release. Mazda and M-O.V. were the first two British makers and both firms had examples on the market by November 1931. Because of the slightly later developments of British RF pentodes the screen-grid tetrode remained in current use somewhat longer than in the U.S.

For example, M-O.V.'s MS4B and VMS4 in Catkin versions were released in May 1933.

Output Tetrodes

A highly specialised form of tetrode and one unique to the American scene appeared towards the end of 1932. In spite of being listed as a 'dual grid triode' and invariably being used as a triode, tubes of this class must logically be classed as tetrodes, at least from a constructional aspect. The possession of two independent grids, each connected to separate base pins, surely allows no other classification.

The first of the species, which were also known as 'double grid power amplifiers', was the type 46, a tube designed specifically for use in Class B service. Like its cousin the 47, the 46 originated during the era of 2.5-volt tubes and it used the same type of 'M' filament. The electrode assembly also closely resembled that of the 47 while the same style of base and bulb were also used. Indeed so similar were the two types in both outer and inner appearance that only by the closest examination was it possible to distinguish between them. In its original form, using an S-17 bulb, the 46 was announced in April 1932[8] but by 1933 the bulb shape had been altered to ST-17.

In practice the possession of two grids allowed the 46 to function as a triode whose characteristics could be al-

Some early European screen-grid valves.

tered to suit a given application, depending on the manner in which the grids were connected. As output tubes with the grids connected together, a pair of 46s operating in Class B mode was capable of the then unprecedented output of 20 watts. With the outer grid tied to the plate a single 46 then had characteristics which made it suitable as a driver for the push-pull pair.

In spite of the superficial attraction of Class B operation of output stages the resultant economy in plate current consumption afforded by its higher efficiency was of little or no significance in AC receivers. This was particularly true of later Class B tubes having power outputs of which could just as easily have been obtained by using a pair of pentodes in Class A. Only when economy of plate current was of prime importance, as in the case of battery-operated receivers, did Class B operation offer any worthwhile advantage.

Following the 46 in sequence came two similar generic types, the only other developments of the dual grid amplifier. The first of these was a tube in the 2-volt Air Cell range, type 49, released towards the end of 1932.[9] With 135 volts on their plates a pair of these tubes operating under zero-bias conditions could provide an output of 2.3 watts. The final dual grid tube, type 52, was a filamentary type rated at 6.3 V, 0.3 A. and was announced by Eveready Raytheon at the beginning of 1933.[10] The 52 was specifically designed for 110-V DC line operation and with a plate voltage of 100 volts was capable of an output of 1.2 watts, a figure considerably in excess of any contemporary pentode.

The first power output tetrode in which the outer grid was intended to be connected only to a source of high voltage in the manner of a pentode, was the type 48 which appeared late in 1932.[11] Officially described by RCA as 'a tetrode with pentode characteristics', the 48 is historically significant in that it may be regarded as the progenitor of

all later power tetrodes. The 48 was stated by RCA to be suitable for use in DC powerline receivers but because of its non-standard 0.4-amp heater rating plus the fact that straight DC receivers had largely given way to AC/DC types by this time, the 48 was more commonly used in 32-volt sets designed for operation on farm lighting systems. In this application the low available plate voltage made it necessary to use as many as four type 48 tubes in push-pull parallel in order to secure an adequate power output. In spite of the fact that the 48 was a true tetrode and was listed as such by all tube makers, the author has discovered that one manufacturer, Raytheon, produced the tube in pentode form only. The reason for this deviation from standard practice is not known but it is mentioned for the sake of completeness.

In chronological sequence the next development occurred on the other side of the Atlantic when, in 1935, a newly established independent British company, the High Vacuum Valve Co. (Hivac) announced an entirely different type of output tetrode.[12] This was the Hivac 'Harries' valve; the latter name being that of its inventor, J. Owen Harries. Like the American 48, the Harries valve was a true tetrode, notable for the utilisation of a principle in valve design known as the 'critical distance' spacing of the screen-grid and plate. By the application of this principle it was possible to achieve, and even surpass, the performance of contemporary pentodes. The only known disadvantage of the Harries valve was a purely practical one in that the extremely wide screen-to-plate spacing resulted in a valve of somewhat larger physical size than comparable pentodes.

Valves of this type were produced in all existing standard British ranges, though in spite of their initial promise made little impact on the scene. However, one suspects this to be due more to commercial difficulties rather than to any deficiencies in the valve itself.

Subsequent development of power tetrodes now reverts to the U.S. but before proceeding further with the story it may be apposite to pause and consider the non-rhetorical question—When is a tetrode not a tetrode?, and the answer —When it is a beam power amplifier. The word 'beam' in

this connotation being descriptive of the shaping of the electron stream brought about by the specialised formation of the electrode structure which is characteristic of all such tubes. The distinguishing features of the final form of power tetrodes are:

1. The existence of 'aligned grids', brought about by the turns of the grid and screen being positioned directly in line with each other.
2. The presence of two small 'beam forming' plates held at cathode potential.
3. The use of critical distance' spacing between screen and plate to suppress the effects of secondary emission from the plate.

It is the second of these three features which, because it had the effect of adding a further electrode, has resulted in the still unresolved question of whether such tubes should be classified as tetrodes or pentodes. To further add to the confusion the following definition was applied by RCA in the 1940 Tube Manual RC14:

'A beam power tube is a tetrode or pentode in which the use is made of directed electron beams to contribute substantially to its power-handling capability. Such a tube contains a cathode, a control-grid, a screen, a plate and, optionally a suppressor grid. When a beam power tube is designed without an actual suppressor the electrodes are so spaced that secondary emission from the plate is suppressed by space-charge effects between the screen and plate. . . . In place of the space-charge effect just described it is also feasible to use an actual suppressor to repel the secondary electrons. Examples of beam power tubes using an actual suppressor are the 6V6 and 6GG'.

The author must admit to being particularly confused over the last sentence as he has never seen a 6V6 with a suppressor grid nor ever heard of the 6G6G as being other than a true pentode. Because the sentence in question was withdrawn in subsequent editions of the Manual it seems likely that the information was incorrect.

But, to continue with our story—the world's first beam power tetrode was the type 6L6, released by RCA in July 1936.[13] Presumably because RCA's efforts were being concentrated on the production of metal tubes at the time, the 6L6 was first issued in this form. In the following year a glass version, the 6L6G, was issued in an ST-16 size bulb whilst later still other variants followed. The final version, type 6L6GC, was fitted with a tubular T-12 bulb and also carried an increased plate dissipation of 30 watts compared with 19 watts for the earlier versions.

Although listed as a receiving type the 6L6 was never widely used in this application because the output of a push-pull pair even when used in class A mode was excessive for all but the largest and most powerful receivers. In any case the 6L6 was primarily designed to operate in Class AB mode as its characteristics were specifically suited to this class of service. Thus the tube found its widest application in high power amplifiers and also became popular with amateur transmitters. Not until a lower power version appeared did the beam power tube become a rival to the well-established power pentode.

As the originator of the species not surprisingly it was RCA who developed the first lower power version which, like its bigger brother, was initially issued in metal form. Towards the end of 1937 the type 6V6 (metal) and the type 6V6G (glass) both appeared at much the same time.[14] The final version, type 6V6GT, was introduced in 1939.[15]

A twenty-year history of the 6L6.

In this form the tube was to remain in continuous production for over 40 years and must be counted as one of the most successful designs of any class of tube ever produced. In turn its characteristics were incorporated into the loktal-based 7C5 of 1939 and the miniature type 6AQ5 of 1947.

Following the introduction of beam tetrodes no further new output pentodes were developed with the exception of battery-operated types. In this case the fact that the emitter (filament) was spread out over a greater area, by comparison with an equivalent indirectly-heated cathode tube, made the application of the beam-forming principle somewhat more difficult to implement. By 1940, however, RCA had produced two 1.4-volt types (1Q5GT and 1T5GT), as well as one dual-voltage 1.4/2.8-volt type (3Q5GT).

In the manufacture of these and subsequent similar types the time-honoured vee filament had to be abandoned and a new design used wherein the filament took the form of two parallel wires. Because this style of filament was not adaptable to miniature tubes these had perforce to remain as pentodes.

The 25-year history of the 6V6.

British Aligned-Grid Tetrodes

Apart from the Hivac-Harries output tetrode previously mentioned apparently no further British development work took place, or at least none was visible until mid-1937. At this time the Marconiphone Co. and GEC Ltd. jointly launched their so-called 'International Octal' range of valves. These were similar, and in some cases identical, to the American octal-based glass series and appear to have been developed with the active co-operation of RCA who at that time had an interest in the Marconiphone Co.

The first beam tetrodes released in the U.K. were types KT32, KT63, and KT66; the letters KT in the type numbers standing for 'kinkless tetrode'. Of the three, only the KT32 was directly equivalent to any American type, in this case the 25L6G. The KT63 was similar to the 6V6G but had ratings and characteristics identical to the 6F6G pentode. The KT66 was comparable to the 6L6G but had a somewhat higher plate dissipation. Like the 6L6 it also underwent developmental changes over the years ending up carrying maximum plate and screen ratings of 500 volts when by this time a Class AB2 pair was capable of 50 watts output.

Initially the development of kinkless tetrodes by M-O.V. was confined to the production of output types but by 1938 RF types had been added to both the new International range as well as the older 4-volt series. This development was without precedent either in the U.K. or in other countries and remained unique to Marconi-Osram. Coinciding with the production of the first output tetrodes in 1937 M-O.V. adopted a policy of gradually phas-

Osram KT63, the later version is on the right.

Marconi-Osram KT66 power tetrodes. The earlier version is on the right.

72

ing out all their existing output pentodes, including battery types, and replacing them with equivalent kinkless tetrodes. In this connection it is interesting to note that the production of beam-type battery tetrodes occurred some three years earlier than in the U.S.

By 1938 other valve makers, initially Cossor and Mazda, had marketed output tetrodes while Hivac continued production of their Harries design. In the same year Brimar produced the American types 6V6G, 6L6G, and 26L6G in their newly introduced International Octal range. These same three types were also included among the valves listed by Cossor, Mullard, and Tungsram in 1940.

Apart from the marketing of the three American-type valves mentioned this was Mullard's only acknowledgment of the threat to the supremacy of the pentode as an output valve. This was obviously because their parent company, Philips, as owners of the basic pentode patent could more profitably continue along established lines.

Continental Developments

In continental Europe the output tetrode made little impression on the scene and always remained a relatively rare breed of tube. The known manufacturers of this class of tube—Fivre, Loewe, Telefunken, and Philips-Valvo—between them produced only about half a dozen types which, apart from those made by Fivre, were all in the form of multiple tubes.

The first continental use of a tetrode output tube occurred in 1938 when Telefunken produced a dual tetrode, type VEL11, for use in one model of the Nazi-inspired German 'Peoples Receiver' known as the Kleinemfanger.[16] The first section of the VEL11 operated as a screened-grid detector whilst the second section was a power tetrode capable of 2 watts output. A second Telefunken multiple tube, type VCL11, consisted of a triode-cum-tetrode having an output of 0.8 watts. Two somewhat similar tubes, types ECL11[17] and UCL11, followed in 1939; these had a much higher power output of 4.2 watts.

An indication of the relatively unimportant position occupied by the output tetrode in continental Europe can be obtained from a study of Brans' *Vade Mecum*. For example, in the 1948 edition of this work there is listed only one manufacturer, Fivre, who made any American-type beam power tetrodes while amongst the few manufacturers who did make other types of output tetrodes none made single-section, i.e., non-multiple, types.

REFERENCES

1. See advt. C.E. Mfg. Co. Inc., *Radio News*, June 1928, p. 1367.
2. New A.C. Tubes Developed, *Radio News*, April 1929, p. 946.
3. Recent Advances in Radio Tube Design, *Radio Craft*, May 1931, p. 599.
4. New Types of Receiving Tubes, *Radio Craft*, May 1931, p. 686.
5. What's New at the Trade Show, *Radio News*, July 1931, p. 51.
6. *Rider's Perpetual Troubleshooter's Manual*, Vol. II, p. 8, 'ERLA' model 636 schematic dated April 20, 1931.
7. New Types of Receiving Tubes, *Radio Craft*, April 1931, p. 663.
8. See *Radio Retailing*, May 1932, p. 33.
9. Still More New Tubes, *Radio Craft*, Sept. 1932, p. 142.
10. New Tube Announcements, *Radio Craft*, Jan. 1933, p. 398.
11. New Tube Announcements, *Radio Craft*, Dec. 1932, p. 334.
12. J.H. Owen Harries, *Wireless World*, Aug. 2, 1935, pp. 105–106.
13. The New Beam Power Tube, *Radio Craft*, July 1936, p. 12.
14. The March of Tubes, *Radio Craft*, April 1937, p. 636.
15. A Guide to the New Tubes, *Aerovox Research Worker*, July 1939, p. 2.
16. The People's Set, *Wireless World*, March 1939.
17. See Philips' publication *The Bridge to Higher Radio Entertainment* dated Sept. 1939, p. 10.

Chapter Ten

Double-Filament and Multiple Tubes

American Developments

The idea of fitting a tube with more than one filament goes back to the earliest days for it was in 1909 that the first double-filament De Forest Audions were produced. Several years later other manufacturers took up the idea, the Cunningham AudioTron and the Moorhead Electron Relay being the best-known examples of unbased double-filament tubes of the period.

The first American double-filament tube to be fitted with a standardised base was a type made by Moorhead in 1922 which was known as the A-P Two-in-One. It consisted of a dual cylindrical electrode assembly joined 'Siamese twin' fashion by means of a one-piece anode formed in a figure-of-eight pattern. The anodes and grids were effectively in parallel while the two axial filaments were joined in series and intended for operation from a stan-

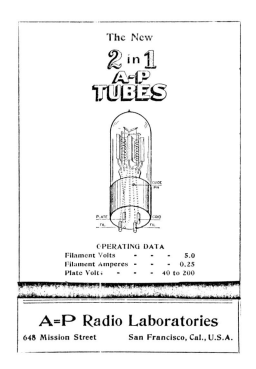

The New

2 in 1 A-P TUBES

OPERATING DATA
Filament Volts - - - 5.0
Filament Amperes - - 0.25
Plate Volts - - 40 to 200

A=P Radio Laboratories
648 Mission Street   San Francisco, Cal., U.S.A.

dard 5-volt supply. However, as the common point of the two filaments was connected to the brass base-shell it was possible to use one filament at a time from a 2-volt supply.

Apart from a slightly later tube known as the Apco, no other double-filament tubes appeared until 1940 and by then they had been developed for an entirely different reason. Originally the reason for the fitting of a second filament was to allow an extension of the tube's operating lifetime, as after the first filament had burnt out the second one could be brought into use. In the case of more recent tubes, however, the fitting of a double filament allowed either series or parallel operation as desired.

The need for series/parallel filament operation had arisen in 1940 with the production of mains/battery portable receivers which used 1.4-volt dry-cell tubes. As a matter of design convenience when these receivers were operating from mains power all tube filaments were connected in series, but as the filament current of most output tubes was twice that of other tubes in the set it became necessary to produce an output tube having two filaments which could be operated either in series or parallel as required. The first standardised double-filament type, type 3Q5GT, was produced expressly to meet this requirement and thereafter double-filament output tubes remained in use for as long as tube-operated portable receivers were in production.

British Developments

One of the earliest-known examples of a British-made double-filament valve was advertised in 1923[1] by Phillips Valves Ltd. of Southall, Middlesex, a small independent who also made conventional single-filament types. The Phillips double-filament valve was a bright emitter type which was unique in being fitted with a composition base at a time when all other makes still had metal-shell bases. A small link-arm on the underside of the base allowed the second filament to be brought into use after the first one had failed.

An unusual, indeed unique, valve known as the 'Nelson Multi', was produced by the Nelson Electric Co. Ltd. towards the end of 1925.[2] This valve had no less than three filaments, any one of which could be brought into use separately by means of a scissors type switch on the underside of the base. In addition it was possible to adjust the switch to allow two filaments to be run in parallel and so use the valve as a power amplifier. Two versions, known as types A and DEA, were offered initially and early in 1926 a further two, types DE2 and DE06, were added to the range. Shortly after this, however, the Nelson Electric Co. ceased advertising and nothing further was heard of the company's products.

As in the U.S.A., several years elapsed before double-filament valves again appeared on the scene and when this occurred they were not of British design. In May 1940 only two manufacturers, Brimar and Tungsram, listed any such valves and in both cases it was the American type 3Q5GT. By then, however, World War II had been in progress for some six months and British valve makers were becoming too occupied with catering for military demands to have time to develop new types for commercial use, so it was not until the post-war years that other makers engaged in the production of the 3Q5GT and similar types.

Early Multiple Tubes

Sooner or later it was inevitable that someone would get the idea of putting two or more identical electrode assemblies inside a single bulb, thus creating a two-in-one or three-in-one tube. Superficially at least the idea was attractive as it would appear to offer economies in production costs which, if it did not result in two tubes for the price of one, did make it cheaper than using separate tubes.

It was in Germany that multiple tubes were first developed seriously and in that country the firm of Loewe Radio AG became the undisputed leader, not only in the manufacture of multiple tubes but also in the production of small receivers incorporating them.[3,4] Loewe had previously made conventional tubes under the name 'Loewe Audion' but from 1926 onwards specialised in the production of 2-in-1 and 3-in-1 types.

The Loewe 3-in-1 was unique in that it contained within the bulb not only three separate electrode assemblies but also all the associated resistors and capacitors necessary for a 3-tube receiver; only the tuning circuits were, of necessity, outside the bulb. To prevent contamination of the vacuum within the bulb each capacitor and resistor was individually sealed inside a glass phial, and the completed assembly of electrodes and components was supported by an intricate arrangement of glass rods and beads. Although German glassblowers have always been renowned for their workmanship the overall effect in this case was of German ingenuity gone mad. Even with the most proficient glass workers such a form of construction must have been expensive and in addition was far from robust. Another rather obvious drawback of the Loewe tube was that in the event of a filament burn-out a major part of the receiver had to be discarded, though in the Vaterland this

Loewe receiver using 3NFB tube.

75

was overcome by the provision of a repair service whereby new filaments could be fitted to a burnt-out tube.

In later productions of the Loewe multiple tubes most of the complicated glass work was done away with and use was made of mica spacers and supports. As if ashamed of the changed internal appearance of these later productions Loewe sprayed the bulbs with aluminium paint which had no functional purpose and served merely to hide the internal structure from view.

In its original form the Loewe receiver consisted of a non-regenerative detector followed by a two-stage resistance coupled amplifier but later productions were modified to incorporate regeneration in the detector circuit. This necessitated an additional external connection on the tube base, the seventh contact being located in the centre of the existing pin circle. The original 6-contact tubes were designated 3NF, while the later 7-contact types were known as 3NFB in Germany and RNF7 in England. In both cases the letters NF indicated Nieder Frequenz (low frequency or AF).

Another Loewe tube, though one with completely different functions, was also produced at this time. It consisted of two screen-grid tetrodes arranged as a two-stage RF amplifier and was known as type 2HF (HF = Hoch Frequenz). The same type of 6-contact base as used on the 3NF was fitted to the 2HF and a similar sized bulb was used.

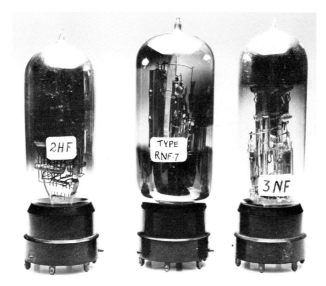

Loewe multiple tubes, the centre tube was originally coated with aluminum paint.

In later years Loewe went on to make AC versions of their multiple tubes and by 1935 four different types were in production. These included such complex types as an RF pentode, detector triode and output pentode combination which required 13 external connections. The production of such tubes remained unique to Loewe and was never attempted elsewhere.

At much the same time as the Loewe multiple tubes first appeared, or a little earlier if the absence of any visible gettering is any indication, another German firm also brought out 2-in-1 and 3-in-1 types. These were produced by the Suddeutsche Telefon Apparate, Kabel & Draht Werke and were sold under the brandname TKD or Te Ka De. Both types were noteworthy for their compact con-

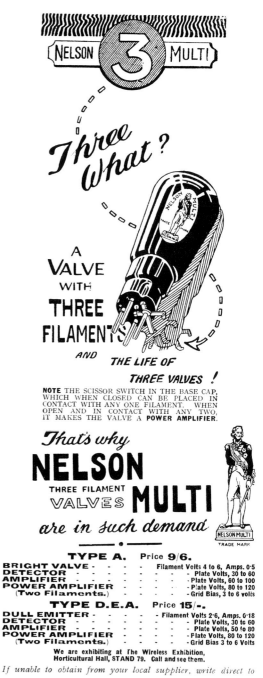

struction and small physical size; the 2-in-1 type VT126 having a maximum diameter of only 40 mm, while the 3-in-1 type VT139, which used the same sized electrodes, measured 50 mm. These and other TKD tubes are notable for the use of one-piece punched sheetmetal grids—the so-called ladder grid—as well as for the use of oxide-coated filaments.

The only early American multiple tube was one which made a brief appearance during 1927. In March of that year a company named the Emerson Rad Val Corp. of New York marketed a 3-in-1 tube known as the Emerson Multivalve type E.M.V.-3A.[5] This tube had three small cylindrical electrode assemblies each having an axial filament. The filaments were series-connected, the terminal voltage being the standard American 5-volt rating. A standard S-14 size bulb was used, together with a standard 4-pin UX base. The base was modified by the addition of a flange or collar which carried four screw terminals, giving a total of eight external connections. The Multivalve was almost certainly made by Cleartron as the bulb had the characteristic flattened spike on the seal-off tip which was a hallmark of Cleartron tubes.

In 1927 the Multivalve tube is known to have been used in a receiver marketed under the name 'Baby Emerson' and also in one made by the Standard Radio Corp. of Worcester, Mass., under the name 'Standardyne'.[6]

The first British multiple valve appeared late in 1927, being produced by Ediswan as type ES220. In essence it consisted of two triodes but these were not constructed in the form of separate assemblies; instead one section was built inside the other, resulting in the most extraordinary electrode formation imaginable. The ES220 appears to have been in the nature of an experimental or prototype valve although an Ediswan receiver known as the 'One-

TeKaDe 3-in-1 (L.) and 2-in-1 (R.) multiple tubes.

Der' was produced in 1928. Like the valve itself, the receivers also seem to have been prototypes only.

A year later B.T-H produced a two-in-one valve not identified by any type number but it was a fairly conventional representative of the genre in that it had two independent sections provided with a common filament.[7] A standard British 4-pin base was used with two additional connections provided by means of two terminals mounted on opposite sides. B.T-H marketed two models of receivers using Duplex valves, in fact as far as can be ascertained, the valves were developed solely for use in B.T-H receivers and were not marketed separately.

Later Twin Triodes

Except in the case of Loewe who continued the production of multiple tubes, no further developments occurred until 1933 when the first of the so-called 'twin triodes', intended for Class B output stage use, appeared in the U.S. These tubes were first produced as battery-operated types and it was in this application that they were most widely used. This was because the inherent efficiency and economy of Class B operation was of greater importance in the case of battery-operated receivers. The type 19, which was in the same 2-volt range as the '30' Air Cell series, was released early in 1933[8] and found ready acceptance by receiver manufacturers. It was capable of 2 watts output under zero bias conditions with 135 volts on the plate. Under these conditions the static plate current was 10 mA, though for greater economy this could be reduced to 1 mA by the application of −6 volts bias, when the output fell to 1.6 watts. Either way this was a remarkable

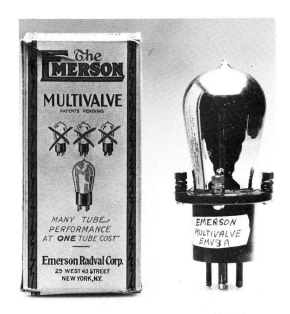

Emerson Multivalve and carton (1927).

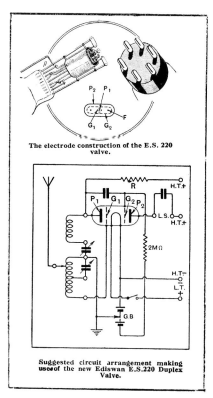

The electrode construction of the E.S. 220 valve.

Suggested circuit arrangement making use of the new Ediswan E.S.220 Duplex Valve.

Ediswan ES220 multiple valve (1927).

performance when compared with the type 33 pentode operating in Class A mode. An octal-based version of the 19 was released in 1936 and a lower-power version, type 1G6G, followed in 1939.

In mid-1933 a 2.5-volt AC version, type 53, and a 6.3-volt version, type 79, were released,[9] but as Class B operation in mains-operated receivers and car radios was little used these two tubes were relatively unimportant commercially. Even so there was apparently sufficient demand to warrant the development of further types, examples of which are types 6A6 and 6N7, though these were probably more often used as other than output tubes—for instance as phase inverters or audio mixers.

Meanwhile, on the other side of the Atlantic similar developments had been taking place. It is probably true to say that Class B operation of the output stages of battery sets was even more enthusiastically taken up in England than it was in the U.S. This was because of the proportionately greater number of battery-operated receivers in use in Britain and because economy in battery current was more sought after.

By the end of 1933 all valve makers had at least one Class B twin triode in production whilst some offered two different types. As in the U.S., the filament voltage was standardised at two volts and most valves had characteristics which were quite similar to the American type 19. Examples of some of the first issues are: Cossor 220B,

Osram B21, Mazda PD220, and Mullard PM2B. An unusual, indeed unique, Class B valve was marketed briefly by Hivac towards the end of 1934.[10] It was known as type DB240 and included a driver triode in the same bulb as the output pair. As far as can be determined this Hivac valve had no counterpart anywhere else in the world and it is mentioned here just 'for the record'.

In spite of the initial enthusiastic reception accorded the Class B output stage it did not enjoy as long-lived popularity as in America. One reason for this was that a somewhat similar type of output stage known as quiescent push-pull (QPP) had always been popular because it did not require the driving power needed in Class B operation. Apart from this there had been continuing and intensive development of highly efficient battery-operated output triodes and pentodes which had no counterparts amongst American tubes and which had the effect of making Class B less attractive.

On the European continent the adoption of Class B appears to have taken place rather later and to a lesser extent than occurred in Britain and the U.S., judging by the small number of manufacturers who produced suitable tubes. The first offering from Philips, the type B240, did not appear until 1935. This was followed in 1937 by the KDD1 in the 2-volt 'Golden' series of side-contact types. Examples from other makers are: Dario TB402, Telefunken RE402B, and Tungsram CB220.

Class B operation of output stages in mains-operated receivers was almost unheard of in Europe with the result that there were no valves developed for this class of service. However, by 1940 some of those British manufacturers making American type valves listed certain Class B types though no single maker listed all types. Osram was the only maker to assign a private type number to any such tube, their type B63 being the direct equivalent of the 6N7.

The first twin-triode voltage amplifiers were the types 6C8G and 6SC7 which appeared in 1940.[11] These were followed in 1945 by the better-known 6SN7Gt and the lesser-known 7F8. When in 1948 RCA introduced noval-based miniature tubes it so happened that the first two types issued were twin-triodes–types 12AU7 and 12AX7. They were followed by the 12AT7, the three types being made by all American manufacturers.

Direct-Coupled Tubes

A peculiarly American breed of tube, the direct-coupled amplifier, first appeared early in 1932 when the Cable Tube Corp. of Brooklyn, N.Y. announced their Speed 'Triple Twin' type 295 in March of that year.[12] The term Triple Twin was explained as indicating that the tube had three times the output of the type 45 triode and twice that of the type 47 pentode. That this claim was slightly exaggerated can be confirmed if the published figure of 4.5 watts for the 295 is compared with the figures for the other two tubes.

It is probably not stretching the imagination too much to suggest that, coming at the time when it did, the tube's production was an attempt to capitalise on the publicity which had surrounded the Loftin White direct-coupled amplifier during 1930–31. Be that as it may, the Speed 295 proved to be the progenitor of a line of similar tubes, the development of which continued for the next five years or so.

The Triple Twin was a two-in-one tube consisting of an indirectly-heated driver triode directly coupled to a directly-heated output triode and was the first American multiple tube to employ two dissimilar triodes. The type 295 carried a 2.5-volt heater/filament rating and was soon followed by a 6.3-volt version, type 293 and an AC/DC version, type 291. As befitted their applications the last two types had much smaller power output capabilities, though were otherwise identical in construction apart from having smaller bulbs.

was that towards the end of 1933, some 18 months after the arrival of the 295, Arcturus announced the type 2B6.[13] The main difference between the new tube and its predecessor lay in the use of an indirectly-heated output section, resulting in a considerably reduced heater wattage. Other differences were the abolition of the top-cap connection and the use of a large 7-pin base and an ST16 bulb.

Coinciding with the release of the 2B6 was the release of receivers by two companies, Lincoln and McMurdo Silver, using the new tube. However, apart from its use by one or two small manufacturers of public address amplifiers, this appears to have been the only occasion when the 2B6 was used in a commercially built receiver. In spite of this the 2B6 had made its mark and further developments were soon to follow.

The first direct-coupled tube to achieve real commercial success was the type 6B5 announced by Triad in April 1935.[14] Other manufacturers who made this tube were National Union, Raytheon, Champion, and Tung Sol. Unlike earlier direct-coupled tubes the 6B5 found ready acceptance amongst manufacturers of both home and automo-

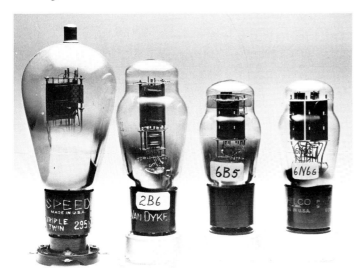

Direct-coupled output triodes 1932–1937.

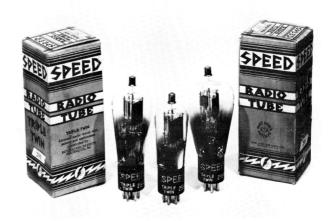

Speed 'Triple-Twin' direct-coupled output triodes.

In spite of having had the advantage of extensive publicity in technical journals of the day, coupled with plentiful advertising, the Triple Twin tubes were not even moderately successful, as to the writer's knowledge they were never used in any commercially built receiver or amplifier. The tube's main drawback was not so much the result of any shortcomings in its design as the need for rather complicated input and biassing circuitry. For example, a special AF choke was needed in the input section's cathode circuit and such a component was an anathema in the days of resistance-coupled audio stages.

For some reason Speed, in spite of being the originators of direct-coupled tubes, did not continue with their development and it was left to two other companies, Arcturus and Triad, to carry on further developmental work. So it

bile receivers, it being used by such large companies as Crosley and United Motors. Undoubtedly the main reason for the success of this new tube was its ability to replace the commonly used type 42 output pentode simply by omitting the usual biassing circuitry. Because the operating conditions of the 6B5 matched those of the 42 quite closely no circuit redesign or other alterations were required in the receiver, even the base connections were the same. What more could any radio manufacturer ask? The direct-coupled tube had arrived!

Compared with earlier designs the 6B5 had the advantage of requiring no external biassing arrangements and in addition had somewhat improved characteristics. It differed from earlier tubes in having an internally mounted resistor connected between the two sections, the stated

SPEED
TRIPLE-TWIN

a master achievement from the Speed Laboratories

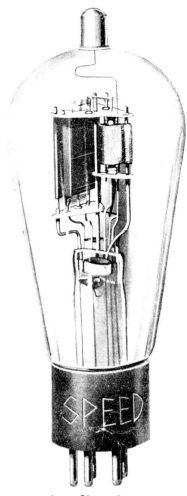

The SPEED "TRIPLE-TWIN," a combination power output and detector tube, far surpasses all recent developments and is comparable in importance only to the invention of the vacuum tube itself.

Its features are outstanding:

- Triple the 245's output and double the 247's without increased plate voltages.

- One "Triple-Twin" supplants complete DETECTOR and AUDIO System.

- Super sensitivity allows elimination of pre-stages in special applications.

- Flat frequency response, 30 to 50,000 cycles. A boon to television.

- Economy in chassis construction.

Complete engineering data available

Applications

- Radio Broadcast Receivers
- Special Receivers
  (Army, Navy, Police, Aircraft)
- Television
- Sound Projectors and Recorders
- Theatre Sound Equipment
- Public Address Systems
- Centralized Radio
- Carrier Current Systems
- Communication Repeater Systems
- Broadcast Transmitters
- Automatic Phonographs
- Industrial Applications

CABLE RADIO TUBE CORP.

230 North Ninth Street
BROOKLYN, N. Y.

purpose of which was to prevent warm-up surges. Because the output section operated with a positive bias it had to have a high-mu characteristic (to prevent excessive plate current) and this was achieved by using two separate control grids connected in parallel.

Following the introduction of octal-based tubes the 6B5 was issued in this form as type 6N6G in 1937. A metal-glass version, type 6N6MG, was made by National Union, Raytheon and Triad. Triad also originated two lower power versions, types 6AB6G and 6AC6G, as well as an AC/DC version, type 25N6G.

In summary it may be said that although the direct-coupled tube in its later forms enjoyed a certain amount of success it never became a serious threat to the well-entrenched pentode or beam tetrode output tubes. Direct-coupled output tubes were largely unknown outside the U.S. though types 6B5 and 6N6G were made, or at least listed, by Brimar from 1938 onwards. Whilst these were probably intended as replacements for use in imported American receivers it is known that at least two British set makers, Pilot and Halford, used 6N6G valves in certain models of receivers made during the late 1930s.

Other Multiple Tubes

A type of multiple tube which originated in the U.S. was an output pentode cum rectifier combination intended for use in small AC/DC receivers. The first of such types, type 12A7, was released late in 1933 and it was followed in 1939 by the 25A7G. In 1940 RCA first issued beam output tetrodes combined with rectifiers, examples of which are types 32L7GT and 70L7GT.

Another early American combination was a vari-mu pentode combined with a triode, the type 6F7 issued in 1933. This tube remained the sole representative of its class in the 6.3-V. range though in 1939 a few manufacturers produced a similar tube with a 12.6-V. heater rating known as type 12B8GT.

The final combination tube issued prior to World War II was the type 6AD7G which appeared in 1940. It consisted of an output pentode combined with a driver triode and it remained the sole representative of this class of tube.

REFERENCES

1. See advt. Phillips Valves Ltd., *Amateur Wireless*, Sept. 15, 1923.

2. See advt. Nelson Electric Co., *Wireless World*, Oct. 7, 1925, p. ad. 12.

3. Tubes Within Tubes, *Radio News*, July 1927, pp. 30–31.

4. Loewe Type RO433 receiver, *Wireless World*, March 12, 1930, p. 286.

5. See advt. Emerson Radval Corp., *Radio News*, March 1927, p. 1081.

6. Trend of Development, *Wireless World*, Oct. 5, 1927, p. 482.

7. Show Report, *Wireless World*, Sept. 26, 1928, p. 401.

8. New Tube Developments, *Radio Craft*, Jan. 1933, p. 398.

9. Radio Tube Progress, *Radio Engineering*, June 1933, p. 28.

10. See *Wireless World Valve Data*, Nov. 30, 1934.

11. See *RCA Tube Manual*, RC14, July 1940.

12. See advt. Cable Tube Corp., *Radio Engineering*, March 1932.

13. C.H. Strohmeyer, Audio System with the new 2B6 tube, *Radio Engineering*, August 1933, pp. 11–12.

14. Clifford E. Denton, The New 6B5 Dynamic-coupled A.F. Tube, *Radio Craft*, April 1935, p. 590.

Chapter Eleven

The Return of the Diode

American Developments

Following the invention and first use of the diode from 1905 onwards, a period which spanned little more than a decade, the progenitor of all radio tubes was quickly eclipsed by the arrival of the triode detector and many years were to pass before the diode once again came into its own. Aided by the use of regeneration the superior performance of the triode detector ensured its dominance for the next 15 years. Not that the triode was without its drawbacks; drawbacks which became increasingly important as developments in receiver circuitry took place.

One of the drawbacks exhibited by the triode when used in the original leaky-grid mode was its inability to handle large signal inputs without introducing distortion. In the days when pre-detector amplification was either small or non-existent this drawback was of no significance, but following the invention of the screen-grid tube with its inherently high amplification factor, the increased pre-detector stage gain led to the detector becoming a bottleneck. This weakness was further emphasised with the coming into use of the superheterodyne circuit with its extremely high gain.

As a result receiver manufacturers were soon forced to seek a better detector and although both triode and screen-grid tubes were used in the so-called 'biassed detector' or 'anode bend' mode for a few years, it soon became apparent that further improvement was desirable. The shortcomings of amplifying tubes when used as detectors led directly back to the diode, which when resurrected was found to be as near ideal a detector as could be devised.

Once this fact had been established it only remained to put it into practice, but at the time there was no such things as diode detector tubes in production. Receiver manufacturers were therefore forced to adopt the makeshift practice of using triodes as diodes. This was simply done by using the grid as the anode while the true anode was usually earthed and thus functioned solely as a shield. Connected in this manner the type 27 tube was successfully used by several American manufacturers until the arrival of specialised detector diodes.

The earliest-known commercial use of diode detection carried out in this manner occurs in the Edison models R4 and R5 receivers marketed in mid-1929.[1] In the following year Philco similarly used diode detection but in this case with the addition of automatic gain control (AVC), even though vari-mu tubes had not then made their appearance. In both cases the receivers were of the TRF variety but in 1931 the Philco model 90 (late) appears to have been the first superheterodyne to incorporate diode detection. In the same year Grigsby-Grunow were the first to use full-wave detection using two type 27 tubes, connected as diodes, in their model 25 receiver.[2]

Duo-diodes 6H66 and GH6 (1936).

The first duo-diodes (1931).

Finally, after more than two years of these makeshift arrangements, the first 'modern' diode detector tube was put into production. Even then it was not available for general sale as the tube in question was made by a receiver manufacturer solely for use in the company's own sets. In December 1931 the Grigsby-Grunow Co. released their model 200 receiver which used the newly developed Majestic type G-2-S duo-diode tube. This tube, together with the later G-4-S, remained unique on the American scene until the advent of the type 6H6 metal tube in 1935.

The arrival of the G-2-S may be said to have signalled the start of a world-wide swing towards the use of diode detection using tubes specially designed for the purpose. Even so triodes were still being pressed into service as diodes as late as 1933 by several well-known manufacturers, such as Crosley and Philco, although by this time duo-diodes in combination with triodes or pentodes had come into general use.

Another factor of perhaps equal importance in bringing about the general use of diode detection was the invention of the so-called 'automatic volume control' (AVC), a feature which was greatly facilitated by the use of diode detection. Prior to this AVC could only be obtained by the use of a separate tube, often needing a rather complex circuit in order to obtain the requisite control voltage. When diode detection was used it was a simple matter to obtain 'free' AVC by using the rectified signal voltage. So it was that within the space of two or three years diode detection came to dominate the scene and has retained its popularity to this very day, even though vacuum tube has been superceded by crystal.

Because of the exceptionally small emission requirements of a signal diode it was soon realised that it was possible to incorporate a couple of diodes into the same envelope with an existing triode without the need to increase either the heater wattage or the size of the electrode assembly. Furthermore, the triode could directly follow the diode in receiver tube sequence as a first stage audio amplifier so that the combination of the two stages within a single bulb was a logical step. This led to the development of the so-called duo-diode-triode tube wherein two tiny diode plates were incorporated into the structure of a triode and shared a common cathode. The first of such tubes was the type 55 which was announced in July 1932.

Much has been written about the Arcturus 'Wunderlich' tube, a contemporary of the 55, which was announced in May 1932.[4] Like the 55 the Wunderlich was essentially a form of diode-triode but because of the unusual method of combining the functions of detection and amplification in one electron stream (unlike the three-stream 55) it deserves special mention. Firstly the German-sounding name was that of the tube's inventor, Norman E. Wunderlich, a former engineer of the old Radio-Victor Corp. who appears to have invented and patented the tube before selling the rights to the Arcturus Radio Tube Co.

The distinguishing feature of the Wunderlich lay in the structure of its twin grids. These were arranged in co-cylindrical, or to be more precise, co-planar fashion around a common cathode and in turn were surrounded by a

Norman E. Wunderlich

The Wunderlich tube and its inventor.

common (triode) plate. Functionally the tube could be regarded as either a leaky-grid triode having two grids, or as a tube having two open-mesh diode plates which allowed the electron stream to pass through and reach the outer plate. In practice the Wunderlich was always used as a full-wave detector and in fact this mode of operation was inherent in its design. As with the 55 it was a simple matter to obtain an AVC control voltage from the rectified signal, though the full-wave circuit configuration was somewhat inflexible when it came to other than 'simple' AVC. To obviate this shortcoming a final form of the tube known as type 'B' was announced in March 1933 wherein an entirely separate diode plate was added to the existing assembly. However, due to its comparative late arrival this particular tube was destined to become little more than a curiosity as it was never used commercially.

Historically the Wunderlich was a dead-end tube; its invention did not give rise to a new generation of similar tubes and within the space of a few years it was all but

Radiotron 85 (6.3V) and 55 (2.5V).

forgotten. The original 2.5-V Wunderlich tube was not allocated any type number but after the production of a 6.3-V car radio version, identified as 'A-Auto', the 2.5-V version became known as type A.

Contrary to a widely-held belief, the Wunderlich design was not unique as at much the same time two other tube makers had released similar types. These differed only in that they were two-stream variants, but the principle of operation remained the same. Whereas the Arcturus Wunderlich used a common cathode, tubes made by Ken-Rad and Sylvania used twin cathodes each with its own grid, the twin assemblies being surrounded by a common plate. Examples are: Sylvania types 29 and 69;[5] Ken-Rad KR20 and KR22.[6] Although the Wunderlich was used by several receiver manufacturers during 1932–33 there is no record of any commercial use of either the Ken-Rad or Sylvania versions.

For the next forty years the duo-diode triode was to reign supreme as the most commonly used multi-function radio tube and even though diodes were later combined with either AF or RF pentodes these particular combinations never became as widely used as the DDT.

By 1933 duo-diode pentodes in both 2.5-and 6.3-volt versions (types 2B7 and 6B7) had appeared and by 1937 they were joined by a 2-volt battery version, type 1F6. It should be mentioned here that the combining of diodes with output pentodes or tetrodes was unknown in the U.S. in spite of its popularity in Europe. When the first 1.4-volt miniature battery tubes were released in 1940 it is interesting to note that a duo-diode triode was not included in the range, only a diode-pentode, type 1S5. In the case of the 7-pin indirectly-heated miniatures it was impossible to produce a duo-diode pentode due to the limitation of the number of base pins.

During World War II the first American miniaturised twin diode, type 6AL5, was introduced by Sylvania. This tube quickly became an industry standard, made by all other makers. Prior to its advent it had been necessary to use a triode strapped as a diode when a miniature type was required. It may be recalled that a similar situation had arisen many years earlier in the case of standard sized tubes. The 6AL5 was announced in August 1944 and was, of course, intended for military applications. After the war it found extensive use in FM and television receivers.

British Developments

Following American practice the use of diode detection, together with AVC, became commonplace in Britain from 1933 onwards. The first British receiver known to have utilised both these features, the Murphy model A8, was being advertised in November 1932. An article in *Wireless World* stated that a Mazda type AC/DD valve was used.[7] For some reason this particular valve was almost immedi-

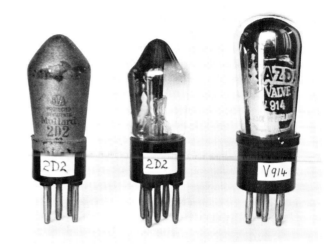

L. Mullard duo-diodes for 2-volt battery operation. R. Mazda V914 (formerly AC/DD) 4-volt AC.

ately superseded by the type V.914, the earlier type being no longer listed after 1934.

Initially British valve makers offered plain duo-diodes only and not until later in 1933 did the first duo-diode triodes appear. In addition to producing duo-diodes for AC and AC/DC operation British and continental manufacturers also made battery-operated types, a class of tube completely unknown in the United States. Of the last named the first British example was the Cossor 220DD which appeared in 1934.[8] A variation also unknown in the U.S. was a 2-volt battery type having an indirectly-heated cathode. This particular type of valve was produced only by Philips-Mullard and was intended for use in their own receivers. The Mullard 2D2 and the Philips KB2 were first listed in 1936. In spite of being indirectly heated these valves consumed only 0.09 amps, a figure about half that of most ordinary 2-volt types.

During its heyday the plain duo-diode was much more widely used in Britain than in America, which may seem surprising in view of the fact that British receivers of the period generally used fewer valves than their American

Philips and Mullard duo-diodes. They came in various shapes and sizes.

84

counterparts. The reason for the popularity of such valves with British set makers may have been due to a drawback connected with the use of some types of diode combinations which manifested itself as an unwanted coupling between the sections. Such coupling could be completely eliminated only by the use of two separate valves for the functions of detection and AF amplification. Be that as it may, the duo-diode retained its popularity in the U.K. up to the cessation of domestic receiver production early in World War II.

From the more conservative British standpoint the use of a separate valve solely for the purpose of detection and AVC could be considered wasteful. That the overall number of valves was not necessarily increased by this procedure can be explained by the fact that in such cases the use of an extremely sensitive output pentode, plus a heavily delayed AVC system, allowed a penultimate stage to be dispensed with.

The first British duo-diode triodes appeared during 1933, one of the earliest being the Marconi-Osram MHD4 announced in May of that year.[9] By comparison the first Mullard combination valve, type SD4, did not appear until the end of 1933. This valve was a single-diode tetrode and was not marketed separately but formed part of the complement of a British-built Philips receiver, model 634A. The equivalent Philips 'Binode' type E444, was used in continental Europe.

By the end of 1933 most valve makers were producing a variety of duo-diode triodes suitable for operation in all

Philips E444 'Binode' fitted with American 6-pin base.

A group of dual-grid detector tubes (1932).

85

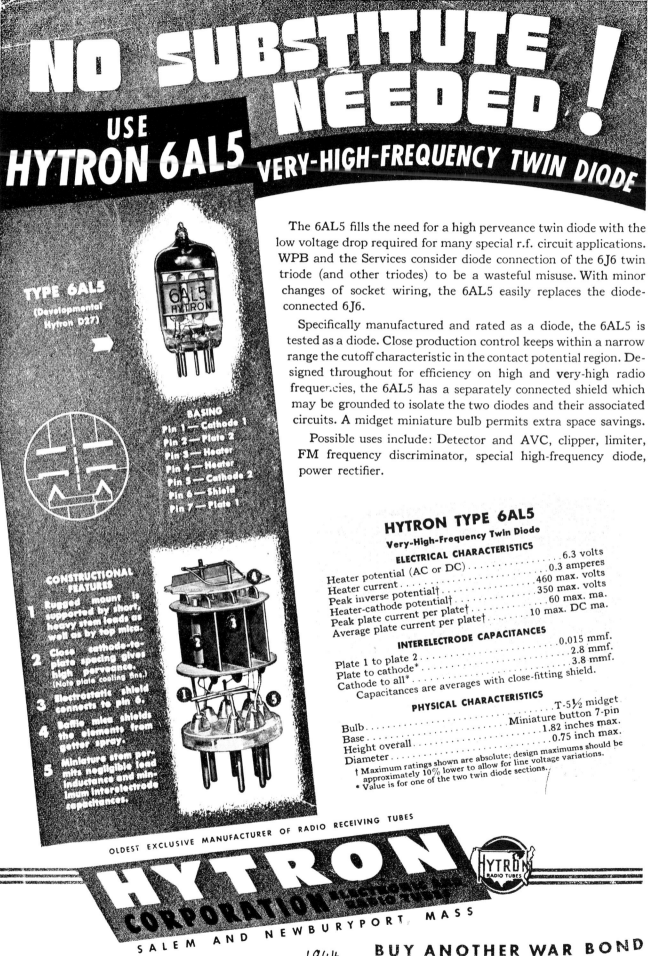

classes of service. As in the U.S., diode-pentode combinations were less common and those that were available differed in that the diode units were usually combined with output pentodes. American practice was to combine only voltage-amplifying pentodes with diodes. One or two exceptions to the British norm may be mentioned: in 1933 Cossor introduced their DD/Pen in which the pentode unit was designed to operate as an AVC amplifier, while in the same year Lissen produced a vari-mu pentode combined with a single diode. A similar valve incorporating two diodes, the Marconi-Osram WD40, was marketed in 1935. Apart from the Mullard example mentioned earlier, no other British manufacturers made diode-tetrode combinations although they they were fairly common on the continent and were marketed in the U.K. by Triotron and Tungsram.

The first duo-diode output pentode to appear was Mazda's AC/PenDD, marketed in 1934.[10] The pentode section of this valve was of the high sensitivity variety, identical to the AC2/Pen. Following this came Ferranti's PT4D in 1935, and by 1936 other manufacturers had similar types in production. Surprisingly, Mullard's Pen4DD was not listed until 1937.

In 1934 Mazda became the world's first valve maker to issue a combination triode-triple-diode valve known as type AC/HLDDD. It was one of the first valves to use the newly introduced 9-pin base.

Following this came the Philips-Mullard triple diode, type EAB1.[11] This class of valve was quite a rarity both at the time and subsequently, and was intended mainly for the equipping of Philips and Mullard receivers which used an elaborate system of distortionless delayed AVC. The EAB1 was announced in 1938 and no similar valve was produced by any other British manufacturer. In the U.S. no similar tube was seen until 1953 when the type 6BC7 appeared.

With the introduction of FM broadcasting in the U.K. in the post-war years the need arose for a triple diode for use in combined AM/FM receivers. In this case three diodes were combined with a high-mu triode, the best-known example of which was type EABC80.

Before leaving the subject of diode detectors a peculiarly British contribution to the genre remains to be discussed. This is the 'Westector', a small radio version of the Westinghouse copper-oxide rectifier better known for its battery charging and radio HT supply applications. Although a solid-state device no apology is offered for including reference to it here for none other than the august *Wireless World* published details of Westectors year after year in its valve data pages. And what is good enough for *Wireless World* is good enough for the author!

Westectors were a product of the Westinghouse Brake & Saxby Signal Co., being first marketed in 1933.[12] Due to their inherently high self-capacity the earliest types were limited to use as second detectors in superheterodynes where the intermediate frequency did not exceed about 150 Kc. By 1934 the upper frequency limit had been extended to 1500 Kc, allowing their use at higher intermediate frequencies or even in TRF receivers. In spite of this Westectors found only limited acceptance in the pre-war years and at no time were they able to challenge the superiority of the thermionic diode. In the years following World War II production of Westinghouse copper-oxide diodes was continued for several years in spite of the coming into use of germanium and other types of diodes which, incidentally, the company also produced.

WESTECTORS
HIGH FREQUENCY METAL RECTIFIERS

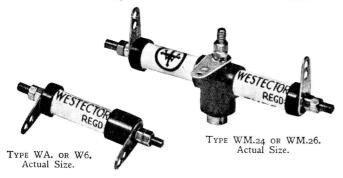

TYPE WA. OR W6.
Actual Size.

TYPE WM.24 OR WM.26.
Actual Size.

Model.	Type.	Length.	Maximum Safe Input Voltage.	Maximum Current Output.
W.4. ..	Half-wave.	1 15/16″	24 v. peak carrier.	0·25 m/a
W.6. ..	Half-wave.	1 15/16″	36 v. peak carrier.	0·25 m/a
WM.24.	Full-wave centre tapped.	3″	24 v. each side of centre tap.	0·5 m/a
WM.26.	Full-wave centre tapped.	3″	36 v. each side of centre tap.	0·5 m/a

REFERENCES

1. See *Rider's*, Vol. 1, p. 7, Edison models R4, R5, dated May 1929.

2. See *Rider's*, Vol. 2, p. 8, Majestic model 25, dated Nov. 11, 1929.

3. Service, July 1932, p. 160.

4. More New Tubes, *Radio Craft*, May 1932, p. 654.

5. Still More New Tubes, *Radio Craft*, Sept. 1932, p. 142.

6. See *Ken-Rad Data Sheet*, dated August 1932.

7. Practical Automatic Volume Control, *Wireless World*, Jan. 6, 1933.

8. See *Wireless World Valve Data*, Nov. 30, 1934.

9. The Double Diode Triode, *Wireless World*, May 19, 1933, p. 355.

10. New Diode Pentode Output Valve, *Wireless World*, March 2, 1934.

11. The Westector, *Wireless World*, March 3, 1933, pp. 173–74.

12. New Range of Valves, *Wireless World*, June 2, 1938, p. 499.

Chapter Twelve

Frequency Changers

Pentagrid Heptodes

In order to trace the origin of tubes designed to incorporate the functions of oscillator and mixer in one unit (for use in superheterodyne circuits) it is necessary to know something of circumstances surrounding their introduction. The earliest superheterodyne receivers made use of a separate oscillator tube coupled to another tube which rectified (detected) the incoming signal. This was the so-called 'additive' system in which the mixer tube became known as the 'first detector' to distinguish it from the normal detector, now known as the 'second detector'. This system was quite satisfactory and in some cases remained in use for many years after the introduction of special multiple tubes.

Initially at least, it seems to have been economic rather than technical considerations that led to the development of special tubes designed to combine the functions of oscillator and mixer in one unit. Because the superhet circuit came into general use at a time when the prevailing economic depression had forced most receiver manufacturers to produce small low-priced models, it was consequently necessary to devise ways of making a cheaper superheterodyne before this class of receiver could compete with the TRF type. The first step in pruning production costs was achieved by dispensing with an RF stage and using in its place a pre-selector (bandpass) input circuit, while later the use of a higher intermediate frequency enabled even this to be dispensed with. The second step consisted in using a self-oscillating mixer tube thus avoiding the need for a separate oscillator tube. Coupled with other economies these two steps made possible the production of a highly efficient five tube receiver which remained the mainstay of the industry for many years. So it was that the single-tube mixer circuit, known as the 'autodyne', came into use, but within the space of two years it had been rendered obsolete by the coming of combination mixer-oscillator tubes.

In the case of battery-operated receivers although it was possible to use the autodyne circuit practical difficulties made it less popular than in mains-operated sets. Because the autodyne mode of operation called for the tube's (filamentary) cathode to be at an RF potential with respect to B- or earth it was necessary to isolate it by using RF chokes in the filament leads. As a result of this complication many receiver manufacturers preferred to use a separate oscillator tube coupled to the first detector. Late in 1932 a unique indirectly-heated 2-volt battery tetrode, type 15,[1] was released by Sylvania to facilitate the use of the autodyne circuit. So efficient and reliable was the 15 that it remained popular even after the introduction of battery-operated pentagrid tubes in the following year.

Whilst the self-oscillating mixer did save the use of one tube this was just about the only virtue it had. Amongst its drawbacks was the fact that because, like its predecessor, it had to rectify the incoming signal this made it impossible to apply any form of gain control to the mixer stage. Because, as an economy measure, most small receivers had no RF stage, a satisfactory control of gain was difficult to achieve when its application was confined to the IF stage alone. The need for a single tube which could combine the functions of oscillator and mixer and at the same time allow the application of an AVC voltage was never greater.

In April 1933 RCA announced the type 2A7, and the pentagrid converter was born.[2] Although this tube was not strictly the first in which the functions of oscillator and mixer had been combined—the French bi-grille tubes had earned this distinction—it was the first to achieve the so-called 'multiplicative' mixing. The 2A7 was single-stream tube with all the elements disposed radially around the cathode, with the two innermost grids forming the oscillator section. The next electrode in sequence deserves special mention as it acted as a space-charge grid and formed a so-called 'virtual cathode' for the control grid (G4). It was this feature which allowed the control grid to be given vari-mu characteristics thus permitting the application of gain control to the mixer stage.

So successful was this design that it remained an industry standard for many years and later formed the basis for the development of 'octode' converters. Subsequent versions of the 2A7 differed only in heater voltage or type of base, the sequence being 6A7, 6A8, 6A8G, 6A8GT, 12A8GT, 7B8. Battery-operated equivalents of the 2A7 were not long in making their appearance, the first of which was type 1A6.[3] Unfortunately, due to the minimal filament current used, the 1A6 was somewhat deficient in performance. In particular the mutual conductance of the oscillator section was rather on the low side resulting in the 1A6 being unsuitable for short-wave working; in fact the tube was even prone to stop oscillating on the broadcast band. As an expedient to overcome this problem, pending the arrival of an improved type of tube, receiver manufacturers sometimes wired a separate triode in parallel with the oscillator section, a practice which led some wag to dub the 1A6 'The tube with an outboard mutual conductance'.

An improved version of the 1A6, known as type 1C6, appeared in August 1934,[4] and due to an increased emission (obtained by an increase in filament consumption) and improved mutual conductance of the oscillator section, no further troubles were experienced.

Early American frequency changers. The tube on the left was a 2-volt battery tetrode with an indirectly-heated cathode.

Little time was to pass before the pentagrid crossed the Atlantic (where it became known as the heptode), for by the end of 1933 Ferranti had produced the first British version, type VHT4.[5] Because of the short time lapse between the appearance of the American and British types, coupled with the similarity of the Ferranti version, it seems likely that Ferranti Ltd. with their on-the-spot representation in the form of Ferranti Inc. of New York, must have obtained a manufacturing license from RCA to enable them to be first in the field in Britain. This suggestion is given credence by the fact that Ferranti Ltd. was a newcomer to valve production, having been engaged in valve making for only one year at this time.

Nearly a year was to elapse before other British valve makers marketed heptode converters, but by the end of 1934 all except Mazda and Mullard had full ranges in production. The fact that two of the largest makers did not produce heptodes may be taken as an indication that this class of valves never dominated the British scene in the way that the pentagrid dominated the American market. Within a year of the heptode's British debut other types of frequency changers were on the market and had found ready acceptance by receiver manufacturers.

Hexodes and Octodes

Apart from the pentagrid the only other early American multiple tube capable of being used as a converter was the type 6F7, a triode-pentode originated by RCA in 1933.[6] Unlike European types the 6F7 was not specifically designed as a frequency changer and was in fact more often used in other applications as evidenced by a contemporary magazine article entitled 'Six Uses for the 6F7'. The two sections of the 6F7 were electrically independent apart from the use of a common cathode, the need for which was dictated by the maximum number of base pins (7) available.

At a slightly later date the triode-pentode mixer enjoyed a limited degree of popularity in both Britain and the continent. In 1934 Mazda produced the first British ver-

RCA 6F7 triode-pentode (L.) and RCA 2A7 pentagrid converter (R.) 1933.

FERRANTI USE FERRANTI VALVES
........SO SHOULD YOU !

HUNDREDS of thousands of Ferranti Valves are at present in use, giving daily demonstration of their efficiency and reliability. What finer testimony than the acclamation of even the most critical of Radio experimenters ?

Ferranti Ltd. have had great experience in the precision manufacture of fine Mechanical and Electrical details. This, especially applied to the design and manufacture of valves, has resulted in a very high standard of quality and remarkable uniformity of valve performance. Every Ferranti Valve is subject not only to normal valve tests but also is tested in a receiver under normal working conditions.

Designed and constructed entirely in the famous Hollinwood works, Ferranti Valves have taken their place in the forefront of Progress towards true Radio reproduction.

The valve illustrated is the Ferranti Heptode V.H.T. 4, the first valve of its kind made in England, which combines in one valve the function of both oscillator and modulator and in addition is a variable Mu type enabling full A.V.C. to be obtained in sets with only one I.F. stage.

There are A.C. Mains, Battery and Universal valves available.

Price 20/-

Write for Valve Catalogue to
FERRANTI LTD., HOLLINWOOD, LANCASHIRE

FERRANTI

sion, type AC/TP,[7] and at much the same time the Mullard TP4 appeared. However, as Mullard were pushing the use of the Philips-designed octode at this time little was heard of their TP. Unlike the American 6F7 the British TPs were intended solely for frequency changing but because, in both cases, the method of combining the oscillator output with the incoming signal was additive it suffered from the same drawbacks as did the antodyne.

For the record, a type of mixer developed in Germany and known as the hexode had a basic similarity to the American pentagrid but the relative positions of the mixer and oscillator sections were reversed. This design proved to be inferior and was not encountered outside continental Europe. Examples of hexode mixers are Philips E448 and Telefunken RENS1224.

Successful though the pentagrid design was on the broadcast and long-wave bands it proved to be less efficient on short-wave, its performance becoming progressively worse as the working frequencies were increased. Attempts to remedy the inherent defects resulted in the appearance of the European octode in 1934. This class of tube was basically similar to the pentagrid in the arrangements of its electrodes but had an additional grid. The effect of the extra grid was to impart pentode characteristics to the hexode section thus improving its performance. But in spite of the octode's superior performance it did not render the penta-grid obsolete, at least not in countries outside continental Europe.

The octode was originally available in two different versions, the Philips-designed 'suppressor grid' octode and the Tungsram 'velogrid' octode. In the latter design the sixth grid was internally connected to the screen, thus accelerating or increasing the velocity of the electron stream. Rather obviously this feature also provided a means of naming the particular version.

As a type the octode was produced by comparatively few makers, British examples being Mullard's FC4 of 1934 and Tungsram's VO4 of 1935. Continental examples are Philips' AK1 and AK2 and Telefunken's EK1 all of which are from the same period. A later development known as the 'beam octode' was released by Philips, Mullard, and Tungsram in 1938[8] and represented the final development of the species. The type EK3 released by these three firms in 1939 was the only example of this class of tube.

On the American scene the first and only octode, type 7A8, was announced by Sylvania early in 1939.[9] This tube was, in essence, a single-ended version of RCA's 6A8 pentagrid converter modified by the addition of a suppressor grid.

With the introduction of metal tubes by RCA in 1935 a new type of mixer, the 6L7, appeared. This tube was described as a pentagrid mixer to distinguish it from the

earlier pentagrid converter; it required the use of a separate oscillator tube coupled to a special 'injector' grid. By comparison with the pentagrid converter the pentagrid mixer could provide superior short-wave performance but the need for a separate oscillator tube tended to restrict its use to higher-priced all-wave receivers.

A European tube having a close functional similarity to the American 6L7 was the so-called 'mixing hexode' which was used to a limited extent, mainly in Germany, during the late 1930s. As in the case of similar American tubes it is necessary to distinguish between hexode mixers and hexode converters; the former type requiring the use of a separate oscillator tube. Unlike the 6L7 which had grids 2 and 4 internally connected, the continental mixing hexodes had these two grids brought to separate base pins thus allowing the tubes to be used in other applications. Examples of such tubes are types AH1 and EH2 made by Philips, Telefunken, and Tungsram. The mixing hexode appears to have been quite unknown in Britain as, unlike the continental-designed octode, it was not made by Mullard.

American 7A8 octode (L.), Philips EK2 octode and American 6K8 triode-hexode (R.).

When RCA introduced single-ended metal tubes in 1939 the production of a frequency changer presented something of a problem in that a minimum of eight external connections was needed. With one of the eight pins (No. 1) of the octal base being reserved for grounding the metal envelope this was consequently an impossible requirement to satisfy. This restriction made it necessary to design a modified form of pentagrid needing only seven external connections.

The manner in which RCA solved this problem is interesting because it resulted in a tube needing quite a different type of oscillator circuit from anything previously used. It was also an example of a tube being tailored to fit within the restriction in the number of external connections available. In the first single-ended converter, type 6SA7, the former oscillator anode (G2) was discarded and the former G3 now funtioned as a combined oscillator anode and screen-grid electrode; the fifth grid now became a suppressor grid, internally connected to the cathode. Because the oscillator anode and the screen grid were now one and the same electrode, which had to be bypassed to earth for RF, the normal 'tickler' feedback oscillator circuit could not be used. Instead the so called 'electron-coupled' circuit, wherein feedback was obtained by trapping the cathode connection into the grid coil, was used.

In 1940 RCA introduced a new range of 1.4-volt battery tubes, the first 'button base' miniature types. The converter in this series, type 1R5, although a pentagrid differed yet again from pervious designs. While the 1R5 was basically the same as the 6SA7 it was not readily adaptable for use with the same cathode coupled oscillator circuit because of its directly-heated cathode. Because of this a conventional tickler feedback circuit was used instead, the common electrode forming the oscillator plate and screen-grid in and being left unbypassed.

Following the battery series of 7-pin miniatures came

AC and AC/DC ranges which were introduced towards the end of 1945. The converter tube in the 6.3-volt class was type 6BE6, a pentagrid resembling the 6SA7. In this case the same oscillator circuit could be used so no circuit redesign was involved. In the loctal range of tubes pentagrid converters were produced in 6.3-V, 150mA AC/DC, and 1.4-V types.

The final pentagrid converters were types 6SB7 and 6BA7 which appeared during 1950. Both were intended for use in FM receivers and featured a high conversion conductance of 950 micromhos.

Triode-Hexodes

An important development in frequency changers occurred during 1934 when a mixing hexode and an oscillator triode were combined in one bulb to create the triode-hexode. An early example of this class of tube, the German ACH1, was produced in 1934 by Telefunken and used extensively during the next few years in receivers made by this firm.

The first British company to offer a triode-hexode was Lissen Ltd. who late in 1934 listed a type ACFC, though it is not known if they were the actual manufacturers. The

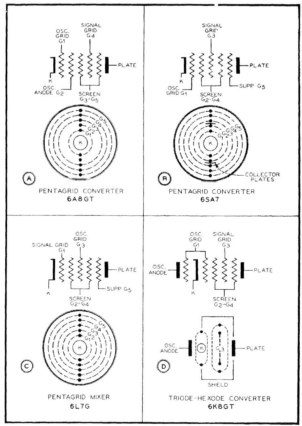

Element arrangements of typical mixer and converter tubes

From Frequency Conversion in Superheterodynes,

M.A. Charles, RADIO, September 1945.

92

Philips CK1 octode   Philips AH1 hexode

first triode-hexode produced by a major British manufacturer was the Marconi-Osram X41 released in mid-1935. By 1936 other valve makers had caught up, examples being Cossor's 41STH, Mazda's ACTH1, Mullard's TH4 and Tungsram's TX4. An octal based version, M.O.V's X65 became available late in 1937. By mid-1938 Mullard had produced a side-contact version, type ECH3, and in 1939 the octal-based ECH35 was issued.

In the post-war B8A series of miniature valves the first 6.3-volt triode-hexodes were Mazda's 6C9 and Mullard's ECH41. The Mazda version was of unusual construction in that the triode and hexode sections were arranged to face each other on either side of a common cathode and in this respect the valve resembled the earlier American 6K8 of 1938. Another unusual valve which appeared at much the same time was M-O.V.'s X78, the world's only triode-hexode to be made in 7-pin miniature (B7G) form. To achieve this seemingly impossible feat it was necessary to cheat by using one of the heater pins to do double duty and serve as the external connection for the cathode at the same time. This procedure could obviously only have been adopted in the case of a valve intended for operation with one side of the heater earthed and the result was the production of a non-standard valve unique to M-O.V. The X78 was later issued in noval-based (B9A) form under the type number X79, this time with a separate connection for the cathode. In 1952 an Australian version of this valve was made by A.W.V. under the type number 6AE8.

As mentioned earlier, the first American triode-hexode

did not appear until 1938 when RCA announced the type 6K8. The design of this tube was unique in that the two sections were arranged to face each other on opposite sides of a common cathode and thus operated in independent electron streams. This most unusual electrode arrangement was never used in any other American tube, the 6K8 remaining the sole representative of the species. By low conversion conductance of 350 micromhos at a time when figures of up to 800 were not uncommon in Europe, which may have been one reason why the triode-hexode did not achieve the same degree of popularity in the U.S. as it did in Europe and elsewhere.

Mullard triode-hexodes TH4A, TH4B and FC4 octode (R.).

Triode-Heptodes

The final development in frequency changers occurred with the advent of the triode-heptode, a tube which was in essence simply a triode-hexode modified by the addition of a suppressor grid to the hexode section. In the U.S. a tube of this type actually appeared before the trode-hexode when Raytheon and Sylvania marketed the type 6J8G in 1937. As this was not an RCA-designed tube it was never produced in metal form nor was it issued as a GT type. In view of its low conversion conductance of 290 micromhos it is not surprising to find that the 6J8G was never a widely used tube, in fact only one receiver manufacturer, Philco, ever seems to have made use of it. Nevertheless, it deserves mention if for no other reason than it was the first American tube of its class.

Following the 6J8G the next triode-heptode was the

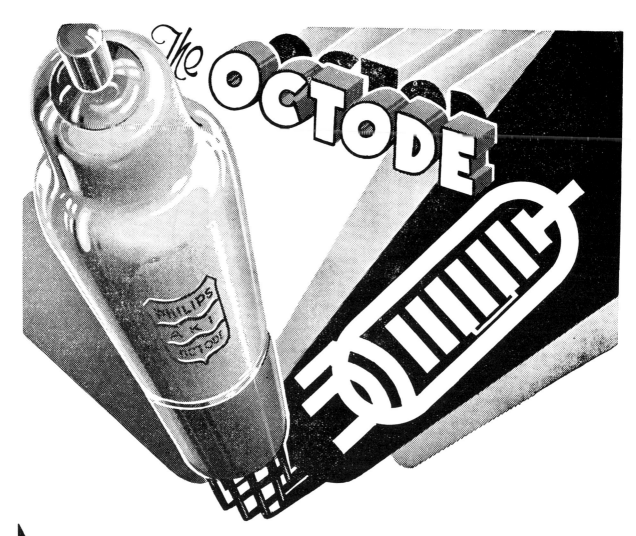

AN AMAZING AIR RECORD

The heavy initial demand in New Zealand and Australia for the Philips wonder-valve, the OCTODE, necessitated urgent action to secure additional supplies.

An aeroplane service was commissioned in London to carry HALF A TON OF OCTODE VALVES to Sydney.

This was safely accomplished within a few days, thus creating a record-breaking air freight feat.

While this is a striking example of the possibilities of aviation, it represents the emphatic endorsement of a great public of the service the OCTODE Valve renders to fidelity reproduction.

As a frequency changer the functions of the OCTODE virtually eliminate "background hiss" and "set noise" long accepted as inevitable in superheterodynes.

Aided by the OCTODE Valve, reception acquires a golden richness and purity of tone of a perfection hitherto unknown.

The OCTODE is a PHILIPS contribution of such import to radio users that to satisfy a record-breaking demand it became necessary to create a record-breaking air freight feat.

High Fidelity **PHILIPS**

(*Advertisement of Philips Lamps (N.Z.) Ltd., 286-288 Wakefield Street, Wellington.*)

1935

loctal-based, 7J7, issued during 1940 by several manufacturers including RCA. However, in spite of being a later development the 7J7 could offer little if any improvement over its octal-based predecessor and, like it, was never widely used. Not until the coming of an improved type, the 7S7 in 1946, could the triode-heptode be said to have earned a place for itself. With a conversion conductance of 550 micromhos the 7S7 could provide an improved performance by comparison with existing types of converters and it remained the final American development of the species.

On the British scene a triode-heptode had first appeared in 1936 when Mazda introduced their type ACTH1. In connection with this valve it should be noted that although it was described by its originators as a triode-hexode it was in fact a triode-heptode, as reference to page 19 of the 1937–38 Supplement to the Mazda Radio Valve Manual will clearly show. Furthermore, in all post-war editions of the *Wireless World Valve Data* it was also correctly listed as a triode-heptode. The same remarks also apply to later Mazda octal-based frequency changers such as types TH41 and TH233. With the release of the B8A series of miniature valves in 1947 both types of Mazda frequency changers in this range were correctly described and identified, e.g., 6C9 = triode-hexode and 6C10 = triode-heptode.

In 1946 the first continental designed loctal-based triode-heptodes, types ECH21/UCH21, were released by Mullard. Although intended primarily as frequency changers these valves differed from any previous types in that the two sections were electrically independent thus enabling their use in other applications. In the early post-war years Brimar, Cossor, and Emitron produced the American designed 7S7/14S7 while M-O.V. issued a quite similar type known as the X81. The final triode-heptodes produced were the noval-based (B9G) types ECH81/UCH81 which were first issued in the U.K. by Mullard in 1953. The same types were also made by Cossor, Ferranti, and Tungsram whilst Mazda's 6C10 and 10C14 were interchangeable with them.

Three versions of the ECH21.

REFERENCES

1. New Tubes Announced, *Radio Craft*, June 1933, p. 398.

2. See *Radio Retailing*, March 1933, p. 40.

3. See *Radio Retailing*, August 1933, p. 40.

4. See Pink Pages *Radio News*, August 1933, p. 1.

5. See advt. Ferranti Ltd., *Wireless World*, Nov. 1933, p. 24.

6. See *Radio Retailing*, June 1933, p. 35.

7. See *Wireless World Valve Data*, Nov. 30, 1934.

8. New Range of Valves, *Wireless World*, May 26, 1938, p. 474.

9. 48 New Tubes!, *Radio Craft*, May 1939, p. 656.

10. See *Wireless World Valve Data*, Nov. 30, 1934, p. iii.

Chapter Thirteen

Metal Envelopes

For several reasons glass as the container or envelope of receiving tubes has always been the most widely used material in spite of onetime attempts to find an alternative. Not that there was ever any pressing need for an alternative as glass was an entirely suitable material as proven by its continued use throughout the history of tube production. It was in the area of transmitting tubes with their higher operating temperatures and associated cooling problems that the first attempt to dispense with the use of glass bulbs was made.

British Metal Valves

Shortly after the end of World War I the first transmitting tubes appeared in which the anode took the form of a copper cylinder having its outer surface completely exposed in order to facilitate cooling. The anode cylinder was fused to a lower section of glass by a special technique known as the Housekeeper seal. In the U.K. valves of this description were made by the M-O.V. Valve Co. and were referred to as cooled anode transmitting, abbreviated to C.A.T. It has been stated that the type of construction used in these valves served as a basis for the development of the first metal receiving valves which appeared about a decade later.

The release of the world's first metal valves, under the Marconi and Osram names, was announced in May 1933.[1] Like their bigger brothers, these valves also made use of external copper anodes fused to lower sections of glass and it was this similarity which led to their being named 'Catkins'. The Catkins represented a complete break from existing valve-making traditions as, apart from the exposed copper anode, a completely new type of electrode mounting and sealing was incorporated in their structure. The conventional glass mounting stem and pinch were abolished and instead the lead-out wires were disposed in a circle and sealed through the squared-off end section of the glass portion of the envelope.

Only four types were included in the initial release—

Marconi-Osram 'catkin' valves.

Marconi-Osram 'catkin' valves produced without screening cans.

96

VMS4, a vari-mu screen-grid; MS4B, a normal screen-grid; MS4, a medium-mu triode; MPT4, an output pentode. All four were functionally identical to existing glass types and bore the same type numbers. Originally all types were fitted with hexagonal perforated metal containers made of cadmium plated brass but later productions were sometimes issued minus the outer containers. The container served the dual functions of preventing accidental contact being made with the otherwise exposed anode and, in the case of RF types, of providing an effective screen or shield.

In 1934 the Catkin range was increased by the addition of three more types, two vari-mu pentodes types W30 and VMP4K and an output pentode type N30. These three differed from the initial release in two respects: the containers were now made of aluminium instead of brass and were of tapered shape, and newly introduced 7-pin bases were fitted. It was the larger diameter of the new base that necessitated the change in the shape of the container. The types N30 and W30 had heaters rated at 13 V, 0.3 A and were intended for series-string heater operation. As in the case of the earlier types their characteristics were identical to existing glass types.

The issuance of only two types in the 300 mA AC/DC range may occasion some raised eyebrows, it being the writer's personal opinion that the manufacturers purposely limited production to two types with the intention that they serve as 'guinea pigs'. Be that as it may, the fact remains that no further issues were ever made in the Catkin range, the total remaining at seven.

In view of the few types produced and their comparatively short production lifespan of less that three years one may be pardoned for expressing doubts as to the success of the specie. In spite of claimed superiority the Catkins made little impression on the market, even though they were sold at the same price as their glass equivalents. Just two years after their appearance only one Catkin was listed in the 1935 Osram Valve Guide, and by 1936 Catkin types were no longer included in the *Wireless World* valve data charts.

However, regardless of its success or failure it must be said of the Catkin that its design represented the first break with lamp-making tradition, and even though its construction may not have been ideally suited to mass production it did set the stage for further developments in other countries. In describing the Catkin as a 'metal' valve it is realised that this description may be disputed on the grounds that only the top two-thirds of the envelope were of metal. But in spite of this the Catkin has surely earned for itself a place in history.

Before concluding this section it is convenient to mention another type of Marconi-Osram valve which is sometimes referred to as a battery Catkin but is correctly known as the 2-volt 'K' type. While in no way a metal valve the 'K' type did use the same method of electrode assembly and the same type of annular seal as was used in the mains-operated types. Only three types were produced—VS24/K, HL24/K, and PT2/K—and they were identical to existing types without the 'K' prefix.

American Metal Tubes

To what extent the British effort served as a spur to the production of American metal tubes is hard to assess but it is known that in 1934 an engineer from RCA visited England in order to study Catkin production methods.[2] By this time developmental work was well under way in the U.S. and in April 1935 the first public announcement of American metal tubes was made.[3]

The American tubes differed from their British counterparts in several ways, mainly in that they were more nearly all metal. Originally the only glass used consisted of a tiny bead surrounding each lead-out wire. Due to high production costs this method of sealing was later, in 1937, changed to a type known as a 'button' seal in which the wires were embedded in a glass disc. A somewhat similar form of seal had been used on the British Catkins where the lead-out wires were taken directly through the bottom of the glass part of the envelope. Another difference, and one immediately obvious to a casual observer, was the smaller size of the American tubes, mainly in the reduced overall height of most types.

Unlike the Catkins the American metals were issued as a full range of types, almost from the start, and the range continued to grow year by year. Viewed with hindsight it is doubtful whether the inclusion of output tubes and rectifiers in metal form served any useful purpose other than to enable RCA to offer a full range in the new format. It may also have helped to forestall any criticism that might have resulted from the non-production of such types. As it happened, early productions of some makes of 6F6 pentodes and 5Z4 rectifiers did give trouble in service to the

Two completely different versions of the 5Z4 rectifier. Both were original releases in 1935.

97

extent that receiver manufacturers using them turned to octal-based 'G' types as soon as the latter became available. Although such teething troubles were soon overcome the bad taste lingered on for many years.

When metal tubes were first announced, as distinct from being actually released, included in the list of six types was an indirectly-heated output triode assigned the type number 6D5. The reason for including such an odd-ball type will probably never be known as such a tube had never previously been made or distributed by RCA. Coupled with this was the initial absence of any output pentode in the metal range and it is interesting to speculate why no such tube was included and whether there was any intention to promote a return to the use of triodes as output tubes in preference to pentodes.

The first metal tubes actually released consisted of a range of nine types—5Z4, 6A8, 6C5, 6F5, 6H6, 6J7, 6K7, 6F6, 6L7.[4] Of these only four call for any comment as the remaining five were simply metal versions of existing glass types. The 5Z4 rectifier in its original form differed from all other types in that the slim tubular 'pencil' anodes themselves formed vacuum-tight enclosures. This form of construction necessitated the electrodes being enclosed in a perforated metal can both for reasons of safety and to protect the tube during handling. Presumably because of high production costs this type of construction was soon abandoned and replacement types were issued in standard metal form. The 6H6 was a duo-diode, a type of tube which had never previously been produced by any American manufacturer with the exception of Majestic. The 6F5 was a high-mu triode, a type not previously, nor subsequently seen except in combination forms. Finally, the 6L7, classed as a pentagrid mixer-amplifier as distinct from a pentagrid converter, was basically a new type intended for use with a separate oscillator tube.

Undoubtedly the most significant development in the history of metal tubes was one that had no direct relationship to the species as such—the introduction of the so-called 'single-ended' types which offered improved performance while dispensing with the need for top cap connections as formerly used on RF pentodes and first-stage AF amplifiers. The design of these tubes represented a completely new departure which set the stage for the eventual world-wide abandonment of double-ended construction in radio receiving tubes.

The initial release of four types—6SJ7, 6SK7, 6SF5, 6SQ7—was announced by RCA late in 1938.[5] It is interesting to note that of the four two were AF voltage amplifiers and this may be explained by the fact that comparable double-ended types had met with some criticism in the matter of excessive hum levels when used in high gain circuits. This hum was mainly attributable to the use of widely spaced lead-out wires and base pins for the heater connections, resulting in stray magnetic and capacitive couplings. In the case of the 6SF5 and 6SQ7 this was

avoided by keeping the heater leads and base pins adjacent even though this had the unfortunate result of breaking the established standard for the position of the heater pins.

It was probably this same hum problem and its solution that allowed British Mazda to profit from the American experience and keep the heater connections of all their own octal-based valves strictly adjacent and always on the same two pins where, we can say with hindsight, the American connections should have been in the first place.

A group of single-ended metal tubes.

In the case of the two RF pentodes, 6SJ7 and 6SK7, advantage had been taken of the opportunity to improve the characteristics, the latter tube in particular had a considerably increased mutual conductance while at the same time required a lower plate current. Two other single-ended types, RCA's 1852 and 1853, later known as 6AC7 and 6AB7, were high gain RF pentodes intended for television use and were actually released several months ahead of the first radio types.

The reason underlying the production of the American metal tubes is said to have been a desire on the part of the General Electric Co., who at the time were planning to re-enter the field of receiver manufacture after an absence of five years, for a unique sales feature which could be incorporated in their forthcoming receiver production. The metal tube was intended to fill this role.

The reason for GE's five-year absence from the entertainment field is of no particular concern except that one consequence of it was that receiving tube manufacture had also been given up for the same length of time. In 1930 the RCA Radiotron Co. had been established for the purpose of manufacturing receiving tubes formerly supplied to RCA by General Electric and Westinghouse. This meant that although GE had the laboratory and engineering facilities needed to develop metal tubes they did not have the necessary production expertise or facilities. For this reason it was necessary to arrange with RCA to have the metal tubes made in what was, by a quirk of fate, GE's former Harrison Lamp Works which had since become RCA's tube factory.

Not for long did RCA have a monopoly on the production of metal tubes as existing licensees were quick to get in on the act and by the end of 1935 five independents—Ken-Rad, Raytheon, National Union, Sylvania, and Tung Sol had all commenced production.

Although new types continued to be released up to the early 1940s metal tubes never completely superseded glass types, at least for use in domestic receivers. Once the initial impact of the 'all-metal' tube had worn off most receiver manufacturers seemed content to use octal-based glass tubes.

Whilst the introduction of metal tubes in the U.S. was technically interesting the manner in which they were introduced was another matter. One effect of the strong element of 'oneupmanship' associated with their commercial exploitation by GE was that Philco, who claimed to be the world's largest receiver manufacturer, completely and permanently eschewed the use of metal tubes. Additionally Philco were sufficiently incensed at the time to conduct an advertising campaign belittling metal tubes, an action which inaugurated a long-standing feud with RCA. Eventually Philco did go so far as to offer metal tubes for replacement use in other makes of receivers in order that they could justify their claim 'Philco tubes improve the performance of any receiver'.

Some of the first American metal tubes.

Metal-Glass Tubes

Because of high tooling costs not all of the independent tube manufacturers elected to enter the metal tube field, one of the most notable abstainers being Arcturus. Because of the large initial impact made by the advent of metal tubes any independent company not producing them could expect to be in for a lean time in the highly competitive tube industry. This situation resulted in the emergence of a hybrid which looked superficially like a metal tube and had almost identical characteristics yet could be produced more cheaply and by conventional methods. Because of their resemblance to metal tubes these hybrids were known as metal-glass or MG types when they first appeared in 1936.[6]

In essence the MG was simply a normal glass tube fitted with a small-diameter bulb and encased in a closely fitting metal jacket to which was attached an octal base. Such

Raytheon 4-pillar radio tubes.

tubes carried the same type numbers as their metal counterparts but with the letters MG added as a suffix. All MGs differed in being considerably taller than corresponding metal tubes and this was particularly noticeable in the case of such types as 6A8MG and 6K7MG.

Companies making MG tubes included Arcturus, Hytron, Ken-Rad, National Union, Raytheon, and Triad. Of these companies Ken-Rad and Raytheon produced so few that it seems doubtful that tubes carrying these names were actually made by them. As a species MG tubes were one of the most short-lived ever produced as within the space of a couple of years they were completely eclipsed by octal-based glass types.

The Arcturus version of the metal-glass tube, known as the 'Coronet', differed in appearance from other brands in that the overall height was considerably less; in this respect the Coronets more nearly resembled metal tubes. The reason for the difference in height is interesting because it resulted from the use of a radically different type of stem of an annular style which had some resemblance to that used on the earlier British Catkins. It was this feature which with its fancied resemblance to the spikes of a coronet gave rise to the name Coronet being applied to the Arcturus tubes. Nine types, corresponding to RCA's original nine metal tubes, were released in March 1936.[7]

In addition to the normal range of 6.3 V and 300 mA AC/DC types Arcturus also produced certain earlier 2.5-volt types in Coronet form. Such odd-ball tubes were fitted with octal bases but were sold with conversion adaptors to enable their use in 5-pin sockets. Arcturus' action was apparently an attempt to standardise their production on the Coronet design but in the event the idea was short-lived. In common with other manufacturers Arcturus soon gave up production of MG tubes in favour of GT types.

As with metal tubes, the production of metal-glass types was confined almost entirely to the land of their origin though it is known that some MGs, patterned on the American design, were made in France, an example being Neotron 6E8. The only other country known to have made metal-glass tubes was Hungary where Tungsram briefly made a series based on the German metal design.[8] The Hungarian tubes, released some six months after the

2.5-volt Arcturus 'Coronet' tubes with socket adaptors.

Telefunken metal tubes, were identical in concept to the American MGs—it was simpler and cheaper to stick to known production methods.

German Metal Tubes

Some years were to elapse before the first metal tubes appeared in continental Europe, though it may be imagined that the American and British developments had not gone unnoticed. Towards the end of 1938 Telefunken announced a new range of tubes which, apart from output tubes and rectifiers, were of all-metal construction.[9] During the following year Philips-Valvo followed suit in issuing an identical range under the same type numbers.[10]

The characteristics and ratings of the new tubes closely followed those of existing European glass types though a horizontal style of electrode mounting was used. Following American practice glass beads with fernico eyelets were used to insulate and seal the lead-out wires, though by then the American tubes were using button-base seals. Not surprisingly the horizontally mounted electrode assemblies caused the German tubes to be considerably fatter than their American counterparts and as chassis space in a horizontal direction has always been of more importance than that in a vertical direction the German tubes were at a disadvantage in this respect.

The German tubes were all of single-ended construction

Arcturus 'Coronet' metal-glass tubes.

Metal-glass tubes by five different makers.

and this feature was claimed by one writer as being 'Yet another new departure . . . ,' but at the time RCA's single-ended series were already on the market.[11] A new type of 8-pin base was developed for use on both metal and glass types in the range and while it had some similarities to the American octal it differed considerably in detail. The most noticeable difference lay in the style of the contact pins which had a 'waisted' shape and were designed to have a lock-in action when the tube was inserted into its socket.

Russian metal tubes carrying markings of a British distributor c. 1958.

Telefunken metal tubes c. 1939.

Although the German tubes appeared not much more than a year before the outbreak of World War II they were put to use, mainly by Telefunken, in both domestic and automobile receivers as well as in televisions. However, because of their higher price they were not used in any models of the famous state-sponsored Peoples' Receivers—the Volksemfanger and Kleinemfanger. Metal tubes were also widely used in German military radio equipment and in this connection it is interesting to note that Telefunken produced a series of four 2-volt battery types which were the only battery-operated metal tubes made anywhere in the world.

Russian metal tubes. Note open date coding indicating manufacture in 1953.

Russian Metal Tubes

Apart from Britain, Germany, and the U.S.A. the only other country known to have made metal tubes was the U.S.S.R. Although information is lacking as to when such tubes were first made several types were listed in the 1948 edition of Brans' *Vade Mecum*. Russian metal tubes were still being marketed many years after the manufacture of American-made tubes had ceased and at the time of writing (1978) are still available, though not of recent manufacture.

The Russian tubes were patterned quite closely on American designs and although differing slightly in external appearance were in most cases interchangeable with equivalent American types.

REFERENCES

1. See announcement *Popular Wireless*, May 13, 1933.
2. Bro. Patrick Dowd, The History of the All Metal Receiving Tube, *Old Timer's Bulletin* (Organ of the Antique Wireless Association, Holcomb, New York), Vol. 16, No. 4, p. 15.
3. All-metal Receiving Tubes, *Electronics*, May 1935, p. 148.
4. Dowd, op. cit., Vol. 17, No. 1, p. 21.
5. New Tubes for 1939, *Radio Craft*, Dec. 1938, p. 330.
6. Recent Tube Developments, *Radio Craft*, June 1936, p. 750.
7. The Latest in Tube Developments, *Radio Craft*, March 1936, p. 524.
8. Footless Valves, *Wireless World*, May 25, 1939, pp. 487–488.
9. Steel Valves, *Wireless World*, Nov. 10, 1938, p. 404.
10. See Philips catalogue, The Bridge to Higher Radio Entertainment, Nov. 1939.
11. See advt. *Electronics*, Oct. 1938, back cover.

Chapter Fourteen

Octal-based and All-Glass Tubes

American Developments

Only a few months after the introduction of metal tubes came the announcement of the first octal-based glass types in August 1935.[1] That such tubes should have been produced so soon after the highly publicised 'all-metal' type was due to a feud which had developed between Philco and RCA-GE which resulted in Philco refusing to have anything to do with metal tubes, at least as far as using them in their own receivers went. Octal-based glass tubes were originally developed at Philco's behest in order to provide them with some sort of 'answer' to RCA's metal ones and to allow them to claim superiority over the latter.

By the end of 1936 there were 34 types of octal-based glass tubes in production[2] with Sylvania and Raytheon being two of the largest producers. Eventually all tube makers including RCA undertook the manufacture of 'G' type tubes which, until the advent of the later 'GT' types, accounted for a large proportion of total tube production.

Because G type tubes were, so to speak, already in ex-

istence, albeit in other forms, at the time of their introduction it may be wondered whether their production achieved any useful purpose. One argument justified their existence on the grounds that it would assist in making the octal base the U.S. industry standard but this argument did not justify the production of so many existing glass types in octal-based form, an action which resulted in a quite unnecessary proliferation of 'same but different' tubes on the market.

It is possible to divide the G series into two groups, those which were glass versions of metal tubes and those which were octal-based versions of existing glass types. The former carried the same type-numbers as their metal counterparts but with the addition of the suffix G, to indicate glass, while the latter were assigned new type-numbers in line with the modified RMA system applicable to metal tubes. Examples of the second category are the type 6U7G (formerly 6D6) and 1F5G (formerly 1F4). In general those G type tubes which had metal counterparts were interchangeable with the latter, though in the case of RF and IF amplifiers differences in inter-electrode capaci-

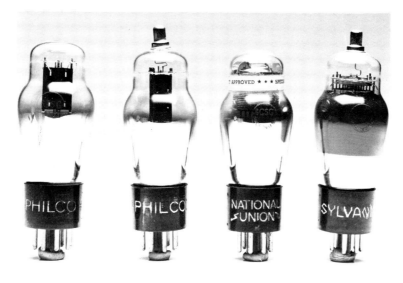

Octal-based glass tubes c. 1937.

102

NEW
LOW-DRAIN BATTERY TUBES!

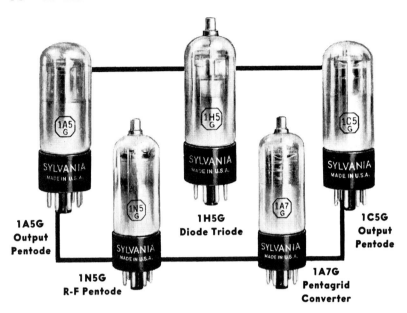

1A5G
Output
Pentode

1H5G
Diode Triode

1C5G
Output
Pentode

1N5G
R-F Pentode

1A7G
Pentagrid
Converter

Sylvania presents an important contribution to the radio industry

A new and completely different line of tubes for battery radios has been perfected in our engineering laboratories. These new tubes are conspicuous for features embodying a highly desirable combination of both operation and space economy in battery radio sets.

Note these characteristics:

Low current drain—.05 ampere at 1.4 volts on all types except 1C5G, .10 ampere.

Twice normal battery life.

Less battery space—only 90 volt B battery required—no C battery needed.

Less tube space—T.9 envelope used.

These five Sylvania low current drain tubes are a complete complement for the design of any type of battery receiver. To the farm market, to the extra set and portable set market which reaches into every family, this new development is most significant. Write today to the Hygrade Sylvania Corporation, Emporium, Pa., for complete technical information.

SYLVANIA
SET-TESTED RADIO TUBES

tances sometimes necessitated the re-alignment of receiver circuits and furthermore separate tube shields were usually required.

The first completely new tubes to be issued as octal-based glass types was a series of 1.4-volt battery types initially produced by Sylvania in 1938.[3] From the point of view of appearance these tubes are interesting in that they reverted to the use of tubular style bulbs which had previously been used in the early 1920s on the first dry-cell tubes and later used in 1930 on the first 2-volt air-cell tubes. Examples of the 1.4 tubes are types 1A5G and 1H5G, the series remained the only G types to be fitted with T9 style tubular bulbs.

An important development of the G type occurred in mid-1938 when Hytron announced a new range of tubes which were marketed under the name BANTAM.[4] These were simply smaller editions of existing glass types having shortened T9 bulbs and metal base-shells in place of bakelite. The reduction in height was achieved by shortening the section of the stem below the pinch thus placing the pinch almost at the bottom of the bulb. With its reduced dimensions the Bantams were little bigger than comparable metal types and could be used as replacements for the latter without the necessity for any alterations to the receiver. To identify the series the suffix GT was added to their type numbers, the letters indicating 'glass tubular'.

Originally all GT types were fitted with metal base-shells but when RCA commenced production they favoured the use of bakelite bases for all types except RF amplifiers. Eventually Hytron too used bakelite bases for all GT types.

With the arrival of the GT series the situation soon arose where individual tube types were available in three different styles, a most undesirable state of affairs to say the least. Although the GTs could offer no improvement in performance their compactness made them the logical choice when it came to deciding which of the two glass styles should become the industry standard. By 1939 production of G types was on the wane and henceforth all new releases except for certain output tubes and rectifiers were produced in GT form. In 1945 production of GT tubes exceeded that of any other type, the actual figures being GT:52 million, metal:27 million, all other types: 56 million.

One outgrowth of the GTs was the production of certain twin triodes, types 6SN7GT and 6SL7GT, which had separate cathodes and thus needed eight external connections. By making use of number one base pin (normally unused or omitted in bakelite-based tubes) all eight contact pins were available for element connections, thus allowing production in single-ended form. By their very nature such tubes could have no counterparts amongst all-metal types.

The final development of GT types occurred in 1948 when Raytheon introduced a limited range under the name

Raytheon 'Bantal' (L.) 1948. Hytron 'BANTAM' (R.) 1938.

BANTAL.[5] Although consisting of but four types the Bantals were a brave attempt to introduce improvements into the existing GT style of construction. The Bantal's claim to fame centered around the use of a glass button stem of similar design to that used in lock-in tubes; in fact, the Bantal could be described as a loctal tube with an octal base. However, Raytheon retired from receiving tube production shortly after marketing the Bantals and the idea was not immediately taken up by other manufacturers.

Nearly a decade later the Bantal style of construction was resurrected and used by RCA and other manufacturers who issued certain selected types of GT tubes using glass button stems in place of the conventional flat press. Such tubes may be recognised by the presence of a shortened or 'low rise' bakelite base, officially described as 'short intermediate octal'. Examples of tubes in this category are types 6SN7GTB, 5U4GB, and 6L6GC.

British Developments

On the British scene valves equivalent to American G types were marketed within a year of the latter's introduction in the United States. First off the mark was the Marconi-Osram 'International Octal' range announced in 1937.[6] That M-O.V. were first in the field was probably because EMI as half-owner of the company had rather close connections and cross-licensing arrangements with RCA. The British valves closely resembled their American counterparts in physical appearance and had similar characteristics though they were assigned M-O.V. type numbers. Of the nine types comprising the initial release all

104

THEY SAID IT COULDN'T BE DONE!

Back in 1938, Hytron began designing new dies and converting production machinery for the first BANTAM GT tubes. The industry said in effect: "You're crazy; it won't work. You can't telescope standard glass tubes to BANTAM size and get the same results." Beam tetrodes, such as the 50L6GT, particularly were considered impossibilities. The intense heat developed during normal operation would warp the elements and crack the small glass bulb.

But Bruce A. Coffin, originator of the BANTAM GT, stuck to his guns. In a few short years, Hytron developed over fifty GT types. The GT became the most popular receiving tube.* Short leads, low capaci-

tances, advantages of shorter bombardment at lower temperatures, ruggedness of compact construction plus both top and bottom mica supports, smaller size, standardized envelopes and bases — all contributed to that popularity.

The BANTAM GT permitted new space economies in pre-war receivers. Only its universal acceptance as standard by all manufacturers makes possible fulfillment of the Services' demands for receiving tubes. In increasing numbers, as this war draws to its ultimate conclusion, Hytron will continue to supply you with the popular BANTAM GT tubes which everyone said just couldn't be made.

*1941 industry production figures: GT—52,000,000; metal—27,000,000; standard glass, G, and loctal—56,000,000.

OLDEST EXCLUSIVE MANUFACTURER OF RADIO RECEIVING TUBES

HYTRON

HYTRON RADIO TUBES

SALEM AND NEWBURYPORT, MASS.

BUY ANOTHER WAR BOND

carried 6.3-volt heater ratings with the exception of the rectifier which, following American practice, was rated at 5 volts.

Next to commence manufacture of octals was Brimar (another firm with close American connections) who in their 1938–39 catalogue listed a range of 21 types. With one exception (type 6P8G) these were identical to American tubes and carried the same type numbers. From this time on Brimar became one of the largest, if not the largest, British manufacturer of American type valves.

By 1940 four other firms—Cossor, Ferranti, Mullard, and Tungsram—also produced fairly comprehensive ranges of octals and all four used American type numbers to identify their products. In addition to producing standard American types Mullard in 1938 introduced a new range of their own known as the Red E series. These were really only 'octalised' versions of their existing Red E side-contact types which had been introduced in the same year.

After the war the production of octal-based G types was continued for a short time, mainly by Brimar, but from 1947 onwards these were mostly superseded by GT types. Commencing in 1946 M-O.V. produced a number of British designed valves which differed slightly in appearance from the American GTs in that they were slightly taller. Examples of these are types B65 and KT76. Other firms producing G or GT types in the post-war years were Ferranti, Mullard, and Tungsram.

The use of the term 'international octal' to describe either the octal-based valves or just the base itself was first used by Marconi-Osram in 1937 when at the time only two countries were involved. Since then, however, the octal base has become truly international for in addition many other countries, including Australia, Italy, France, Germany, Japan, and Russia, have all produced octal-based tubes.

Lock-In Tubes

A little over three years after the appearance of the GE-RCA metal tubes the first indication of another new departure in tube development was given by the announcement of an 'all-glass' tube to be released by Sylvania. The first of such tubes to be marketed was type 1231, an RF pentode intended for television applications which was announced in November 1938.[7] It is not quite clear why this particular tube should have been chosen as first release ahead of regular radio tubes but the fact that RCA had just announced two similar metal tubes may have had something to do with it.

Sylvania, though early on the scene with metal tubes had concentrated on the production of octal-based glass types presumably at the behest of Philco who were using them to total exclusion of metal types. Philco, as the arch-

rival of RCA were desirous of having a counter to the much-vaunted metal tube and an all-glass tube was to be the answer. So it was that the word Loktal became as closely associated with the name Philco as it did with the company producing the tubes, Sylvania.

The Loktal was something of a landmark in tube development for it was the first type (not counting RCA's 'acorn') in which the bakelite base had been dispensed with and the lead-out wires made thicker so that they formed the connecting pins. This feature had been achieved by the use of the so-called 'glass button stem', a type of construction first developed by RCA for use in their later type metal tubes and modified by Sylvania for use in their Loktals. The elimination of the bakelite base in favour of having the contact pins protruding directly through the bottom of the bulb was an important step in securing improved performance at the higher radio frequencies for it resulted in lower losses coupled with shorter leads. Eight contact pins were provided, all of which were available for element connections, while the metal base-shell was grounded through the central metal spigot. In the Loktal tubes the spigot actually served a threefold purpose for apart from providing an earth connection and a means of pin indexing it also served to lock the tube in its socket. From this last feature the name Loktal was derived but because the word was a Philco-Sylvania trade-mark other tube makers referred to their products as loctal or lock-in tubes.

Philco 'Loktal' tubes, made by Sylvania.

In May 1939 both Raytheon and Sylvania announced a range of lock-in tubes totalling twelve types.[8] The variation in the style of type numbering used with the lock-in tubes calls for a word of explanation. Normally all 6.3-volt tubes carried the figure 6 as the first digit which implies that the figure 7 would indicate 7 volts. In the case of lock-in tubes the R.M.A. seems to have been prevailed upon to allow a departure from the established system in order that the new tubes could be recognised as a group by their type numbers, thus 6.3-volt types carried the figure 7 as the initial digit while 12.6-volt types used the figure 14. In the case of 1.4-volt battery tubes the figure 1 was correctly used as the first digit and group identification was achieved by using the letter L as the second digit, e.g., 1LA6.

By 1946 there were 53 different types of Loktal tubes listed in the Sylvania Technical Manual and most of these types were also available from other manufacturers such as Raytheon and Tung Sol. Sylvania's total reached 100 by 1954 after which time no new types were produced. For the benefit of tube collectors it may be mentioned that one Sylvania-Philco Loktal carried an odd-ball type number, FM1000; it was an FM detector developed in 1950 for use in Philco receivers.

The all-glass construction pioneered in the Loktals undoubtedly influenced the course of future tube development in both American and Europe as even miniature tubes show signs of Loktal ancestry.

European All-Glass Tubes

At much the same time as the development of continental metal and metal-glass tubes was going on the first European all-glass tube also made its appearance. It is not possible to speak of the initial release as a 'range' for the simple reason that there was but a single type issued. In February 1939 Mullard announced their first all-glass valve, type EF50,[9] which was jointly released by Philips.

In appearance and construction the EF50 had many similarities to the American loctal but differed in having a metallised bulb and a 9-pin base. In spite of having a vertical electrode assembly the EF50 was of somewhat larger diameter than loctal types, measuring 32 mm in diameter as against 28 mm. The original 1939 production appears to have been in the nature of a prototype, judging by external changes apparent in later issues. The bulb metallising was discontinued in favour of a separate metal jacket and the extremely unorthodox type of 'hooked' contact pins were changed to conventional straight ones. The original use of bent or hooked pins was in connection with a unique method of locking the tube into its socket whereby after insertion it was given a slight clockwise twist. Presumably because such an arrangement carried with it an inherent danger of cracking the glass around the contact pins it was quickly discontinued and conventional straight pins used instead.

The EF50 had a working transconductance of 6.6 mA/V, a figure considerably higher than that possessed by

War-time versions of the EF50/VR91 metal-glass RF pentode.

HIGH FREQUENCY TUBE ALSO BEST FOR ALL RADIOS

"Lock-In" Not Only Ideal For FM, Television, But Better For Other Type Sets

any other existing types, and was intended for use as a wide-band amplifier in television receivers. However, due to the outbreak of World War II and the consequent cessation of television broadcasting the EF50 was not used in this application until after the war when in 'disposals' or war surplus form it once again resumed its rightful role, albeit for but a short period. It was in wartime radar equipment that the EF50 was most widely used and indeed so great was the demand that British valve makers were unable to cope and this led to arrangements being made to have supplies made in the U.S. by Sylvania.

Another pre-war all-glass tube, the Philips-Mullard EE50, appeared at almost the same time as the EF50 and closely resembled it in outward appearance.[10] There the similarity stopped as the EE50 was a radically new type of amplifier utilising the phenomenon of secondary emission to secure greatly increased transconductance, which in this case reached a figure of 14 mA/V.

Following the end of the war five further types were added to what was by then known as the B9G range in the U.K. They were two RF pentodes, types EF54 and EF55; two double pentodes, types EFF50 and EFF51; and a secondary emission amplifier type EPF60. Apart from

these 9-pin types the only other post-war European all-glass tubes were the Philips-Mullard 8-pin E21/U21 series which were basically similar to the American loctals.

REFERENCES

1. Latest Radio Equipment *Radio Craft*, Aug. 1935, p. 86.

2. Newest Tubes for the Radio Industry, *Radio Craft*, Nov. 1936, p. 271.

3. See advt. *Electronics*, August 1938, p. 39.

4. Recent Radio Tubes, *Radio Craft*, May 1938, p. 751.

5. See advt. *Radio Maintenance*, August 1948, p. 2.

6. See announcement *Wireless World*, April 23, 1937.

7. Fifteen New Tubes!, *Radio Craft*, Nov. 1938, p. 282.

8. 48 New Tubes!, *Radio Craft*, May 1939, pp. 656, 657.

9. All-Glass Valves, *Wireless World*, Feb. 16, 1939, pp. 155, 157.

10. Amplification by Secondary Emission, *Wireless World*, Feb. 23, 1939, pp. 178, 180.

Chapter Fifteen

Power Rectifiers

Although the first 'radio' application of the two-element tube was as a detector of wireless signals this was soon overshadowed by the diode's ability to rectify alternating current mains power to enable its use in receiver and transmitter power supplies, and it was many years before diode detection returned to favour. In the broadest sense of the term any two-element tube is a rectifier, of course, but from the time mains power started to replace battery power (initially during 1926–27) the term rectification has come to mean the conversion of low frequency power line current to pulsating direct current.

The earliest work in this direction was being carried out in Germany at much the same time as Fleming was working on his detector valve. In January 1904 Dr. A. Wehnelt applied for a patent on a 'valve-tube'; the patent DRP 157,845 was granted on January 13, 1905. In a paper[1] entitled 'Concerning the Emission of Negative Electrons from Glowing Metallic Oxides' Wehnelt mentions the use of these substances for the cathodes of discharge tubes. Furthermore, under a sub-heading 'Practical Application of Discharge Tubes with Glowing Metallic Cathodes', Wehnelt states: '. . . the tube acts like an electric valve, allowing one phase of the alternating current through. Thus the tube may serve to transform alternating current to pulsating direct current'. (Note, for 'phase' read 'half-cycle'.)

From the foregoing it is readily apparent that Wehnelt had invented and patented a diode rectifier, albeit in a very different form, nearly a year before Fleming; a seemingly little-known fact, judging by the way it is often ignored by radio historians. Even so it must be borne in mind that Fleming was able to patent his valve in Germany so the German Patent Office apparently found nothing which could have been regarded as a prior claim. In the event it does not appear to have been contested by Wehnelt. However, the oxide-coated, or 'Wehnelt' cathode as it was sometimes called, was in itself to become an important contribution to the development of the electron tube in general, even though many years were to elapse before oxide-coated emitters came into general use.

Of all the electron tubes ever manufactured one of the most widely used must surely have been the full-wave high vacuum rectifier. Because it was such a basic and elementary member of the family it did not undergo the rapid developments associated with other types of tubes; in fact it would be fair to call it the Cinderella of the tube world—a tube that was largely taken for granted. Indeed at one period in history it was British practice not to count in the rectifier when referring to the number of valves in a receiver.

General

This practice stemmed from the days when battery eliminators were in common use and if a valve rectifier was incorporated (which was not always the case) it was naturally considered to be part of the eliminator, not the receiver proper. Furthermore, many early British mains-operated sets incorporated Westinghouse 'metal' rectifiers in their power supplies, a situation without parallel in other countries, which further reinforced the idea that rectifiers, whether thermionic or otherwise, were things apart. With the decline in popularity of Westinghouse HT rectifiers British set makers soon realised the advertising value of counting the rectifier valve in with the other valves when compiling receiver specifications. Whereas previously receivers had been described as having so many valves plus rectifier it soon became common practice to describe a four-valve-plus rectifier model as a five-valve set, as had always been done in America.

But, to begin at the beginning: because the earliest receivers were invariably run from batteries, and transmitters run from motor-generators, little or no demand existed for rectifier tubes until after World War I. For example, in three De Forest catalogues of the 1920–21 era, listing nine different models of radio telephone transmitters only one was equipped to operate directly from the AC mains by the use of thermionic rectifiers. This particular transmitter used two half-wave tubes made by Moorhead Laboratories Inc.

Some of the earliest developmental work on rectifier tubes had been initiated in the General Electric laboratories as far back as 1915 and the resultant tubes given the generic name of 'Kenotrons'. Originally they had been designed to handle extremely high voltages but for various reasons were not initially developed commercially.

American Developments

With the resumption of amateur transmitting activities following the end of World War I the need arose for a rectifier to power the new 'tube' transmitters, and in 1921 the first commercially available GE rectifier, type UV-216, was released by RCA.[2] This tube was a bright emitter type, the filament consuming 2.35 amps at 7.5 volts, the output being 50 mA at 350 V. At the time of its release, and for some years later, the 216 was marketed under the name Kenotron, following GE's practice of referring to all their high-vacuum rectifiers in this manner, but in 1925 when superseded by a thoriated filament version, type UX-216B, the designation was changed to 'Rectron' for a short period before RCA dropped this method of referring to rectifiers.

Before continuing with the story of mainstream developments it may be of interest to mention an 'odd-ball' rectifier which appeared briefly in 1925. At that time the Dubilier Condenser & Radio Corp. of New Jersey were marketing a B battery eliminator using a type of tube which can be politely described as unconventional.[4] The tube itself was made by Westinghouse and was designated Rectron UV-196. Although a full-wave type it was unique in having two electrically separate filaments operating in conjunction with a common plate. No sound technical reason can be imagined for such an unorthodox style of construction and no practical advantage resulted from it. In fact there were two disadvantages in that an extra filament winding had to be provided on the power transformer and because five external connections were needed it became necessary to adopt the clumsy expedient of using the brass base shell to provide the fifth connection.

Like so many simple ideas, later taken for granted, the

Rectron UV-196 single-anode full-wave rectifier (1925).

Kenotron UV-216 (1921).

RCA Rectron UX-213 (1926).

The successor to the 216B was the UX-281 which appeared towards the end of 1927.[3] With its oxide-coated filament consuming 1.25 amps at 7.5 volts the 81 was capable of 85 mA output at 700 volts input. Although originally used in solo form, two type 81s were later often used to provide full-wave rectification in circuits where the plate voltage was higher than could be handled by existing full-wave rectifiers. The original S-19 size bulb remained in use until the early 1940s after which time tubes having ST-19 bulbs were issued for replacement purposes.

idea of combining two half-wave rectifiers in one bulb was a logical step which resulted in considerable economies in receiver construction. Because the construction of full-wave rectifying tubes was practicable only when comparatively low plate voltages were involved, combination tubes did not come into general use until more efficient output tubes operating at lower voltages had been developed. In September 1925 the first full-wave rectifier, type UX-213, was announced by RCA.[5] This tube had a thoriated filament rated at 5 volts, 2 amps and could provide an output of 65 mA at 170 volts input.

110

Such was the pace of receiver development at this time, particularly in the matter of the increasing number of tubes used, together with increases in audio output, that within a space of two years the need arose for a higher power version of the 213. In May 1927 what was to become a landmark tube was announced.[6] Known as the UX-280 it was the first rectifier to make use of an oxide-coated filament, a feature which resulted in a greatly increased emission with no increase in filament consumption. The rated output was 125 mA at 300 volts input, though the input rating was upped to 350 V in 1929, after which time the ratings remained unchanged throughout the production lifetime of the tube, a matter of over 50 years.

With its increased rating the 80 was capable of supplying the requirements of even quite large multi-tube receivers but even so it was ever a hard-worked and hard-working tube which, throughout much of its history, was frequently over-run by receiver manufacturers. For example, it was quite common at one time to find the 80 being expected to handle input voltages running as high as 385 volts which naturally shortened its operating life. In a commendable attempt to lessen the effects of this abuse some tube makers produced modified versions in which the plate area was enlarged in order to obtain cooler running. For example, in 1929; Raytheon marketed an 80 in which the plate area was about 75% greater than normal. A completely different approach to the problem of enlarging the plate area resulted in the production of a tube having corrugated plates, and in 1935 such a tube was marketed by National Union. In both cases the improved versions did not remain in production for long, presumably because they were more expensive to manufacture.

The shrinking 80, 1929 and 1969.

During the course of its lifetime the 80 went through three reductions in bulb size, from the original S-17 to ST-14 in 1933 and thence to the diminutive T-9 in the 1970s, all without any impairment to its performance. The 80 rectifier remains unique amongst all tubes ever made for it is the oldest type which, at the time of writing, is still in current production in certain countries.

Some six years after the introduction of the 80 a growing demand for a higher power rectifier resulted in the production of the type 5Z3 in 1933.[7] When used under capacitor input filter conditions this tube was rated at 225 mA output at a maximum plate voltage of 450 volts. An octal-based version, type 5U4G, was issued in 1937 which emerged in its final form as type 5U4GB in 1956.

Compared with the situation existing in Europe in the days before World War II where multitudinous numbers of rectifiers having only slightly dissimiliar ratings were commonplace, American requirements were adequately catered to by just one type which remained the sole representative of its class in the application for which it was intended. In general it may be said that there was only rectifier for a given application. As the specifications of the 80 were carried over unchanged into the octal-based versions, 5Y3G (1936) and 5Y3GT (1946), these were counted in with the 80 for the purposes of this claim. Only one misdemeanour in the issuance of rectifiers can be attributed to the American tube industry, the duplication of two existing octal-based types which resulted in versions having different base connections. The tubes in question were types 5Y3G/5Y4G and 5U4G/5X4G. No valid reason existed for this unnecessary duplication and it can only be attributed to oneupmanship on the part of the originator of the later variants.

Gaseous Rectifiers

One of the earliest developments of the diode rectifier occurred with the production by GE of a specialised type

Radiotron UX-281 (R.) compared with an 81, c. 1935.

of gas-filled tube designed for service in automobile battery chargers. In turn it was the adoption of the six-volt wet battery for radio purposes that created a market for a charger suitable for home use. Whilst the motorist at least had a built-in charger in the form of a generator the radio fan was initially forced to take his battery to the nearest charging station for regular recharging. Clearly a market existed for a home battery charger.

Initial work on gas-filled rectifiers had been carried out by GE as far back as 1914 while in 1917 the first commercially available types were marketed under the brandname Tungar. These were argon-filled tubes, more commonly known as bulbs, and were made in two sizes rated at 2 amps and 5 amps. Some time later the 5-amp size was replaced by a 6-amp size and a 15-amp type was added to the range. In October 1926 a Tungar trickle charger fitted with a diminutive half-amp bulb was announced.[8]

The argon-filled rectifier had a somewhat lower efficiency than either vacuum or mercury vapour types yet had the ability to provide a high output current at low plate voltages. The tubes had a fixed voltage drop of 10 volts which resulted in heavy power losses unless several batteries were charged in series at the one time, but this was normally possible only in the case of commercial use. Nevertheless the Tungar rectifier remained the most widely used thermionic rectifier for battery charging purposes right up to the advent of modern solid-state devices.

Although the name of GE became synonymous with argon-filled rectifiers, similar tubes were also marketed by Westinghouse under their brandname 'Rectigon'. In addition at least two independent manufacturers, e.g., Argus and National Union, produced replacement types, presumably under license. In the U.K. Tungar bulbs were made by the British Thompson-Houston Co. when they were known as Tungar Valves. The Dutch firm of Philips

British-made 2-amp Tungar valve.

also produced a range of mercury-vapour rectifiers included in which were types intended for Tungar replacements.

Another type of gas-filled rectifier with origins going back almost as far as those of the Tungar was the so-called 'cold-cathode' or filamentless rectifier. As early as 1916 work on such tubes had been carried out in France though it was in America that the development took practical form.[9] The first commercially available cold-cathode rectifiers were marketed in 1922 by the American Radio & Research Corp. under their brandname Amrad. This company specialised in the manufacture of transmitting apparatus and presumably for this reason the Amrad tubes were made only for transmitting use. The design of the Amrad tubes was attributable largely to one Charles Grover Smith and it is believed that the initial letter of his surname was chosen as a sort of generic type indicator, resulting in the rectifiers being known as 'S' tubes.

Initially the S tube was rated at 400 V input, 50 mA output but this rating soon proved to be inadequate for transmitting use and the tube went through several stages of redesign resulting in it having a final rating of 1000 V, 100 mA. This made it a much more attractive proposition to the radio amateur as the tube could now compete favourably with the bulky and expensive Radiotron UV-217.

Following the takeover of the Amrad Corp. by Crosley in 1925 the production of S tubes ceased and the patents were acquired by a company known as the American Appliance Co. of Cambridge, Mass. In November 1925 the first of these new tubes were offered for sale under the brandname 'Raytheon'.[10] The Raytheon was a helium-filled full-wave rectifier known as type B, indicating that it was intended for use in B battery eliminators. The company underwent reorganisation during the first month of operation and in December 1925 its name became the Raytheon

Two versions of the 2-amp Tungar bulb (outer) and a 6-amp (centre).

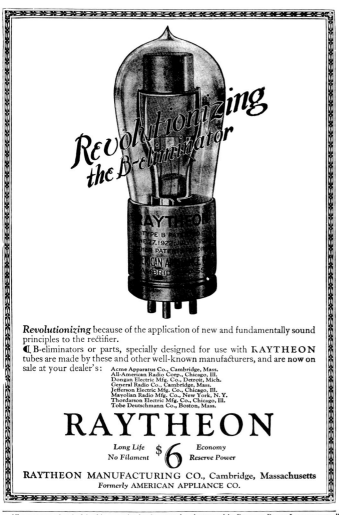

Revolutionizing because of the application of new and fundamentally sound principles to the rectifier.

¶ B-eliminators or parts, specially designed for use with RAYTHEON tubes are made by these and other well-known manufacturers, and are **now on** sale at your dealer's:

Acme Apparatus Co., Cambridge, Mass.
All-American Radio Corp., Chicago, Ill.
Dongan Electric Mfg. Co., Detroit, Mich.
General Radio Co., Cambridge, Mass.
Jefferson Electric Mfg. Co., Chicago, Ill.
Mayolian Radio Mfg. Co., New York, N.Y.
Thordarson Electric Mfg. Co., Chicago, Ill.
Tobe Deutschmann Co., Boston, Mass.

RAYTHEON

Long Life $6 Economy
No Filament   Reserve Power

RAYTHEON MANUFACTURING CO., Cambridge, Massachusetts
Formerly AMERICAN APPLIANCE CO.

All apparatus advertised in this magazine has been tested and approved by POPULAR RADIO LABORATORY *1925*

Manufacturing Co.[11] At this time the B tube was being advertised for sale under the slogan '60 milliamps for $6.00'.

Late in 1926 an improved version known as the BH was marketed, this tube having an output of 85 mA. At much the same time a new high power version, type BA, was also introduced. The reason for the production of a tube with such a large output is dealt with in another chapter.

Looking back to the heyday of the Raytheon gaseous rectifier in the middle and late 1920s it is perhaps a little difficult to understand why it was so readily accepted and widely used. At the time of its introduction it certainly compared favourably in price with its high-vacuum contemporary the Radiotron UX-213 which was listed at $7.00, and even more favourably with a pair of UX-216B Rectrons at $7.50 each. The price advantage alone could not have accounted for its rapid acceptance because the tube was not without its drawbacks, so it is necessary to look elsewhere for the reason. That reason was undoubtedly to be found in the fact that the Raytheon Mfg. Co. did more than just make tubes; they maintained a laboratory which offered a unique service to receiver manufacturers who could call on Raytheon to design a complete power pack to any individual maker's requirements, needless to say incorporating a Raytheon tube.

Judging from the number of manufacturers who took advantage of this service not too much was known about this new branch of the art. It was this service, plus abundant advertising, that gave Raytheon a prominent place in the rectifier market of the day with subsequent renewal sales largely, but not exclusively, assured.

By 1927 numerous other manufacturers had similar gaseous rectifiers on the market amongst which were At-

THE NEW S-TUBE

Co-operating with leading amateurs, we made certain mechanical improvements to the AMRAD S-Tube in order to meet still further amateur requirements for "the Rectifier Without a Filament." These improvements result in:—

Increased mechanical strength—The internal elements are now so supported that breakage in handling is minimized.

Improved looks—The shape is now tubular which further facilitates handling as well as improving appearance.

Increased dielectric—The large Mogul base provides greater dielectric strength resulting in increased efficiency.

Improved production facilities are now materially reducing the existing shortage of S-Tubes. If your dealer cannot supply you, amateurs may send remittance direct to us and we will make promptest possible delivery.

From time to time we have published unsolicited letters from amateurs praising the S-Tube. Many of these refer to the first type. Later, the ratings were increased and even more favorable comments were received. Now, with the mechanical improvements above noted, still greater value is offered to those desiring an economical, dependable, source of d. c. plate supply or for use in charging storage B Batteries.

Send for Bulletin J-2. This describes type 4000 which is identical with new type 4000-1 illustrated, except for the improvements. (New Bulletin is not quite ready).

AMERICAN RADIO AND RESEARCH CORPORATION

QST Oct 1924.   **Dept. Q, Medford Hillside, Mass.**
Dealers in Principal Cities and Towns

113

water Kent, CeCo, C.R.A., Epom, Majestic, Manhattan, Q.R.S., Schickerling, Speed, and Supertron (Supertheon). Several of these appeared to be identical to the Raytheon while others differed in various ways. The Epom was an argon-filled tube made by the Connecticut Telephone & Electric Co. and intended for use in a B eliminator made by the company.[12] The only manufacturer of any significance was the Q.R.S. Music Co. of Chicago who also made the Majestic Super-B tube for Grigsby-Grunow-Hinds.

Because the manufacture of all the above named tubes ceased after a comparitively short time it is reasonable to assume that they were either unsuccessful or else they infringed Raytheon's patents. In the case of the Q.R.S. Co. it is known that they were prosecuted by Raytheon with the result that Raytheon took over the Q.R.S. tube division in settlement of the patent suit.[13]

Gaseous rectifiers were little used outside the U.S. but it is known that they were made in at least three European countries—Britain, France, and Germany. In England a

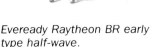
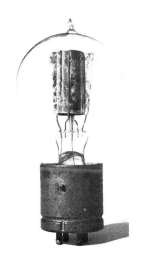

Eveready Raytheon BR early type half-wave.

Schickerling neon-filled rectifier.

QRS gaseous rectifiers, 400mA (L,) 85mA (R.).

tube known as the Ethertron Filamentless Valve was made by Burndept under license to Raytheon,[14] while in France a 'valve sans filament, license Raytheon' was made by La Radio Technique in 1928.[15] Also in 1928 the German firm of Siebt made a gaseous rectifier under the name Anotron. In all cases production was limited to a single type produced over a short period with no subsequent development as occurred in the U.S. In view of their initial success it is perhaps a little surprising to find that by the end of 1928 Raytheon rectifiers had almost completely disappeared from the scene and not until a new field opened up were they to make a reappearance, albeit in a somewhat modified form.

When in 1932 the first self-contained car radios appeared Raytheon developed a small half-wave tube espe-

cially for this class of service. Known as type BR,[16] this tube was first used in a power pack unit developed by P.R. Mallory Inc. under the name Elkonode. In June 1933 the Galvin Mfg. Co. incorporated this unit in their Motorola car radio, thus bringing the gaseous rectifier back into use after an absence of five years.

The use of half-wave rectification was of short duration, however, as by the end of 1933 it had been completely superseded by the more efficient full-wave system. For the record it may be mentioned that Raytheon produced an early full-wave tube known as type OZ3[17] but no trace exists of its having been used commercially and in the event it was withdrawn from the Raytheon catalogue by 1936. In spite of this inauspicious start Raytheon continued with development and when in February 1936 the metal shell type OZ4 was announced the tide once again turned in Raytheon's favour, though never again was the gaseous rectifier to enjoy the same degree of popularity as in the heyday of the BH type. Both the OZ4 and the glass version, type OZ4G, were widely used and were still being manufactured right up to the early post-war years.

Amrad—the first gaseous rectifiers c. 1922.

Even at the peak of its development it must be admitted that the gaseous rectifier retained its original drawbacks. In the case of car radio rectifiers the requirement of a minimum striking voltage was sometimes hard to meet under conditions of low battery voltage and resulted in erratic operation or failure of the tube to conduct. With the coming of the first tube/transistor hybrid car radios in 1955 the days of the vibrator power supply were numbered and with its passing went the need for any sort of rectifier tubes.

Raytheon gaseous rectifiers 1925–1927.

Raytheon gaseous rectifiers, 300mA output.

During and after World War II Raytheon continued to develop their cold-cathode rectifiers; the 1955 edition of the *Radio Amateurs Handbook* listed no less than eleven different types, not including the earlier types long since obsolete. An interesting representative of the genre was Raytheon's CK1012,[18] ostensibly a receiving type though probably never used as such. It differed in being fitted with a heater element which could be used to assist ionisation under certain operating conditions. A study of published characteristics fails to reveal any significant difference in performance when used in either manner.

Quite early in the development of the thermionic tube it had been found that the maximum useable emission was limited by a fundamental characteristic known as the space charge. A search for a means of overcoming this limitation resulted in the development of gas-filled rectifiers, one variety of which was the hot-cathode mercury-vapour type.

Like all gaseous rectifiers m-v types rely on the principle of gas ionisation, which occurs during operation, to neutralise the space charge. Unlike other types which are filled with gas during manufacture, m-v rectifiers contain a small amount of liquid mercury which during operation is heated by the filament and forms mercury vapour. In operation the ionised gas exhibits a visible blue glow which is characteristic of all mercury-vapour tubes.

Raytheon gaseous car-radio rectifiers.

Because of certain pecularities connected with their operation m-v rectifiers were seldom used in receiver power supplies though they found extensive application in transmitters and large audio amplifiers. Like all gaseous rectifiers m-v types generate RF 'hash' when in operation and additionally they are liable to flashover when used under certain operating conditions. It was these two factors that limited their use in domestic receivers.

During 1932–33 mercury-vapour rectifiers enjoyed a brief popularity in the U.S., being used mainly in larger multi-tube receivers having high power Class B output stages. Because of their inherently good voltage regulation m-v rectifiers were eminently suited to this application.

The first American m-v rectifiers were marketed in 1932,[19] two standard types, the 82 and 83, being produced by most manufacturers. Both were full-wave types having oxide-coated filaments and they may be regarded as being the counterparts of the high-vacuum types 80 and 5Z3. In addition to these there were several non-standard types isued during 1932–33, all of which quickly vanished from the scene. Arcturus made four types under their letter des-

115

American mercury vapour rectifiers type 82 (L.) and 83 (R.).

Osram G.U.1 half-wave mercury vapour rectifier.

ignations AD, AE, AF, and AG, the last two being equivalent to the types 82 and 83. All four were unique in being fitted with internal fuses,[20] a tacit admission of the danger of flashover! At much the same time Ken-Rad made their types KR1, KR31, and KR98, the first two being small indirectly-heated half-wave types. Ken-Rad also issued mercury-vapour versions of the 80 and 81 as types 280M and 281M.[22]

On the British scene the use of m-v rectifiers in radio receivers was even less common than in the U.S., in spite of the fact that M-O.V. had issued their type GU1 as early as 1931,[23] a year before the appearance of m-v types in America. The GU1 remained the sole British representative of the species until 1934 when it was joined by Mazda'a MU1, after which time no further releases occurred.

In general it may be said that the mercury-vapour rectifier remained unsuited to receiving applications though it retained its popularity in transmitting applications for as long as thermionic tubes remained in use.

Indirectly-Heated Rectifiers

Even though directly-heated amplifying tubes had been almost completely superseded by indirectly-heated types by the early 1930s directly-heated rectifiers remained in general use in the U.S. for at least another decade. From a later viewpoint the reason for this may not readily be apparent but it should be borne in mind that at the time i-h rectifiers cost twice as much as d-h types. Whether it was a case of a small demand resulting in higher production costs or higher prices restricting the demand is a moot point but the fact remains that the i-h rectifier always remained a rarity in the U.S. except where circuit dictates made its use imperative. Apart from the question of price there also seems to have been a distrust for the breed which probably arose from a lack of understanding of its inherent difference.

The first American i-h rectifier for use in transformer powered receivers appeared considerably later than comparable British types for it was not until 1934 that RCA's 83-V was released.[24] With the advent of metal tubes in 1935 the first rectifier in the series was an i-h type of most unusual construction consisting of two separate half-wave units sealed within long thin glass tubes which were protected by a perforated metal shell. This type of construction was obviously expensive and towards the end of the year a new version contained within the standard MT-5 metal envelope was issued; it was the first true all metal rectifier tube.

In 1937 an octal-based version of the 83-V was issued under the type number 5V4G and it remained the only i-h type in the range. The first rectifier in the loctal range, type 7Y4, carried a 6.3-volt heater rating making it suitable for use in either small AC powered receivers or in car radios. The one and only 6.3-volt, 7-pin miniature rectifier, type 6X4, was issued in December 1945 and carried identical ratings to the earlier 6X5 and 7Y4.

In Britain the development of the indirectly-heated rectifier took place considerably earlier than in the U.S., the first example being announced by Mazda in January 1931.[25] The reason for this early lead is not entirely clear but it should be noted that only one company was involved. The Mazda rectifiers were from the same stable as the earlier Cosmos AC valves which had been made by Met-Vick, a firm which while pioneering the manufacture of i-h valves had had no experience in the production of d-h types. While d-h rectifiers were also made by Mazda it is interesting to note that i-h types were sold at the same prices as the former, presumably in order to popularise their use.

Standard-Micromesh R2, an early indirectly-heated rectifier.

Even though the higher efficiency of i-h rectifiers could have been expected to appeal to economy conscious British users other valve makers were slower in undertaking production and d-h rectifiers remained the most commonly used types. A year was to pass before another manufacturer, Micromesh, announced any i-h types and not until 1933 did the first M-O.V. and Mullard examples appear.

Mazda's advertisements of the day mentioned such desirable features as extremely long life and the prevention of the possibility of a short circuit developing due to burn out of the filament (as could occur with d-h types) under overload. However, it is only fair to say that in spite of the claim to be short circuit proof when overloaded, which may have been true for this particular manufacturer's de-

sign, the i-h rectifier as such was no less affected by external short circuits than its d-h counterpart. It is also a fact that, in some quarters at least, the full significance of the valve's lower internal resistance was not appreciated when it was used in the more common capacitor-input configuration. When so used the omission of anti-surge resistors in the plate leads could result in breakdown of the valve due to current surges when supplied from a low impedance source.

As in the U.S. the valve did not gain general acceptance from receiver manufacturers, in fact two of the largest pre-war makers, HMV and Philips, seldom employed i-h rectifiers in their receivers.

Quite apart from their greater efficiency the use of i-h rectifiers had what might be termed a beneficial side effect resulting from their slower warm-up time. In pre-war receivers using electro-dynamic speakers it was customary to energise the field coil by using it as a filter choke in series with the HT supply. In order to secure adequate excitation of the field coil its resistance had to be very high in comparison with a normal choke and this in turn meant that the initial HT voltage had to be correspondingly higher than would otherwise have been the case. When a directly-heated rectifier was used under these conditions the DC HT voltage could rise to almost the peak AC input during warm-up time of the remaining tubes in the receiver. This resulted in an undue strain being placed on the filter and bypass capacitors during each warm-up period. By comparison, when using an i-h rectifier, having a warm-up time comparable to the other tubes in the receiver, the HT voltage built up slowly to the normal working figure.

In connection with the above it is appropriate to mention here an odd-ball rectifier, known as type 80S, marketed by Brimar in 1938. This was an i-h version of the standard American 80 which was sold as a direct replacement for it. Presumably it was Brimar's intention to give users the benefit associated with the slower warm-up time of i-h rectifiers but in the event the inherent danger of using such valves in circuits not adapted for them sometimes resulted in rectifier breakdown.

For the record, the earliest-known rectifier to use an indirectly-heated cathode was a small full-wave type, the 2506, produced by Philips late in 1928. It was first used in a Dutch built receiver, model 2514, marketed towards the end of 1928. The same model was also sold in Great Britain prior to the establishment of Philips' British receiver factory and the 2506 valve was also advertised for general sale during 1929.[26]

Whilst the introduction of an indirectly-heated rectifier was a pioneering effort on Philips' part it cannot be said that the 2506 was an unqualified success. With hindsight it is obvious that its design was woefully inadequate with the result that production ceased after quite a short time. After 1929 the 2506 was replaced by a directly-heated type known as type 506. By comparison the output of the 2506 was only 45 mA against 75 mA for the 506 yet both types had the same 4-volt 1-amp rating. It was obvious that the design of the 2506 was incapable of further development and it was not until 1933 that another Philips i-h rectifier appeared. This time the Anglo-American design using a closely-spaced small-diameter anode was adopted.

By the end of 1933 there were three i-h rectifiers in the Philips AC range and by 1936 two 6.3-V side-contact types had been added. In 1947 the first European miniature rectifiers, types EZ40 and UY41, were issued in the Philips Rimlock range. These were followed by the first Noval-based rectifier, type PY80, in 1951.

Car Radio and AC/DC Rectifiers

Two receiver developments, both of which originated in the U.S., were the transformerless AC/DC radio and the automobile radio. It was the introduction of these two classes of receivers which led to the production of the first indirectly-heated rectifiers.

As in the case of the first household radios the earliest car radios made use of B batteries for the HT supply, and for exactly the same reasons ways and means were sought to eliminate the need for such batteries. One solution was to use a motor-generator, familiarly known as a 'dynamotor', to supply the HT requirements but these were bulky, expensive, and noisy in operation. The second method was to use a vibrating reed interruptor in conjunction with a transformer and rectifier—the so-called 'vibrator' power supply. Although the latter method was somewhat less reliable in operation it became universally accepted on account of its considerably lower cost and remained in use until the advent of transistorised receivers early in the 1960s.

Initially the so-called synchronous or self-rectifying vibrator was commonly used, thus providing 'free' rectification. Its efficiency was comparatively high and there were savings in both cost and space compared with the use of a separate rectifier. On the other hand there were practical difficulties which soon led to the abandonment of this system and from 1932 onwards the use of a separate thermionic rectifier became standard practice.

The first rectifiers developed specifically for car radio applications were half-wave types such as the Arcturus AD, Ken-Rad KR1, and the standard type 1V. The first two were mercury-vapour types which proved to be largely unsuccessful in car radio service and they were soon superseded by high-vacuum types. In April 1933[27] the first full-wave car radio rectifier, type 84/6Z4 was announced and it remained a standard until the arrival of a metal version, type 6X5, and a glass octal version, type 6X5G, in 1937.

Because the characteristics of these rectifiers made them

Two versions of the STC 4033A half-wave rectifier.

suitable for supplying the HT requirements of smaller AC-operated receivers they were sometimes used in this application. For example, the 84 was extensively used by Philco and the 6X5G by Stewart Warner.

Two reasons were responsible for the introduction of the transformerless AC/DC receiver: firstly the appeal of a small set which, while not strictly portable, could conveniently be carried from room to room; secondly the desire for a low-priced 'midget' set to meet the needs of the depression conditions then prevailing. At the time of the introduction of such receivers, late in 1932, there were no suitable rectifiers in existence and it became necessary to improvise a substitute. Some receiver manufacturers initially made use of a type 37 general-purpose triode as a rectifier by strapping its grid and plate together; others pressed the KR1 car radio rectifier into use pending the arrival of a specially designed type.

Early in 1933 two suitable rectifiers were announced, the types 12Z3 and 25Z5.[28] The former was a conventional half-wave type having a maximum output current of 55 mA, while the latter was unique in having two separate sets of elements which allowed it to be used in different circuit configurations. Whilst the 25Z5 was most commonly used in half-wave mode it could also be used as a full-wave voltage-doubler rectifier when operating from 110-volt AC lines. When used in this manner better receiver performance was attainable as a result of the higher available DC output voltage. The use of twin-element rectifiers in voltage-doubler mode was naturally restricted to countries where 110 volts was the standard mains supply.

A metal version of the 25Z5, type 25Z6, and a glass octal version, type 25Z6G, were both issued in 1937; all carried the then standard 300 mA series heater rating. When RCA introduced the 150 mA series of AC/DC tubes in 1939 the first rectifier included in the range was type

118

35Z4GT. Later rectifiers having the same heater current rating were types 35Z5GT, 45Z5GT, 35Z3, 50Y6GT, 117Z6GT, and 117Z3.

British Rectifiers

In Britain, too, the earliest rectifiers were those developed for transmitting use and in this connection it is interesting to note that as early as 1920 Ediswan were advertising 'double anode' (i.e., full-wave) types.[29] Other manufacturers of transmitting-type rectifiers were M-O.V. and Mullard.

Reflecting the slower acceptance of mains-driven receivers in the U.K. was the complete absence of receiving-type rectifiers before the end of 1926; in fact certain firms did not make any before 1928. By American standards the first British valves were capable of only quite small outputs, many being small half-wave types rated at no more than 30 mA. These small outputs were in keeping with the modest HT requirements of most British receivers of the day which were commonly of the 2-valve or 3-valve variety.

Another factor contributing to the slower development of valve rectifiers may well have been the initial popularity of Westinghouse 'metal' HT rectifiers. However, because of their bulkiness and higher cost, which increased in direct proportion to their power handling abilities, metal rectifiers were seldom used in multi-valve receivers.

Amongst the first British rectifiers were Burndept's U695 and Osram's U4, both of which appeared in 1926. As an indication of the capabilities of such rectifiers it may be mentioned that the U4 was rated at a mere 15 mA output. In the same year Osram also marketed their first full-wave rectifier, type U5, but not until 1927 did other companies commence production. The first and only rectifier marketed under the B.T.-H. brandname was the type RH1 announced in October 1927; while the first two under the Cosmos name were announced in September of the same year. It was well into 1928 before the first Mullard rectifiers came on the scene (types DU2 and DU10) and the same applied to Cossor who issued their types SU6 and BU6 in that same year.

As in the U.S. half-wave rectification soon became obsolete in AC-operated receivers and by 1933 half-wave rectifiers had been dropped from the catalogues of the major valve makers. Also, as in the U.S., the increasing popularity of multi-valve sets led to the development of higher power rectifiers which, in 1930, resulted in the production of the first British type having an oxide-coated filament, M-O.V.'s type U.9. Incidentally, it was the first of this firm's rectifiers to carry, what was by then, the standard European filament rating of 4 volts. Within the next year other British valve makers had similar types on the market, most of which were available in three differ-

Cossor U.3 half-wave rectifier c. 1922.

119

ent sizes. With the introduction of M-O.V.'s International Octal range of valves in 1937 direct equivalents of the American types 5Y3G and 5U4G were issued as types U50 and U52. By 1940 all major manufacturers with the exception of Mazda were producing American type rectifiers which in most cases included the ubiquitous 80 as well as more recent types.

Osram U.3.

Osram U.8 full-wave rectifier.

Philips 506, full-wave. Philips 373, half-wave.

Philips Rectifiers

It is convenient to include mention of Philips rectifying valves here because in the terms of the 1925 Philips-Mullard agreement any two-electrode valves could be sold in the U.K. under Philips' name. The earliest low-power rectifiers made by Philips were intended for use in battery eliminators which were marketed before the firm had commenced receiver manufacture.

In contrast to American practice where 'B' eliminators invariably used full-wave rectification many European eliminators used half-wave. The first Philips eliminator, type 372,[30] used the type 373 h-w rectifier and was capable of 40 mA output. The model 3003 eliminator used a type 506 HT rectifier and a type 3006 h-w grid bias rectifier. The type 1002 h-w rectifier was used only in the model 1001 HT battery charger.

The earliest Philips rectifier to be produced solely as part of a particular receiver was a diminutive h-w type known as the 2504; it was incorporated in the model 2501 receiver which appeared during 1927–28. So tiny was the 2504 that a normal bakelite valve base could not be fitted to it and instead an SBC lamp base was used with the anode connected to the brass base shell.

Probably the best known of the early rectifiers was the type 506 which was first used in battery eliminators before being used in Philips receivers in 1928. By 1929 there were as many as ten different rectifiers in the 4-volt range alone. Not all of these were marketed in Great Britain though by 1938 no less than seven different 4-volt types were listed in the *Wireless World Valve Data* of that year. An altogether more than adequate offering, one might venture.

Following the end of World War II Philips-Mullard somewhat surprisingly included a 4-volt directly-heated rectifier, type AZ41, in their Rimlock range of miniature

valves introduced in 1947. It was surprising because by this time directly-heated rectifiers, except high power types, were obsolete and it is interesting to note that the only other British maker of Rimlock (B8A) valves made only an indirectly-heated type.

Three versions of the Marconi-Osram U.12.

The Diode as a Voltage Regulator

A less common application of the two-electrode tube is as a voltage regulator. Probably the earliest example of such use is to be found in the HT supply of airborne radio transmitters used by the American Army during World War I when the first attempts were made to use radio as a means of communication between aircraft in flight and personnel on the ground. To provide the plate voltage for the transmitter a wind-driven generator, usually attached to a wing strut, was used, and as a matter of interest this system was retained in later civilian aircraft until well into the 1930s. In practice the use of a wind-driven generator suffered from the drawback that variations in the speed of the aircraft caused the generator speed to vary and this obviously called for some form of voltage regulation and here is where a diode tube was put to good use.

The U.S. Signal Corps developed a unique form of voltage regulator using a specialised type of diode manufactured by the General Electric Co.[31] Briefly, the mode of operation was as follows: the tube's filament was lit from a separate winding on the generator and the tube itself was connected in series with a separate differential shunt field coil. With increasing speed both the filament and plate voltages of the tube increased simultaneously, resulting in an increased current through the differential or opposing field coil. This increased current had the effect of bucking the current in the main field coil thus reducing the excitation and preventing the generator voltage from rising appreciably. In practice the output voltage was held constant to within 10% with armature speeds varying between 1800 and 3600 rpm.

The type TB-1 tube used in the regulator circuit was similar in size and shape to other GE tubes of the period, such as types VT-11 and VT-12, and used an S14 bulb fitted with a 3-pin Shaw type brass base. The electrodes consisted of a small-diameter tubular anode together with a spiral filament rated at 7.5 to 10 V.

By its very nature such a tube could be expected to perform equally well as a half-wave rectifier and post-war surplus stocks were offered for sale for this purpose with a claimed output rating of 60 mA at 350 V. Apparently large quantities of the TB-1 had been manufactured as up to seven years after the end of the war these tubes were being advertised for sale to amateurs for as little as $1.50 each.[32]

GE type TB1 regulator diode c. 1917.

REFERENCES

1. *Physikalische Zeitschrift*, Vol. V, No. 1, Oct. 20, 1904.
2. *GE Report*, p. 56.
3. Ibid., p. 57.
4. See advt. *Radio News*, June 1925, p. 1224.
5. *GE Report*, p. 55.
6. Ibid., p. 56.
7. Progress in Tubes for Radio, *Radio Engineering*, Feb. 1933, p. 11.
8. See advt. *Radio News*, October 1926, p. 451.
9. See advt. *Radio News*, December 1926, p. 715.
10. See advt. *Radio News*, November 1925, p. 613.
11. See advt. *Radio News*, December 1925, p. 906.
12. Robert S. Kruse, The Epom Rectifier, *QST*, June 1926, pp. 41–43.
13. See *Radio Engineering*, August 1928, p. 45.
14. The Wireless Show, *Wireless World*, Sept. 8, 1926, p. 348.
15. See La Radio Technique valve catalogue, 1928.
16. Still More New Tubes, *Radio Craft*, Sept. 1932, p. 148.
17. See *Raytheon Technical Data*, 7th Edition, Aug. 1935.
18. See advt. *Electronics*, October 1945, p. 81.
19. Two New Tubes, *Radio Craft*, July 1932, p. 16.
20. Four New Tubes, *Radio Craft*, April 1933, p. 595.
22. See *Ken-Rad Tube Data Chart*, dated August 1932.
23. See *Wireless World Valve Data Supplement*, Dec. 1931.
24. See *RCA Receiving Tube Manual* RC12, 1934, p. 128.
25. See advt. *Wireless World*, January 1931, p. ad. 5.
26. See advt. *Wireless World*, December 4, 1929, p. ad. 6.
27. Here are the New Tubes!, *Radio Craft*, April 1933, p. 586.
28. Progress in Tubes for Radio, *Radio Engineering*, Feb. 1933, p. 11.
29. See advt. *Wireless World*, January 1920, p. xvii.
30. See *Philips Receiving Valve* catalogue, dated 15-1-26, p. 40.
31. J.H. Morecroft, *Principles of Communication*, p. 373.
32. See advt. *QST*, June 1925, p. 89.

Chapter Sixteen

Electron Ray Tubes

American Developments

Visual tuning indicators first came into use in 1933 following the advent of receivers incorporating automatic volume control (AVC) circuits. Due to the AVC action such receivers exhibited an apparent broadening of tuning making it more difficult for a non-skilled user to tune-in correctly. Initially a specialised form of neon lamp was often used as a tuning indicator while in the case of receivers in the deluxe class or in communications receivers a milliammeter was used. As meters were costly items a need arose for a cheaper though equally effective device.

In 1935 RCA introduced the first electronic tuning indicator, type 6E5, which was dubbed a 'Magic Eye' though formally identified as an electron ray tube. Physically the 6E5 resembled a contemporary glass radio tube as it was fitted with an ST-12 bulb. Essentially it was a diminutive cathode-ray tube with a tiny fluorescent screen known as a 'target'. A control electrode was arranged to cast an angular or fan-shaped shadow on the target which varied in width according to the DC potential applied to it. Included in the assembly was a tiode amplifier direct-coupled to the control electrode. In turn the grid of this amplifier was intended to be directly connected to a receiver's diode detector circuit.

Because the 6E5 could handle only a comparatively small input voltage before the edges of the shadow overlapped a new tube, type 6G5, having a vari-mu triode amplifier capable of handling higher input voltages was developed in 1936. In the same year yet another type known as the 6N5 also appeared; it differed from the previous types in being intended for operation in battery sets and had a heater rating of 0.15 amps. This tube was later issued under the combined type number 6AB5/6N5. In 1939 the type 6U5 was issued but as its characteristics closely resembled those of the earlier 6G5 the two were later issued under the combined number 6U5/6G5. The 6G5 was also issued under the style 6G5/6H5.

So far all the types mentioned had the original fan-shaped shadow but in 1937 Arcturus, Raytheon, and Syl-

6E5 (1935)   6G5 (1936)

The first magic eye tubes.

6U5/6G5   6A85/6N5

123

vania introduced the type 6T5 which had an annular shadow. For some reason this type quickly became obsolete, the recommended replacement being the type 6U5.

At the time when the 6E5 was produced 6.3 volts had become the industry standard heater voltage so for this reason it, and all subsequent types, carried the standard 6.3-V, 0.3-A rating. However, because of the existence of a large number of older receivers still in use at the time some tube manufacturers produced a 2.5-volt version of the 6E5 known as the 2E5 and a similar version of the 6G5 known as the 2G5. These tubes were intended to allow radio servicemen to modernise earlier receivers by the fitting of a tuning indicator. Incidentally they were probably the only 2.5-volt tubes of any kind produced long after the figure of 6.3 volts had become the industry standard.

Although the 6E5 was issued after the introduction of the octal base, as first used on metal tubes in 1935, this style of base had not then been used on glass tubes and for this reason the 6E5 made use of a 6-pin base. This set the pattern for the next few years and not until October 1938 did the first octal-based tuning indicator, type 6AF6G appear. This tube differed from previous types in two respects: it was fitted with two control electrodes giving separate shadows and it contained no amplifier; consequently it was necessary to use a separate tube, or tubes, for this purpose. The later 6AD6G was a companion type for use in AC/DC or battery service.

During World War II the 12.6-volt type 1629 (VT-139) was developed for use on 12-volt supply systems. The final indicator tube developed was the type 6AL7GT which appeared in 1950. It was intended for use with FM receivers and differed from all previous types in having two rectangular fluorescent patterns.

British Developments

The first British electron ray indicator was issued by M-O.V. and appeared in their 'International Octal' range

British magic eye valves. The two on the right use Mazda octal bases.

American 'Magic Eyes.' Note octal base on centre tube.

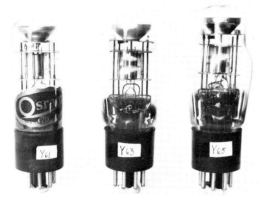

British octal-based magic eyes.

A group of Philips tuning indicators 1936–1949.

124

of valves released in 1937. Known as type Y63 it was the equivalent of the American 6U5 but differed in being fitted with an octal base. Later additions in the M-O.V. range were types Y61, Y62, Y64, Y65.

In 1937 Mullard released their types TV4 and TV6, the equivalents of Philips types AM1 and EM1; both had side-contact bases. Next came Mazda's AC/ME and ME920, both of which were fitted with British standard 7-pin bases. These were followed by types ME41 and ME91 which had Mazda octal bases.

By 1940 Mullard were listing types EM1, EM3, EM4, and EFM1. Of these the EM1 was simply the earlier type TV6 given a different type number. Not until after 1949 was the only octal-based type, the EM34 issued.

American types 6AF6G and 6AD6G Telefunken EF11M combined RF pentode and indicator tube (centre).

Continental Developments

Not surprisingly it was the enterprising firm of Philips who produced the first continental tuning indicator tubes, the 4-volt type AM1 being used in their 1936 receiver models. A 6.3-volt version of this tube, the EM1, was included in the 'Red E' series of tubes released in 1936. These differed from American designs in having a four-bladed control electrode which produced four separate shadows acting in unison. The resemblance of these four shadows to a cross initially gave rise to the terms 'tuning cross' or 'Magic Star' being applied to the early Philips indicators. Philips were the first manufacturers to produce an indicator, type EM4, having two dissimilar control electrodes which resulted in the two shadows having different sensitivities, a useful feature where a wide range of input voltages is to be handled. The EM4 was first used in 1938–39 model Philips receivers.

Included in the Telefunken 'E11' series of tubes announced in 1938 was an unusual tuning indicator, type EFM11, housed in the same bulb as an entirely separate

AF amplifying pentode which had no association with the indicator function. The idea of turning a tuning indicator into a multiple tube in this manner was purely German, though the practical advantages were minimal. Examples of its use occur in Telefunken receiver models D860WK and T898WK. Philips-Valvo and Tungsram also produced the EFM11 as well as a side-contact version known as the EFM1.

Another unusual tube, also of German origin, was the Lorenz EM71, a 6.3-volt all-glass type using an American type loctal base; it was marketed in the U.K. by Brimar under the same type number.

Miniaturisation

With the advent of miniaturisation in the post-war years tuning indicators became just one more tube type to undergo a shrinkage, though in this case the metamorphosis

A group of Noval-based (B9A) indicator tubes c. 1956–1960.

was of European origin. While the first types issued were, like their bigger brothers, intended to be used as radio tuning indicators some later types were more commonly used as level indicators in portable (mains-operated) tape recorders which became popular during the 1950s.

The first miniature tuning indicator, type EM80, appeared in 1953. Although having a conventional fan-shaped shadow the display area was located on the side, rather than the end, of the tube. Later types in this series were EM81 and EM85. In 1956 a completely new type of indicator was introduced in which the fluorescent screen was deposited directly on the glass itself in the manner of cathode ray tubes. The display area was of rectangular shape in place of the earlier fan-shaped format. Tubes of this type were the EM84 and EM87.

The smallest tube having a fan-shaped shadow displayed on the end of the bulb (after the manner of the older standard sized tubes) was the Japanese 6ME10, made by Ten and Toyo. It was unique in being constructed in a T-5½ bulb which was fitted with a miniature 7-pin bake-lite base.

The smallest indicator tubes ever made were two directly-heated luminescent triodes, types DM70 and DM160; the former had a 10 mm bulb and the latter a 6 mm. The DM70 is known to have been used as an ultra-miniature tuning indicator in both battery- and mains-operated receivers.

Japanese 6 ME10
Note miniature
7-pin base

Lorenz EM71
Note loctal base

For some reason American involvement in the development of miniaturised tuning indicators was zero; none of American origin ever appearing in the pages of any RCA tube manuals. In 1961, however, RCA took the unprecedented step of distributing the first European tube of any type on the U.S. market. In this case the type chosen was the EM84 which was listed under the combined type number EM84/6FG6.

Chapter Seventeen

Transmitting Tubes

Not until nearly a decade after Fleming's discovery that a vacuum tube could be used as a detector of electrical oscillations did other workers discover its ability to generate similar oscillations. By then the three-electrode tube had appeared on the scene and it was this tube's amplifying ability which enabled it to also be used as an oscillator. In 1912 De Forest was engaged in developing a multistage audio frequency amplifier for telephone use and in the process had encountered problems with feedback. According to De Forest's own account it was the subsequent investigation of the cause of this unwanted feedback which led him and his assistants, Charles Logwood and Herbert van Etten, to the discovery of the principle of 'regeneration'.

In the following year, 1913, De Forest claimed to have discovered the ability of his Audion tube to oscillate at radio frequencies.[1] His patent application covering what he called his 'Ultra Audion' circuit was filed in March 1914.[2] This patent and others filed in the following year were to be the subject of long, drawn out, and bitter patent litigation extending over the next twenty years.

Once again the triode was to become the centre of a controversy, this time in connection with its newly recognised ability to act as a generator, or oscillator, and also as a 'regenerator' when used in a receiving circuit. In 1913 the young Edwin H. Armstrong, then a student at Columbia University, had independently discovered the principle of regeneration and had filed a patent in that same year.[3]

Apart from these two inventors there were others in the U.S., as well as such people as Franklin in England and A. Meissner in Germany, who were actively engaged in similar work and who had also applied for patents. On the American scene it developed into a contest between Armstrong and De Forest over their attempts to sustain their respective claims to priority.

In 1924 the District of Columbia Court of Appeal ruled in De Forest's favour. Four years later, in 1928, this decision was reversed in Armstrong's favour. Finally, in 1934, De Forest once again had his claim sustained. Incidentally,

this final decision was at the time considered by the cognoscenti to have been a miscarriage of justice.

Because receiving tubes were initially the only ones available it followed naturally that they were pressed into use as the first oscillators for transmitting use. Understandably it was their limited power handling capabilities which led to the development of higher power types designed expressly for transmitting work. De Forest produced his first transmitting tubes, which he termed 'Oscillions', in 1915.[4] Experimental transmitting tubes were also produced by General Electric and Western Electric in this same year. During World War I transmitting tubes for military use were developed on both sides of the Atlantic and from this time onwards the production of transmitting types became a specialised branch of the art.

It was the birth of broadcasting and its subsequent growth which resulted in the call for larger and larger

Radiotron UV-202 (1921).

127

transmitting tubes, tubes which eventually reached output capabilities in the order of tens of kilowatts. Of more interest to tube collectors are the lower-power types first developed in America and England during the early 1920s. Two of the earliest American tubes were the UV-202 and UV-203, both of which appeared in 1921. The first production of tubes intended specifically for short-wave work occurred early in 1926 when the Radiotron UX-852 and the De Forest type H were marketed. Both these tubes had their grid and plate leads taken out at widely spaced points in order to reduce inter-electrode capacitances to a minimum.

By 1930 the De Forest Radio Co. listed 14 different types of transmitting tubes, including rectifiers. By 1938 RCA were offering 33 types of air-cooled tubes, not counting rectifiers. As in the case of receiving types the first Radiotron transmitting tubes were made by GE but in 1933 RCA set up its own transmitting tube division. At this time the collapse of De Forest Radio provided RCA with an opportunity to commence its own production by acquiring the former company's transmitting tube plant. For some years thereafter certain types of tubes were issued under the namestyle 'RCA-de Forest'.

With De Forest out of the running the number of independent producers reached an all-time low. A small New York company known as the Duovac Radio Tube Corp. had commenced manufacturing in 1930[15] and continued to operate for several years, presumably without an RCA license. The remaining manufacturer, Arcturus, made a brief foray into the transmitting tube field during the early 1930s, issuing upwards of 10 types. These carried type

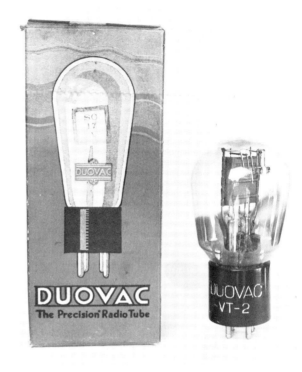

Duovac version of Western Electric's VT-2.

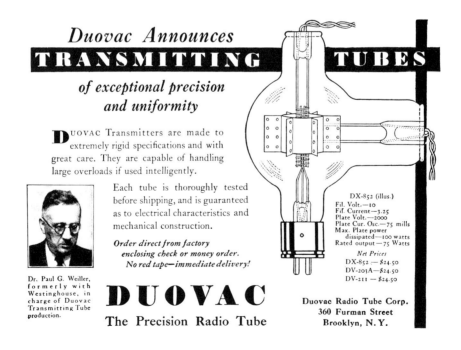

Advertisement for Duovac tubes appearing in QST for December 1930.

numbers commencing with E7, thus E703A was equivalent to UV-203A and so on. Little was heard of these tubes and their production life appears to have quite brief, though the company remained active in the receiving tube field for many years. The next independent to commence manufacturing transmitting tubes was Sylvania who set up a separate factory for the purpose in 1934. Within a short space of time, however, action by RCA forced their withdrawal from this field, effectively leaving the Radio Group a monopoly in the marketplace.

An event of some significance occurred in 1936 when RCA first licensed other companies to make transmitting tubes. As well as allowing existing receiving tube manufacturers to enter the transmitting tube field this action also resulted in the establishment of several smaller specialist manufacturers, most of whom concentrated on the production of tubes for amateur use. In the first category were such firms as Hytron, Ken-Rad, and Raytheon, while amongst the newcomers were Amperex, Eimac, Gammatron, Taylor, and United. The existence of specialist companies not engaged in the production of receiving tubes remained unique to the U.S., although following the takeover of Amperex by Philips after World War II receiving tubes were issued under the Amperex name. Heintz & Kaufman, makers of Gammatron tubes, also issued receiving types during the 1960s, though it is not known whether they were the actual manufacturers.

On the British scene the first transmitting valves were developed by H.J. Round for the Marconi Co. in 1915. The advent of World War I spurred their development and laid the groundwork for the production of high-power types for broadcasting during the 1920s. The rapid increase in the power handling abilities of transmitting valves can be appreciated when it is realised that by 1922 there were 5-kW water-cooled types in production. At this same time air-cooled silica envelope valves of up to 15-kW rating were being produced for naval use. By 1931 Met-

De Forest 'Oscillion' with Shaw base c. 1920.

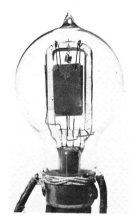

De Forest 'Oscillion' transmitting tube (1917).

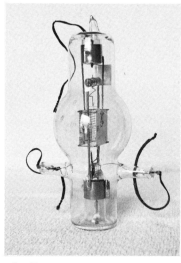

De Forest type 'H' short-wave transmitting tube (1926).

Marconi MT5 triode c. 1922.

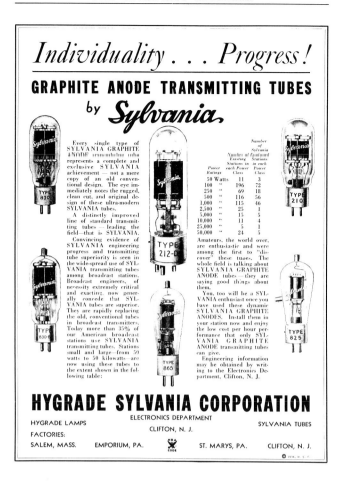
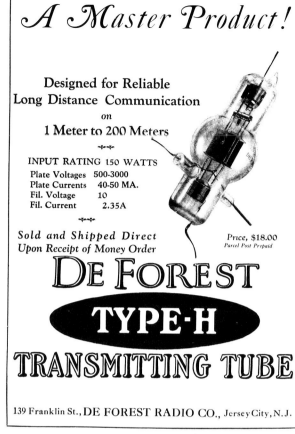

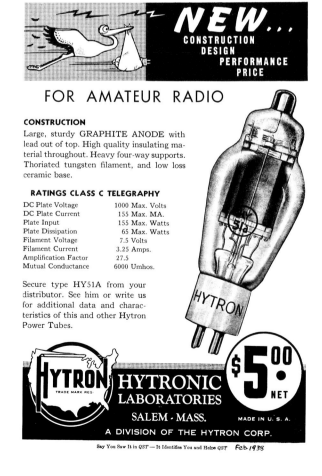

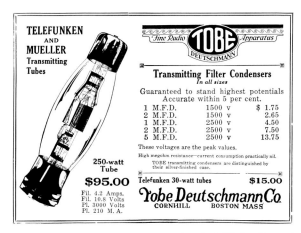

Advertisement for German tubes appearing in QST for November 1925.

RCA de Forest types 802 (L.) and 800 (R.) of 1936.

Philips type Z1 (1924).

Philips ZIIB 20-watt tube (1924).

Mullard 0/30A 30-watt triode (1923).

Three early British transmitting valves c. 1923.

Philips ZIIA 20-watt (1924).

Vick had developed 'demountable' transmitting valves of 500-kilowatt rating.

Of more interest to collectors are the various lower power valves developed during the early 1920s by M-O.V. and Mullard. Amongst these may be mentioned Mullard's 0.10, 0.20, and 0.30, together with M-O.V.'s M.T.1, M.T.5, and T.30.

On the continent the firm of Philips produced their first 'generator lamps' as early as 1919. By 1920 'zendlampen' having output capabilities of 250-watts were available. Philips were one of the few continental manufacturers who early produced low-power tubes suitable for amateur use; their types Z1, Z2A, Z2B, and Z3 were issued early in 1924. Two types of advanced design, known as TCO3/5 and TCO4/10, were introduced in 1930. These had their grid and anode connections taken to widely spaced top-mounted terminals and were intended for short-wave working. It was claimed by their manufacturers that these two tubes could be used to generate oscillations at frequencies as high as 80 MHz. As a matter of fact it is known that they were capable of stable working at much higher frequencies, for in 1931 experimental oscillators operating at up to 212 MHz had been developed.

By comparison with those of Philips the products of other continental manufacturers were less well known outside their respective countries. The American ban on the importation of receiving tubes which was in operation during the pre-World War II years also applied to transmitting tubes. However, it may be mentioned that, for a short period from late 1925 to 1926, German-made Mueller and Telefunken tubes were being sold in the U.S. Whether by coincidence or otherwise the importer of these tubes had the very German sounding name of Tobe Deutschmann and the Mueller tubes, which were made by Radio Rohre Fabrik (R.R.F.), were actually sold on the American market under the name of TOBE. As these German tubes were advertised for only a very short length of time it seems likely that they were either a 'job lot' or else further importation was prevented. In the event Mr. Deutschmann went on to become well known for other American-made radio products.

French Metal low-capacitance 'horned' tube c. 1925.

Three Philips transmitting tubes of the 1930 era. The TB04/10 was the equivalent of the American type 10.

(L.) German Mueller 'MS' 30-watt. (R.) Mueller MSIV 5-watt c. 1926.

REFERENCES

1. Lee de Forest, *The Father of Radio,* p. 317.
2. U.S. Patent application 1,507,016.
3. U.S. Patent No. 1,113,149.
4. Lee de Forest, *The Father of Radio,* p. 333.
5. See advt. Duovac Radio Tube Corp., *QST,* December 1930, p. 85.

Chapter Eighteen

Miniaturisation

Early Developments

Tubes of substantially smaller dimensions than others in general use at the time date back to as long ago as World War I. The reason for the development of such valves (for they were of British origin) was the need for an improved performance at the higher radio frequencies. In this respect it is interesting to note that the development of a much later type of miniature tube also took place during a war—World War II—and in this case, too, it was a similar need for a better high frequency performance that brought about its production. The circumstances were the same, only the frequencies had been changed—in 1942 frequencies in the VHF and UHF ranges were being used. While the World War I valves cannot be regarded as true miniature, having regard for what is understood by the term in relation to the much more recent developments, it is nevertheless interesting to note that their dimensions were quite comparable to those of the 9-pin miniature types developed during the late 1940s and early 1950s.

Undoubtedly the earliest 'minis' were the Marconi types V.24 and Q which first appeared towards the end of World War I. These valves were designed to have very low inter-electrode capacitances to permit their use in cascaded stages of RF amplification in certain Marconi receivers. This required feature was obtained by the use of very small electrodes and by bringing out all external connections to widely spaced points on the surface of the tubular envelope. These valves were thus the first of any type which did not make use of the conventional stem seal (pinch) type of construction. Their design is attributed to Capt. H.J. Round, whose name is associated with several other valves of the period.

Valves of the V.24 type were largely handmade and thus quite unsuited to mass production with the result that even though dull-emitter versions, types DEV and DEQ were developed after the war their comparatively high cost made them less popular than conventional types. Incidentally, both these types were still listed in the 1937 Marconi catalogue and it is understood that they were available up to the outbreak of World War II!

In the United States the first really small tube was the Western Electric type 215A, known coloquially as the peanut tube. The design of this tube dates back to the closing stages of World War I, though it was not actually produced until the early 1920s. The 215A used a concentric style of element assembly having a tubular anode with a dimaeter of about 0.18″ (5mm). To maintain the electrodes in alignment a floating glass press was used at each end of the assembly with the lead-out wires sealed through a depression in the bottom of the bulb. With a diameter of 0.6″ (16mm) and an overall height of 2½″ (64mm) the 215A for many years remained the world's smallest tube. As the

Western Electric 215A (L.) and VT5 (R.). Peanut tubes.

tube was intended for operation from a single dry cell the filament was rated at 1.0 V, 0.25A and was of the oxide-coated type. A special small size bakelite base, unique to this particular tube, was used and it seems likely that in 1923 the 215A was the first tube ever to be equipped with a moulded base. Unlike the Marconi valves the 215A was not intended for RF amplification, its construction being in the form of a scaled-down version of a normal size tube. As with certain other WE tubes of the period a British version was made by STC and it is interesting to note that under the British type number 4215A the peanut valve was being listed until at least 1939.[1]

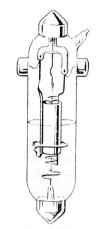
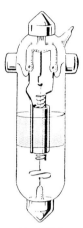

Nearly ten years elapsed before any further developments took place when towards the end of 1934 M-O.V. announced two special types intended for hearing-aid application. These were the H.11 and L.11, both being triodes with filaments rated at 1.1 V, 0.1 A. A special small base fitted with side contacts in place of the usual pins was used, presumably with the intention of securing a reduction of the overall height. The valves measured 50 mm by 20 mm, the relatively large diameter being due to type of base used which was in the form of a cup encircling the lower part of the bulb. The H.11 and L.11 appear to have been the world's first valves designed specifically for use in hearing-aids.

The next step in the evolution of miniatures occurred in 1935 when a recently established British valve maker, The High Vacuum Valve Co. (later Hivac Ltd.), produced the first three types in what was to become a quite extensive range of 'midget' valves.[2] Hivac specialised in the production of this type of valve and must be regarded as a pioneer in the field. They were the first to produce tetrode voltage amplifiers and output pentodes and in addition pioneered the production of a vari-mu pentode and a diode-triode type, the last two intended to allow the use of audio AVC in hearing aids.

Hivac 'midget' valves c. 1935.

A notable feature of the Hivac midgets was the use of a new means of sealing the lead-out wires directly through the bottom of the bulb without the use of a normal stem pinch. This feature enabled the production of a shorter valve than would otherwise have been the case even though the use of a pin type base contributed considerably to the overall height. Originally the Hivac midgets carried a 2-volt filament rating, but later 1.5-volt and eventually 0.65-volt ratings were used. The later productions dispensed with the use of separate bases and were fitted with wire leads which allowed the valves to be soldered directly into the circuit. These later valves were only 10 mm in diameter and varied in length from 24 mm to 30 mm, exclusive of the lead-out wires.

Some three years after the appearance of the first Hivac midgets a somewhat similar range was produced in the U.S. by Hytron. These particular tubes were referred by as 'Bantam Junior' by their manufacturers, the name being derived from the same company's earlier 'Bantam' octal-based tubes. In December 1938 the first three Bantam Juniors were released—a triode, type HY113, and two pentodes, types HY115 and HY125.[3] All carried filament ratings of 1.4 V, 70 mA. The Bantam Juniors were slightly shorter than the earliest Hivac midgets even though a somewhat similar sized bakelite base was used.

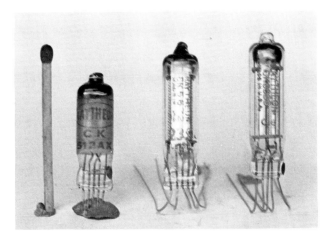

Raytheon 'CK' flat hearing-aid tubes.

In 1940 Raytheon entered the field with their 'CK' series of flat hearing-aid tubes. This was followed by the 'CKX' series in the same year, these being the first tubes to dispense with the use of a separate base and provide wire leads to permit their being soldered in place.[4] Following this Hytron then introduced a range of even smaller hearing-aid tubes known as 'Super Bantam' which in 1941 were claimed to be 'The World's Smallest'. Not long after the end of World War II the development of further hearing-aid tubes was halted by the appearance of the first transistorised hearing-aids, an application for which transistors were a 'natural'.

American Button-Base

With the amount of developmental work that had gone into the making of specialised hearing-aid tubes it was not surprising that the production of smaller tubes specifically designed for use in portable radios should also be considered and early in 1940 the first of such tubes were marketed by RCA.

This event must be regarded as a turning point in receiving tube history as for the first time the use of the so-called 'glass button stem' (gbs) or 'button base' seal was combined with the production of a truly miniaturised tube. In fact the use of the button base was actually a pre-

SYLVANIA NEWS

ELECTRONIC EQUIPMENT EDITION

JAN.   Published by SYLVANIA ELECTRIC PRODUCTS INC., Emporium, Pa.   1946

NEW T-3 TUBE FILLS NEED FOR SMALLER UNIT IN TINY BROADCAST RECEIVERS

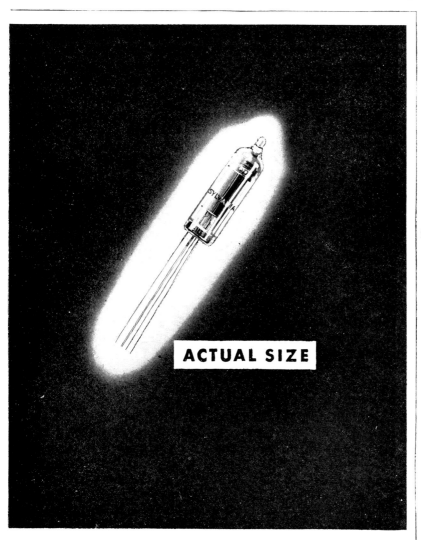

ACTUAL SIZE

For any further details, or questions you may want answered about this tiny, sturdy vacuum tube, do not hesitate to write or call Sylvania Electric Products Inc., Emporium, Pa.

Commercial Version of Proximity Fuze Tube Is Rugged, Has Long Life

Following Sylvania Electric's recent announcement about the sensationally small vacuum tube—originally developed for the now-famous proximity fuze transceiver—have come many inquiries concerning this super-midget.

SET MAKERS ESPECIALLY INTERESTED

Since the commercial version of the "war-baby" is being produced, many set manufacturers are extremely interested in its qualities — with a view toward making radios about the size of the average wallet or package of cigarettes, miniature walkie-talkie sets and other units.

This new tube, then, is being made in a low-drain filament type and is able to operate at 1.25 volts. This takes advantage of a new, small battery developed during the war which, of course, is a further aid in the manufacture of remarkably small radio sets.

WILL BE AVAILABLE FOR ALL TYPES

Future designs of this versatile tube can be incorporated in radios ranging in size from tiny pocket sets up to deluxe receivers. It has a life of hundreds of hours, is rugged and exceptionally adaptable to operation at high frequencies.

SYLVANIA ⓢ ELECTRIC
Emporium, Pa.

MAKERS OF RADIO TUBES; CATHODE RAY TUBES; ELECTRONIC DEVICES; FLUORESCENT LAMPS, FIXTURES, WIRING DEVICES; ELECTRIC LIGHT BULBS

requisite of this form of construction as, apart from reducing inter-electrode capacitances it played an essential part in the process of miniaturisation. The RCA miniatures, like Sylvania's Loktals, made use of specially developed thickened lead-out wires which themselves formed the actual contact pins. Base/socket indexing was achieved leaving a gap in the pin circle.

Late in 1939 the first four tubes in the initial release of button-base miniatures was announced, the range consisting of a pentagrid converter, an RF pentode, a diode-triode, and an output pentode.[5] The filament rating was 1.4 volts at 0.05 amps except for the output tube which was rated at 1.4V, 0.1A. Later output tubes had 2.8 volt center-tapped filaments to allow series or parallel operation. The tubes were fitted with a newly developed T-5½ bulb measuring 0.75"x2.125" (9mmx54mm), the size being uniform for all types.

So far all the tubes referred to have been filamentary

Osram DA2 and Valvo 4676 compared with an RCA955 (R.).

RCA 955, 954, 9004 'Acorn' tubes.

types intended for battery operation but as far back as 1934 RCA had announced the first indirectly-heated miniature known as the 'Acorn' type. The type 955 was a triode of highly specialised construction intended for amateur and experimental use at extremely high radio frequencies. It was followed in 1935 by the type 954, an RF pentode, and in 1936 by the type 956, a vari-mu pentode.

In December 1941 RCA announced the first 7-pin button-base indirectly-heated miniatures, types 9001, 9002, and 9003. These were essentially an adaptation of the Acorn structure modified by being fitted into T-5½ bulbs. Incidentally, they were advertised by RCA as 'midgets', not miniatures, although they used the same sized bulbs as the 1.4-volt miniature battery types of the previous year.

The first 7-pin button-base i.h. miniatures designed as such were types 6C4, 6J6, and 6AG5 which appeared towards the end of 1942.[6] By this time America had entered World War II and consequently the main thrust of tube development was directed towards military needs.

Turning now to the European scene we find that in Nazi Germany, where preparations for war had been going on before 1939, certain types of i.h. miniature tubes had been developed for military use at a comparatively early date. For example, miniature VHF/UHF pentodes were actually in large-scale production at least a year before similar types appeared in the U.S. Evidence of this was obtained as early as 1940 when an examination of German aircraft which had crashed in England revealed that the receivers used miniature tubes exclusively.[7]

The German miniatures differed from American in being fitted with bakelite bases, and in this respect were old fashioned. Losses were minimised by the use of widely spaced radial contact pins in conjunction with the use of a top cap for the grid connections. Bulb diameter was 20 mm, that is 1 mm larger than the American T-5½ size then in use. However, in spite of being true miniatures in respect of electrode structure and bulb size the use of a bulky side-contact base resulted in the 'seated' diameter being as great as many standard sized tubes; thus little or no saving of space resulted from their use.

Due to their unusual construction these tubes were required to be inserted 'head first' into individual recesses in the chassis leaving the underside of the base flush with the associated metal work. Removal could be accomplished only by the use of a special extracting tool which had first to be screwed into a threaded hole in the bottom of the base. The production of these tubes appeared to play no part in German post-war developments.

At this point it should be stressed that the main thrust of wartime miniaturisation was directed at achieving improved performance at higher frequencies, in the VHF and UHF regions; the accompanying reduction in physical size, with its ability to effect a reduction in the bulk and weight of portable or airborne equipment, was of secondary importance. In any case much of the radio and radar receiving equipment used by all countries throughout the war incorporated standard sized tubes.

After the war it remained to be seen to what extent, if any, the development of indirectly-heated miniature tubes was to affect the production of radio and television receivers. Having had the longest experience in this area it was only to be expected that RCA would be first in the field with a range of post-war miniatures intended for use in domestic receivers. In September 1945 dual ranges of 6.3-volt and 150-mA series-heater types first became available; these were the 6BA6, 6BE6, 6AT6, 6AQ5, 6X4, and their AC/DC counterparts.[8]

Even though other tube manufacturers had all had considerable wartime experience in the production of miniature types they were somewhat slower in following RCA's lead. For example, both Raytheon and Sylvania continued to develop standard sized tubes in the immediate post-war years. By 1947, however, all were producing a large range of miniatures.

Presumably in order to allay any doubts as to the ability of miniature tubes to effectively and economically replace standard sized ones RCA emphasised that they were 'comparable in performance and cost' to their bigger brothers. As for their possible usefulness in enabling the production of more compact receivers this factor was insignificant as a practical limit in this direction had already been reached before the war.

Because of the wartime work that had already gone into the development of the 7-pin miniatures, coupled with the extensive production facilities remaining at the war's end RCA apparently saw no good reason to depart from established lines when developing a range of post-war types. Even at the time, however, the decision to stick with the 7-pin T-5½ bulb format was open to criticism on the grounds that this small size was far from ideal for use with output tubes and rectifiers. Further, it resulted in the inability to produce such well-established tube types as duo-diode pentodes and triode-hexodes. Even a pentagrid con-

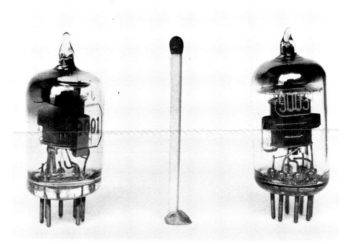

RCA 9001 and 9003. The first 7-pin heater-cathode miniature tubes (1941).

verter only just scraped through by the juggling of its internal structure combined with a modification of the associated receiver circuitry. Power tubes and rectifiers with their larger electrodes could be accommodated only by the use of taller bulbs and even so these bulbs were running at the limit of operating temperature.

Considering the remarkable size reduction that was accomplished in the T-5½ miniatures they proved surprisingly reliable in service and this was no small tribute to the painstaking engineering and quality contol during manufacture that went into their production. Having said that it must now be admitted that in the case of certain early Australian productions a considerable amount of trouble was experienced in service initially.

To keep things in chronological order it is convenient to make brief reference here to the so-called 'T-3' subminiature tubes pioneered by Sylvania. Although the term T-3 was actually the bulb size designation it came to be used as a convenient group indicator for the series which had three-eighths of an inch (10 mm) diameter bulbs. The first of these tubes was advertised by Sylvania in December 1945 when it was described as having been developed from the wartime proximity-fuse tube. The suggested use was for the production of ultra-compact portable receivers, though it is extremely doubtful if any such sets were ever commercially produced.

By 1950 a minimal range of four types—1E8, 1AD6, 1T6, 1AC5—was listed by both RCA and Sylvania. The filament rating for all types was 1.25 V, 0.04 A, and the maximum plate voltage was 67½ V.

Sylvania also developed a large number of subminiature tubes having indirectly-heated cathodes, examples of which were types 6AD4, 6BF5, and 6K4. In addition to these there were many others in '5000' and '6000' series, most of which carried a heater rating of 6.3 V, 0.15 A. Finally, Sylvania produced some even smaller tubes, types

The first 'T5½' button-base miniature tubes 1940.

138

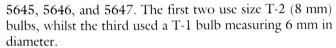
5645, 5646, and 5647. The first two use size T-2 (8 mm) bulbs, whilst the third used a T-1 bulb measuring 6 mm in diameter.

With one exception* what must be regarded as the final step in the development of receiving tubes occurred in 1948 when RCA released the first two types of a new range of miniatures. These tubes were of similar appearance to existing 7-pin types but were fitted with slightly larger (T-6½) bulbs having a diameter of 0.8″ (21 mm), and had 9-pin bases. As may be surmised, it was through the use of nine contact pins that the name of the series, 'noval', was derived.

The first two releases were types 12AU7 and 12AX7, both of which were listed in RCA's RC-15 Tube Manual dated March 1948. They were twin triodes having one side of each heater connected to a common base pin thus enabling their use on either 6.3- or 12.6-volt supplies or in 150 mA series-string heater chains.

The growth in the number of new types of American noval tubes was considerably slower than had been the

*RCA's 'Nuvistor'.

case with 7-pin miniatures because (commendably) no attempt was made to duplicate existing 7-pin types in noval form solely for the sake of doing so. Only where a tube needed more than seven external connections was it issued in 9-pin form, with the result that some six years after their introduction there were only 17 novals in production. Furthermore, the number of new 7-pin types issued continued to exceed the number of novals.

A series of specialised tubes produced as a direct result of the initial impact made by transistors in the field of car radio application came into use in the late 1950s. These tubes were unique in that they were designed to derive their plate voltage directly from a 12-volt system without the use of a vibrator HT supply. Because at this time the development of transistors was still in its infancy (production was confined mainly to audio frequency types) a hybrid type of car radio evolved which used a single output transistor fed by tube-equipped earlier stages.

Listed in RCA's RC-18 Tube Manual of November 1956 were six types of such tubes one of which, the 12K5, is of particular interest to historians in that it was a tetrode designed to operate in space-charge mode as a transformer-coupled driver for the output transistor. By 1961 the number of different types in production had reached the amazing total of 23.

(L.) An RCA 12AX7 with European style markings.
(R.) RCA 6AT6 of 1960 vintage.

European Developments

The development of miniature tubes in Europe took place slightly later than in America largely as a result of wartime conditions which effectively delayed the introduction of any new types of tubes for civilian use. For example, by the time RCA's 1.4-volt miniatures had appeared the war had been in progress for several months. Thus at the war's end there existed a five-year time lag and because of this it was convenient, if not essential, to adopt American designs *in toto* in order to make up for lost time.

Britain, Germany, and Holland were the first countries to produce 7-pin miniatures which in most cases were identical to American types, even to the extent of carrying American style markings. In the U.K. they were known as B7G types and in Germany as Pico 7.

One of the earliest British productions was M O.V.'s Z77 announced in July 1947. It was a steep-slope pentode intended for television applications. By 1949 all British valve makers had a range of 1.4-volt types in production and by this time some had a limited range of 6.3-volt and 150-mA AC/DC types in addition. It may be said, however, that no single manufacturer produced a full range of American types nor were they as widely used as other types of miniatures.

Rimlock

More or less coincidentally with the release of the first British B7G miniatures came the release of the so-called 'Rimlock' 8-pin (B8A) range by Mazda and Mullard.[9] With few exceptions the valves produced by these two companies were interchangeable even though they were slightly different in appearance and carried different type numbers. With a bulb diameter of 21 mm the rimlocks were slightly larger than the B7G types being the same diameter as the American Noval types, which at that time had not appeared on the European scene.

The use of a metal base shell made the overall diameter slightly larger than the actual bulb diameter, a feature which the rimlocks had in common with the much earlier American loctal design. Originally both Mazda and Mullard made use of a separate cemented-on base shell but after about 1953 Mullard dispensed with the shell and increased the diameter of the lower portion of the bulb to compensate for the change. Philips and Telefunken likewise modified the construction of their tubes at much the same time. A final change in bulb style occurred from about 1965 onwards when certain Eastern European manufacturers produced rimlocks having bulbs of a uniform diameter in which the main section had been increased in size to equal that of the lower portion.

The production of rimlock valves was confined almost exclusively to 6.3-volt and 100-mA AC/DC types and in Britain only one battery type, Mullard's DK40 was available. In view of Mazda's dedication to rimlocks it is somewhat surprising to find that this company issued only B7G types in the 1.4-volt range, that is apart from the older Mazda octals. On the continent Philips marketed but four 1.4-volt types whilst Telefunken listed only two.

Although the rimlock design had been proposed as the British post-war standard it failed to gain industry accep-

tance, Mazda and Mullard being the only two companies to undertake production. Once again it was a case of history repeating itself. By about 1957 rimlock valves were no longer being used as initial equipment, having been superseded by American type 7-pin and 9-pin miniatures, or, rather, European designed tubes using the American style of construction.

With the appearance of the first British noval-based valves in 1951 European post-war developments took another step on the road towards Americanisation, or perhaps more correctly, internationalisation. The first release of 9-pin valves using the American noval standards oc-

TeKaDe type RG12D60 rectifiers (1939).

A group of Philips-Mullard 'Rimlock' valves. The earliest types had metal base shells.

A group of Ediswan-Mazda 'B76' valves.

curred when, early in 1951, Mullard announced their types EF80, ECL80, and PY80.[10] Because by this time much of the emphasis on the development of new types was concerned with television it is not surprising to find that these three valves were intended for this application. It is probably true to say that, due to the slightly earlier emergence of post-war television in America, many more types of 7-pin miniatures had been developed in that country before the production of 9-pin types and this accounts for the fact that certain types of tubes, e.g., RF pentodes, were never produced in 9-pin form. This is in contrast to the position in Europe where all types, including TV deflection amplifiers and booster diodes were made in noval form.

Apart from using the same type of construction and following American standards in the matters of basing and bulb dimensions there was little other similarity between European and American productions, two exceptions being types DY80 and DY86; these were TV EHT rectifiers which were directly equivalent to the American types 1X2B and 1S2 respectively. By 1954 there were about 23 different types of noval-based tubes in production on both sides of the Atlantic and thereafter the number of new types continued to increase until about 1965 after which time no further developments took place.

European Subminiatures

The involvement of European countries in World War II served, amongst other things, to delay the development of subminiature tubes, at least for hearing-aid application, until well after the end of the war. Because of this the first types appearing in Great Britain, and probably the whole of Europe, were of American origin. For example, American 'Microtube Valves' [sic] were being advertised for sale in the pages of *Wireless World* during 1942. Not until six years after this were the first subminiatures produced in Britain.

In 1948, after collaboration with the Post Office, Mullard produced a range of three 10 mm size valves for use in government-sponsored 'National Health' hearing-aids. These were types DF70, DL71, and DL72, the filament rating for all three being 25 mA at 0.625 V.

In 1953 Mullard announced a range of seven indirectly-heated subminiatures with 6.3-volt heaters but by August only one type, EC76, was actually available. With one exception, type EA76, all valves in this range had 9.5 mm (10 mm nominal) bulbs. A range of nine directly-heated types was announced in 1957, all of which had 1.25-volt filaments. This was followed by a range of eight 6.3-volt indirectly-heated types in the American 5000 and 6000 groupings which were issued in the same year.

As was not unexpected, considering the pioneering work done in pre-war days on 'midget' valves, the firm of Hivac

Ltd. was also active in the production of subminiatures though this company made only battery-operated types. The first Hivac valves of this class were being advertised in 1951, though the company later, in 1957, claimed to

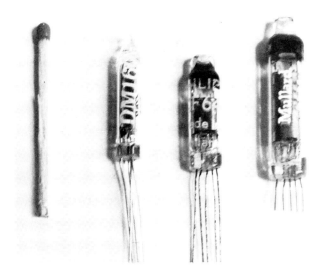

Philips-Mullard sub-miniatures
DM160   DF64   DL66

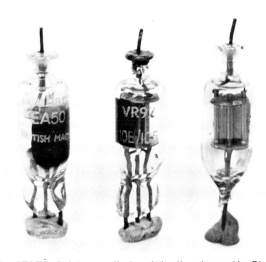

Mullard EA50. A detector diode originally released by Philips in 1939.

have designed and produced the world's first subminiature valves.[11] Hivac had by 1954 issued eight valves in the 0.625-V and 1.25-V groups of battery subminiatures and further additions continued to be made up to 1957.

Speaking of 'world's first' miniatures the author nominates the Philips EA50, a 6.3-volt signal diode contained in an 11.5 mm bulb, for this distinction. The world's first miniature valve to be fitted with an indirectly heated cathode was Mazda's D1 produced in 1937. It was a diode intended for television use and formed the basis for the later Philips Mullard EA50. During WW 2 large quantities of EA50 were produced for radar use under the Royal Air Force number VR94.

Decal

A European development of the noval, appearing in 1965, was the production of a few specialised types of miniatures in a new 10-pin format. On the continent they were known as 'decal', and in the U.K. as 'B10B'. In external appearance decals were identical to novals, apart from the existence of an additional base pin. Only certain multiple tubes requiring more than nine pins were produced in this form, examples being types ECH200 and PFL200. Having regard for the date of their introduction, decals must qualify as being the last new type of miniature produced in Europe and probably in the entire world.

The Nuvistor

What must be regarded as the final development in receiving tubes occurred when RCA released the first of a highly specialised and completely new type of tube under the name 'Nuvistor' in 1960. Nuvistors were intended for use in the VHF and UHF bands as first-stage amplifiers, mixers, or oscillators. As would be expected, having regard for the operating frequencies involved, the nuvistor was of extremely small dimensions, having a maximum overall height of one inch (25 mm) and a diameter of just under half an inch (12 mm). By comparison with conventional subminiature tubes the performance of the nuvistor was phenomenal, some types having mutual conductance figures of over 12,000 micromhos (12 mA/V).

The construction of the nuvistor represented a complete break with traditional methods of manufacture, it being made entirely from metal and ceramic material without the use of glass or mica. Welding of the electrode assembly was replaced by brazing in an atmosphere of hydrogen, and processing and sealing were carried out at higher than normal temperatures.

In July 1960 RCA announced the availability of the first Nuvistor triode, type 7586. Two more followed in 1961, the 6CW4 a high-mu triode and the 6DS4 a vari-mu triode. Because of the specialised nature and limited applications of the nuvistor only a small number of types were produced. Furthermore, RCA remained the only company

A group of three RCA Nuvistors compared with an early transistor (R.).

to manufacture them, production being intended mainly for use in RCA's colour television receivers. A tetrode nuvistor, type 7587 was intended for industrial applications.

The nuvistor was virtually unknown outside the U.S. although a somewhat similar class of tube was produced in Japan by Toshiba; an example of this make being type 3D-HH13. Limited use of nuvistors was also made by radio amateurs in the 1960s.

REFERENCES

1. See *Brimar Valve Manual*, 1938–39, p. 23.
2. See advt. High Vacuum Valve Co., *Wireless World*, Apr. 5, 1935, p. 9.
3. Recent Radio Tubes, *Radio Craft*, May 1938, p. 774.
4. Four Thumb-size Pentodes for Hearing Aids, *Radio Craft*, May 1940, p. 682.
5. Radically New Miniature Tubes, *Radio Craft*, Feb. 1940, p. 465.
6. New Tube Types, *Radio*, Dec. 1942, p. 20.
7. Wireless Equipment of the Luftwaffe, *Wireless World*, Nov. 1940, pp. 450–452.
8. *RCA Review*, Vol. 8, June 1947, pp. 331–341.
9. New Receiving Valves, *Wireless World*, June 1947, p. 228.
10. See, for example, Mullard advt. *Wireless World*, Feb. 1951, p. ad. 48.
11. See advt. Hivac Ltd., *Wireless World*, April 1951, p. ad. 57.
12. See Philips catalogue, *The Bridge to Higher Radio Entertainment*, Nov. 1939, p. 18.

Chapter Nineteen

Contact

Terminology

Before proceeding with a detailed description of the various types of base and socket combinations which were developed over the years it is worthwhile to examine the origins of some of the terms which came into use to describe them. It may be mentioned that in the U.K. there has always existed a rather loosely worded terminology which at times has led to a certain amount of confusion, so an attempt will now be made to set the record straight.

In the case of the earliest 4-pin valves the part which carried the contact pins was commonly referred to as the *base*, a completely logical and justifiable addition to emerging radio terminology because valves were normally operated in a vertical position with their pins at the bottom. However, as most of these early valves were made by lamp makers, who had already developed their own nomenclature wherein that part of a lamp containing the contacts was known as the *cap*, it is not surprising to find lamp-making terminology being carried over into valve manufacturing.

The term cap arose as a result of the manufacturing procedure whereby the contact assembly was cemented to the stem-end of the bulb whilst it was held in an upright position; in other words the lamp was 'capped'. As valve-making techniques closely followed lamp-making practice the same method of attaching the base was used, thus, from a manufacturing point of view, both lamps and valves had caps. Incidentally the term cap was never similarly used in the U.S. in connection with radio tubes even though lamp-making techniques had played a similar part in their manufacture. Eventually the word cap as a synonym for base became obsolete in British radio parlance and was little used after about 1933.

Having, it is hoped, settled the matter of cap versus base another terminological confusion, which also arose in the early days, now requires a word of explanation. This concerns the use of the word base as a synonym for 'valve holder'. With the exception of such valves as the Marconi V.24 and S.625, for example, where the term base is inap-

plicable due to the manner in which those valves were constructed, it must be unequivocally stated that the word base can logically be used to refer only to that part of a valve from which the contact pins protrude. Such usage is entirely appropriate whether a separately constructed base is attached to the bulb or whether the contact pins are embedded directly in the bottom of the bulb. Unfortunately, however, due to the use of three different terms during the early 1920s some lingering confusion has remained to the present day.

As one of the earliest manufacturers of one-piece insulated holders for valves S.R. Mullard A.M.I.E.E. was, during 1920, advertising these items as 'Valve Bases'.[1] At much the same time other manufacturers were using the terms 'valve sockets' or 'valve holders' to describe their products. By about 1925, however, the word 'valveholder' had come into general use following existing electrical parlance where the corresponding term was 'lampholder'. The new word was unambiguous and became the accepted British term thereafter. So, although it may be said that S.R. Mullard as an individual had started off on the wrong foot the Mullard Co. had, by 1926, fallen into line with the rest of the industry in accepting the common usage of the two terms. Many years later, however, Mullard once again got out of step in confusing the words base and valveholder. In Mullard valve manuals issued after World War II, where instructions were given for replacing obsolete valves with later types, the word base was invariably used instead of the correct term valveholder; viz.—'change base' or 'change base wiring'.

Still on the subject of nomenclature, criticism must now be voiced of the widespread and misleading British habit of misusing the term 'UX' as a blanket classification for all American pre-octal bases, or even the valves themselves. This usage arose after about 1937 following the introduction of British-made American type valves. Amongst manufacturers the chief offender was STC-Brimar who, not content with misusing the term UX as a synonym for 'American', added to the confusion by appending this designation to each individual pre-octal valve listed in their

143

1938–39 catalogue, thus 'Type 6A7 Pentagrid Converter (UX base).'

To Americans and others familiar with American terminology such usage was utterly incomprehensible as the term UX had been introduced in 1925 to distinguish the then new 'long pin' style of 4-pin base which had superseded the earlier UV style. And as for the UY base, well nobody in the U.K. ever seems to have heard of it! Even the highly respected *Wireless World* has, since 1940, been guilty of spreading confusion via the pages of its Valve Data Charts by captioning drawings of American type 5-, 6-, and 7-pin valve bases as 'UX'.[2]

No apology is offered for the foregoing diatribe which, it is hoped, will serve to set the record straight in the minds of present-day readers, not to mention future historians.

Early Bases and Sockets

Because a radio tube, like a lamp, has always been an expendable item it has similarly been necessary to provide some means whereby it can readily be connected into and disconnected from its associated circuitry. No matter how good a tube may be in respect of its performance, unless an effective and reliable method of connecting it up can be provided its full potential will never be realised. Thus the means of accomplishing this fundamental requirement has always been an important factor in tube development, even if it has not always received adequate recognition. From the simplest double-contact lamp base to complex multipin button bases is a long jump yet the basics have always remained the same—the need for low contact resistance, the need to resist atmospheric corrosion plus, in some cases, the need to withstand high operating temperatures. That these particular facets of base design have not always been accorded the attention they deserve can be observed by a critical examination of the many and varied styles of contact arrangements that have appeared over the years.

In tracing the development of tube bases it is not surprising to find that several early types were just ordinary lamp bases of the day pressed into use for radio work. Thus Fleming's original experimental two-electrode valves, being no more than electric lamps with a plate added, used either the standard American Edison screw bases or the original Swan base. Later, when commercial production was commenced, the standard British double-contact (BC) lamp base was used. Similarly the early De Forest Audions used a type of lamp base known as candelabra screw. In both America and Europe the standard E.S. lamp base has been used on certain types of rectifiers since the earliest days and such usage has continued until well into the post-World War II era. Similarly, the standard B.C., lamp base has been used in Britain and the continent for certain early types of rectifiers and transmitting tubes. In all cases the lamp base was used to provide the filament connections.

Because a minimum of three external connections is needed for any thermionic tube it was obviously necessary to provide an additional connection of some sort when using a lamp base on a tube. Initially this was done by bringing out the required extra connection(s) in the form of flying lead(s) but this arrangement had the drawback that the rather fragile leads were liable to be broken off by too frequent handling. In spite of this the original De Forest Audions retained the same form of connection throughout their production lifetime, a matter of nearly ten years.

It has to be admitted that it was the exigencies of military demands during World War I that gave rise to the development of standardised forms of 4-pin bases, in both America and Europe, and this in turn led to the adoption of respective national standards on both sides of the Atlantic after the war. So it was that the particular style of 4-pin base first used on the famous French wartime tubes, as well as being adopted as the British standard during the war, subsequently became the industry standard in both countries afterwards.

In Germany because of the wartime differences in tube basing arrangements the German peacetime designs initially followed that country's wartime ones. In carrying over their own wartime style of base the Germans were, of course, doing no more than had been done in Britain and France, and the practice was continued until about 1925. From this time the Franco-British style base was adopted as the German standard though for a short transitionary period tubes continued to be made with both types of base; the newly adopted style being known initially as 'engl-franz'. With Germany having 'joined the club' it could be fairly claimed that a European standard 4-pin base had finally arrived.

Prior to this time there had been in existence in Europe several different styles of 4-pin bases which can be classified as follows: the Franco-British-Dutch types based on the original French wartime design; the French Radiola 'Y' base and at least two different German types of which the 'Telefunken' style seems to have been the more common.[3] In addition, by 1924 some British, French, and Dutch manufacturers were also producing certain types of tubes fitted with the American UV style base. However, as the latter tubes were intended either for export or the servicing of imported American receivers their production should not be regarded as indicative of a trend within the industry. Some examples of European tubes fitted with metal-shell UV bases are: B.T-H. B4, Philips D4, Radio Micro R30.

As in the U.S. metal-shell bases remained in use up to 1925 or slightly later, after which time bakelite bases came into use. Another change occurring at this time was the use of hollow base pins in place of the earlier split pins.

144

A noticeable difference between European and American bakelite bases of the period was that while the latter were required to have a standardised diameter in order that they should fit the earlier UV sockets, the diameters of European tube bases could be varied to suit the individual maker's fancy. This led to each manufacturer using his own particular size and shape of base which in effect served as a sort of trademark; it was often possible to identify a particular make of tube simply by looking at the base.

Another feature which for many years distinguished European bases from American was the presence of resilient contact pins. As originally derived from the wartime French design the pins were bifurcated but after about 1923 most tube makers changed to the use of resilient pins formed by some other means. Originally the corresponding socket contacts were non-resilient but after about 1928 British practice fell into line with American in using resilient contacts. From this time onwards the use of double resiliency remained until the introduction of octal bases during 1937–38.

The earliest type of valveholder used with British and French valves consisted of four individually-mounted tubular metal contacts which were completely exposed and protruded above the surface on which they were mounted. Because the contacts were exposed it was possible to accidentally burn out the filament of a valve if an attempt were made to insert it while the HT battery remained connected during the process. Even though one-piece insulated valveholders were available as early as 1920 their design was such that there was still enough exposed metal on their top surfaces to create a hazard.

With the advent of dull-emitter valves with their more

Example of tube using a Franco-British 4-pin bakelite base c. 1926.

Example of the original French 4-pin metal base.

Example of a European tube using an American-style UV base c. 1924.

The safety cap (Prov. Pat.) which is now fitted to all Ediswan Valves. The filament pins are shorter in length than the plate and grid pins, thus avoiding any chance of them making surface contact with the wrong sockets.

Ediswan's 'Safety Cap' introduced in 1923.

delicate filaments the likelihood of burnt out filaments increased and in a commendable attempt to eliminate the hazard the firm of Ediswan, in 1923, introduced a patented type of base known as the 'Safety Cap'.[4] These Ediswan valves had shorter filament pins than normal which could not make contact until the longer grid and anode pins had been inserted first. The Safety Cap was a stop-gap measure which preceded the arrival of better valveholders some two years later. In 1925 the introduction of fully-insulated unitised valveholders having the upper portion their contacts recessed well below the surface effectively removed the hazard.

The introduction of later types of dull-emitter valves which from 1926 onwards had comparatively long and thin filaments which could vibrate if jarred during use gave rise to a problem known as microphony. When such valves were used as detectors the slightest jar or bump could cause a receiver to emit an audible microphonic howl. One solution to the difficulty was to add some form of damping to the filament during manufacture to elimi-

145

nate the tendency to vibrate but this procedure was not popular with valve makers due to manufacturing difficulties and increased cost. By far the most common method of alleviating microphony was by the use of special anti-microphonic valveholders. In the U.K. such holders were commonly used from about 1926 to 1933 until the development of valves with improved types of oxide-coated filaments rendered their use unnecessary.

Following American practice the use of skeleton or wafer valveholders became standard practice in British mass-produced receivers after about 1931.

The first American tubes to have all the lead-out wires terminated at one end of the bulb and to be equipped with a 4-contact base were produced by the Western Electric Co. early in 1915 for telephone work. Subsequently a modified version of the base was adopted by other companies for radio tubes. First application for radio purposes occurred with the production of tubes made by De Forest, GE, and WE for military purposes just prior to America's entry into World War I in 1916.

At this time two different base styles had come into use; one originated by De Forest for the U.S. Navy was approximately 1.25 inches in diameter and had three bottom contacts with the fourth connection being taken to a side-mounted locking pin, whilst the other style was originated by WE was 1.377 inches in diameter and had four contacts. The variation in diameters is emphasised because it was one of the basic differences preventing interchangeability even though both bases were otherwise somewhat similar.

The WE base was used on tubes made for the U.S. Army Signal Corps and was sub-divided into two variations differing in respect of the placement of the locking pin in relation to the base pins. In receiving type tubes the locking pin was positioned at right angles to the centre line of the grid and plate contacts, whilst in transmitting tubes it was rotated 40 degrees angularly to place it in line with the grid and F+ contacts. This was done in order to prevent accidental insertion of a receiving tube into a transmitting tube socket or vice versa. Other WE tubes such as telephone repeater types and later tubes used in theatre sound systems also used the 'transmitting' style locking pin placement.

Thus far there were in existence two different sized bases used on receiving and low power transmitting tubes, the three-contact one which became known as the Navy type and the four-contact one which formed the basis of the post-war 'UV' style. Another type of 3-contact base, used only on one specialised tube, type TB1, a regulator diode made by GE, differed in that while its dimensions and locking pin placement followed the existing 'Army' pattern the positioning of the contacts did not. Incidentally, the TB1 appears to be one of the few GE tubes to make use of a moulded insert to hold the contact pins, in contrast to the usual GE practice of using a ceramic disc

Example of 3-pin Navy base used on a Western Electric type 201A tube c. 1918.

fastened in a peripheral groove at the lower end of the base shell.

In the foregoing descriptions the word 'contact' has been used in preference to 'pin' as the actual contacts themselves were so short as to be little more than stubs, but hereafter for the sake of uniformity the word pin will be used.

After the war GE commenced making receiving tubes using the same type of base as had been used on their wartime productions: a seamless brass shell having four contact pins rivetted to a porcelain disc fastened to the lower end. Apart from the so-called 'Shaw' base (to be discussed later) the GE style base became the industry standard, retaining its original metal-sleeve form until 1924–25.

These early GE tubes were assigned type numbers commencing with the letters 'UV' which corresponded to the grouping in the UV section of the RCA catalogue. The first tubes to be so listed were types UV-200 and UV-201. It should be noted that the use of the UV prefix was not confined to vacuum tubes as other components such as RF and AF transformers were similarly marked. Examples of these are UV-713 and UV-712 respectively.

In recent years the growing interest in things historical has led to some speculation as to the reason for RCA's inconsistent method of cataloguing. The only definite information available states that the letter 'U' indicates a *unit*, as distinct from an *assembly*; after that it is a matter of guesswork. It seems logical to assume that the 'V' indicate vacuum tube, or even valve as the British term was not unknown and had been used by some independent manufacturers as far back as 1916. Also included in the UV category were ballast tubes and transmitting tubes using quite different styles of base. Attention is drawn to the fact that although RCA originally assigned a UV prefix to all types of tubes these letters had no significance in regard to identifying the type of base used on a particular tube. As a matter of fact there were no less than six completely different styles and sizes of bases used on tubes bearing the UV prefix to their type numbers.

From the foregoing it can be seen that the UV designation was never intended to be used as either a base or socket identification (sockets, incidentally, carried the prefix 'UR') even though the term later became commonly used for this purpose. Actually the need for a system of base identification did not arise for several years because of the very few different series of tubes in use at the time, each of which had individual styles of base. Thus storage battery tubes used the standard sized UV base whilst dry-cell tubes used a smaller version known simply as the '199' size. Initially the only other types of base were confined to two tubes, known as the WR-21 and WD-11, made by Westinghouse for use in their own receivers. Both these Westinghouse tubes quickly became obsolete and their base styles played no part in future developments. Only after the advent of the long-pin base in 1925 did it become desirable to incorporate some means of differentiating between the two styles of base by the use of a code letter in the type number. Because RCA decided to use the letter X in the type numbers of the tubes using the new style base the new bases were sometimes referred to as the 'X' type; conversely the older style base was then referred to as the 'V' type.

Prior to Westinghouse joining the so-called 'Radio Group' in 1921, GE and Westinghouse as competitors had each pursued separate paths in developing their own styles of tubes, tubes which differed not only in their characteristics and ratings but also in the types of bases used. The basing arrangements of the Westinghouse tubes followed the Franco-British practice of using long unequally-spaced contact pins, though these were hollow rather than bifurcated. Thus the Westinghouse tubes required resilient socket contacts in contrast to the Franco-British use of solid sockets. In the case of the WD-11 tube the anode pin was of a larger diameter than the remaining three; this being done to prevent the accidental insertion of a 1.1-volt tube into a socket wired for a 4-volt WR-21 tube. It is interesting to note that the idea of using a larger diameter anode pin was first seen on the wartime German Telefunken RE16 tube—enough said!

Because GE had not produced a 1.1-volt dry-cell tube

RCA apparently decided that it would be worthwhile to have Westinghouse produce a modified version of the WD-11 fitted with the standard sized UV base; a tube known as the WD-12 subsequently appeared late in 1923. Although intended to allow dry-cell operation of receivers using storage battery tubes the WD-12 was never widely used for the purpose, probably because GE had introduced thoriated-filament tubes earlier in the same year. A later version of the WD-12, known as the WX-12, was introduced towards the end of 1925; it differed in having a UX style bakelite base.

Apart from the bases developed by GE and Western Electric (the latter being restricted to use in WE tubes) the only other early base was one which became known as the 'Shaw standard' 4-pin type. This type of base, which was the brain-child of one Henry S. Shaw, had first been used on certain wartime tubes made by GE, De Forest, and Moorhead. The Shaw base was identical to the GE standard UV type in the matter of essential dimensions but differed in the method of manufacture. Whereas the GE base used a porcelain disc to hold the contact pins, in

Shaw UV type bases. The later version on the left is a one-piece bakelite moulding.

Example of a Shaw 4-pin base used on a De Forest type DV1 tube c. 1923.

the Shaw design the pins were embedded in a moulded insulator positioned in the lower end of the base. During manufacture some of the molten insulating substance was forced under pressure through four small holes in the lower edge of the base shell; the resultant protrusions serving to securely lock the insulator to the shell.

After the war Shaw bases continued to be used by Moorhead for the short time that company remained in existence, and by De Forest until about 1923. From 1920 onwards Shaw bases were usually provided with a nickel-plated finish, following European practice. In later years the Shaw Base Co., as successors to the Shaw Insulator Co., became one of the largest manufacturers of moulded bakelite bases, supplying such well-known tube makers as Arcturus and Majestic. Shaw UX type bakelite bases were even used on some British-made Osram valves for a short period around 1926, presumably as a stop-gap measure until the M-O. Valve Co. commenced its own production.

Radiotron tubes were first fitted with bakelite towards the end of 1924, the type WD-11 being one of the first types to be so fitted. In October 1924 bakelite-based UV-201A and UV-199 tubes were being advertised and from then on no further metal-based RCA receiving tubes were produced.

WD11 type base (L.). Note larger diameter anode pin. WR21 type base (centre), note identical contact size and spacing compared with Franco-British style (R.).

Two Moorhead World War I tubes using Franco-British bases made by Shaw.

Before continuing with the story of base developments a word of explanation concerning the side locking pin may be in order. Originally this little pin served two purposes —as a locating device to ensure that the tube was correctly positioned when it was being inserted into its socket, and then as a latching device after the tube had been given a slight clockwise twist in the socket. This combined locating/latching feature was retained on the most commonly used form of UV sockets though non-latching types were later produced by a few manufacturers.

The UV style base/socket arrangement had, with one exception,* an inherent design weakness wherein the spring contacts in the socket pressed only against the solder on the bottoms of the tube pins. This gave only a small area of contact which combined with the unsatisfactory nature of soft solder as a contact material often resulted in poor contacts at these points. Towards the end of 1924 some manufacturers, such as Cutler Hammer and Hart & Hegeman, brought out sockets in which contact was made to the sides instead of the bottom of the base pins. These sockets were of the straight push-in type without the twist-lock feature and may be regarded as being an intermediate step in the evolution of the later 'UX' style base/socket design.

The introduction of the long-pin base by RCA towards the end of 1925 marked an important step forward in the American tube industry as, at one sweep, the disadvantages of the old UV style base were done away with. The new UX style base, together with its associated socket, offered a far more positive form of connection between the base pins and socket contacts. At the same time the increased area of contact allowed a current of up to three amps to be handled. A third, albeit incidental, advantage was a reduction in the number of loose tube bases formerly caused by the twist-lock feature of the UV socket! Finally, the UX sockets were smaller and more compact and were easily adaptable to the so-called wafer or skeleton designs which were soon to come into use in mass-produced receivers using metal chassis.

In designing the new style base thought had been given to the matter of interchangeability with the older UV style. By a slight repositioning of the side pin on the new tubes they were enabled to fit both the old and new style sock-

*Many Western Electric tubes, mainly telephone repeater types, had their pins tipped with precious metal. Their sockets had contacts provided with special alloy areas.

148

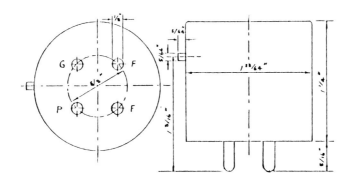

AMERICAN UV

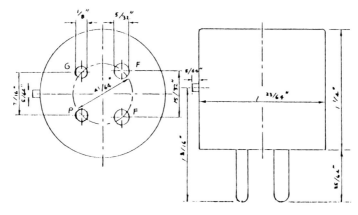

AMERICAN UX

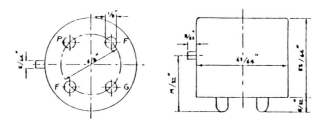

AMERICAN UV-199

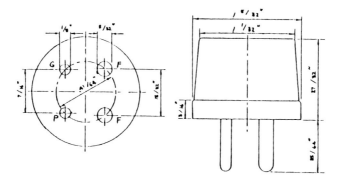

AMERICAN UX-199

149

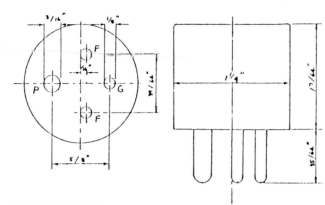

AMERICAN WD-11

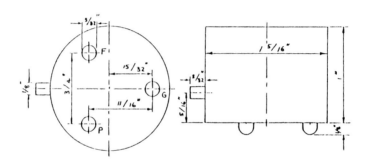

DE FOREST—U.S. NAVY

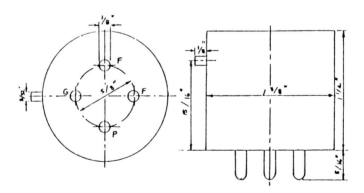

WESTERN ELECTRIC

150

ets. No planned obsolescence here! Because the four pins had to be equally spaced in order to achieve this interchangeability it was necessary to provide some other means of positioning the tube in its socket. This was accomplished by using larger diameter pins for the filament connections. With one exception (to be discussed shortly) the use of larger pins for the filament or heater connections was to become standard practice in the construction of all subsequent American tube bases produced prior to the advent of octal types in 1935.

Because moulded bakelite bases had come into use before the appearance of long-pin tubes it followed that such bases were automatically used for these tubes. However, there were one or two exceptions to be found. For example, the first Raytheon types BA and BH gaseous rectifiers were fitted with long-pin brass bases as were certain early Radiotron transmitting tubes.

After about 1930 the need for retaining the side locking pin on currently produced UX base tubes had passed due to the old-style UV sockets having become completely obsolete.

Two versions of the UV socket. The one on the left has the usual twist lock, the one on the right has a snap lock.

Because much early tube development took the form of the evolution of generic types brought about by the addition of further grids, the need for additional external connections, over and above the original four, soon made itself felt. A minor, or perhaps not so minor, problem confronting the makers of the first non-triodes was how best to provide for this requirement. There were three choices open:

1. Provide a terminal somewhere on the bulb surface.
2. Provide a terminal on the side of the base.
3. Provide an additional base pin.

At one time or another each of these methods has been used, sometimes in combination. The first method was open to objection on the grounds of cost as it was more difficult to achieve in factory production. It was seldom used unless circuit dictates made it unavoidable, as for example in the case of the screen-grid tube. The second method was the most widely used one in the case of double-grid tetrodes; it was also used with early European AF

pentodes where it was desired to promote the use of such tubes in existing receivers having 4-pin sockets. The third method, which although used in non-standard form, e.g., the British Thorpe K4 tetrode and French Radiola bi-grill tubes as early as 1924, did not come into general use in Europe until 1929.

With the introduction of the first American screen-grid tube, type UX-222, in 1927, a new term was added to the American radio vocabulary—'grid cap'. Rather obviously the term originated as a means of identifying the additional external connection needed with this type of tube. In the case of screen-grid tubes circuit requirements called for a wide separation of grid and plate connections and a top contact was the most practicable way of achieving that end. In practice the grid cap took the form of a small metal thimble, having a diameter of 0.036 inches, cemented to the top of the bulb. To make connection with the cap a small push-on connector known as the grid clip was used.

For all American radio receiving tubes it has always been standard practice to use the top cap for the grid connection, while in Europe it was always the plate connection that was taken to the top of the bulb. At least that was the way things started off but after about 1933 European practice gradually fell into line with American. Initially there was also another difference in the actual style of the top connector used on European tubes, where it took the form of an insulated screw terminal. One reason for the use of an insulated connector was that with the plate connection in an exposed position this point was at a relatively high potential with respect to any adjacent earthed metal.

Because the change to American practice could not be accomplished overnight some British manufacturers, notably Mullard, issued valves in either grid-at-top or plate-at-top versions, e.g., VP4A or VP4B. This was be-

Osram VMS4 valve using hybrid top connector (1933).

151

cause it was still necessary to provide the older style valves for replacements in existing receivers. For a short period during 1933 some Osram and Marconi screen-grid valves, e.g., type VMS4, were fitted with a dual-purpose hybrid style of top cap which retained the original bakelite skirted lower part of the connector but fitted it with a solid metal terminal top. As this metal top was the same diameter as the newer thimble caps the user had the choice of using either a snap-on clip or the older lug connector.

When the American metal tubes were introduced in 1935 their comparatively small dimensions called for a proportionately smaller grid cap; thus the officially designated 'miniature' grid cap arrived. With the introduction of glass octal-base tubes a year later, using the same size grid caps, the bottom of the thimble had to be flared out to provide a large enough surface area to ensure satisfactory bonding to the glass bulb. This style of cap was known as the 'skirted miniature' and remained the future standard for all receiving tubes requiring a top connection, including later television types which had the plate connection in this position, e.g., type 6BQ6.

In two cases the Americanisation of European top connections did not go all the way. When, in 1934, the first continental side-contact tubes appeared they had to use the standard sized American grid caps for the simple reason that the miniature style had not yet been evolved in the U.S. Subsequently when Philips introduced their smaller 'Red E' side-contact series in 1937 they continued to make use of the older style grid cap. Similarly the older style cap was used by British Mazda and Canadian Rogers on their octal-based series which also appeared in 1937.

The first standardised American 5-pin base, because it was a national standard, also qualified as the world's first standard 5-pin type. Although 5-pin bases had earlier been used in several European countries such bases were peculiar to individual manufacturers and never became national standards within those countries.

In May 1927 the first tube to use a 5-pin base was the Radiotron UY-227; it was also the first, and almost the only, Radiotron to carry the prefix UY in its type number as it had but a single companion, the UY-224(A). This was because by the time further 5-pin tubes had been issued (in 1929) RCA had adopted a policy of dropping all existing prefixes in favour of the letters 'RCA'; thus when types 235 and 247 appeared in 1931 they were

marked RCA-235 and RCA-247 respectively.* Another factor which resulted in all tube manufacturers eventually dropping type prefixes altogether was the growing practice of using briefer designations when speaking and writing of tubes whereby the first digit of the three-letter type number was omitted. This became general practice from 1930 and remained so until the introduction of the new R.M.A. type numbering system in 1933.

The UY base and its later variants were unique among American long-pin styles in that all the pins were of uniform diameter and were unequally spaced; the latter feature being used as a means of positioning a tube in its socket. In other words it was the only long-pin base that did not make use of larger diameter filament/heater pins as an indexing device. This point is stressed for the benefit of non-American readers as it will frequently be found, when referring to tube data published outside the U.S., that in drawings of base connections the American 5-pin base is depicted as having larger diameter filament/heater pins. Alas! both the respected *Wireless World* and Brans' *Vade Mecum* have been guilty of this minor sin.

Although the 5-pin base was no longer in current use on receiving tubes produced after 1933 its use was continued on transmitting tubes, for example the type 807, which arrived on the scene several years later and incidentally remained in current production until long after the end of World War II.

American UY 5-pin bases. Note all contact pins are the same diameter.

Multi-Pin

The need for bases having more than five contact pins did not really arise until 1932 when the advent of later versions of existing generic tube types called for six external connections. In the case of indirectly-heated output pentodes, for example, initial European practice was to provide a side-mounted screw terminal on the 5-pin base but this method was not acceptable to the American tube industry. In general it may be said that, right from the ear-

Examples of UY bakelite bases made by Shaw. The base on the right has the trademark—S. B. Co. c. 1931.

*Some independent tube makers, for example Ken Rad, continued to use the UY prefix on these two types for a short period.

liest days of bakelite base tubes, the provision of external connections except by means of base pins was not favoured in the U.S.

The use of 6-pin bases originated in the U.S. initially to equip certain indirectly-heated tubes such as output pentodes and RF pentodes; examples being types 42 and 58,[5] respectively. Although earlier versions of both these basic types had been issued in 5-pin form, e.g., types 38 and 39/44, they soon became obsolete. Another reason for the early adoption of 6-pin bases was the American practice of providing an external connection for the suppressor grids of all i.h. RF pentodes produced after about the middle of 1932. At this time, too, the advent of new types of tubes, such as duo-diode triodes and voltage-doubler rectifiers also called for six external connections.

With the rapid development of new tubes, coupled with variations of existing types, which occurred from 1932 onwards the need soon arose for a 7-pin base. The first use of such a base occurred with the production of the type 59 output pentode, a tube which had an externally-connected third grid. The base itself was officially described as 'medium 7-pin' but was commonly referred to as 'large' 7-pin to distinguish it from the later small 7-pin base. It must qualify as the least used of any base as it was fitted to only four receiving tubes, the types 53, 59, 2B6, and 6A6. Because all other American tubes needing 7-pin bases were physically smaller than these four, the need arose for a correspondingly smaller base—hence the arrival of the 'small 7-pin' base. The smaller base was first used on such tubes as the types 2A7 and 6B7 which appeared about the middle of 1933.

Example of tube using American large 7-pin base c. 1932.

Up to the time when 7-pin bases were introduced the development of new bases had been simply a matter of adding extra contact pins as the need arose. However, with the introduction of metal tubes in 1935 advantage was taken of the opportunity to design a new standardised base suitable for all types of tubes. So it was that the 8-pin 'octal' base arrived on the scene and for a while it seemed that future requirements in respect of the number of base pins had been adequately catered to.

As things turned out, unfortunately, it was not long before the development of certain types of tubes tended to be restricted by the lack of sufficient external connections. This occurred because the octal base originally used one pin solely for grounding the metal envelope thus leaving only seven active pins. Both metal and metal-shell GT types were so affected but after the appearance of GT types with bakelite bases (introduced during World War II to conserve metal) the No. 1 pin was no longer required as a ground connection and became available for use as an electrode connection. The production of such tubes as the type 6SN7GT, a single-ended dual triode, was made possible only by the availability of the formerly sacrosanct No. 1 pin.

A criticism (seemingly voiced more outside the U.S. than within) of the octal base, though in no way disparaging to the design as a whole, concerned an allegedly high hum level exhibited by certain tubes when used as first stage AF amplifiers. Such criticism arose because the widely spaced heater pins supposedly gave rise to heater-induced hum. The author believes this criticism to have been largely unjustified for the following reasons: at the time of their introduction all first-stages tubes, e.g., types 6F5, 6Q7, 6J7, had top-mounted grid connections in order to lessen hum pickup. Tests published by the U.S. Bureau of Standards in 1952 indicated that when used with well-designed associated circuitry the types 6F5 and 6J7 developed less than 3 microvolts of heater-induced hum at their grids. Even this low figure was improved upon with the introduction of single-ended versions such as the 6SF5 which exhibited a figure of under one microvolt. It should be mentioned that all these tubes were ordinary run-of-the-mill receiving types and not special quality types; indeed the latter were unknown at the time.

From a practical point of view the octal base offered one advantage never exceeded by any other design—unsurpassed ease of tube insertion even when working 'blind'. This design feature was accomplished by providing an extension of the bakelite base which was located in the centre of the pin circle and protruded slightly below the ends of the pins. This central 'spigot', as it was sometimes termed, was fitted with a guide key which mated with a corresponding keyway in the socket. So efficient was the design that not only was it widely adopted outside the U.S. but later series of tubes such as the U.S. loctal and the German metal used adaptations of the basic octal idea.

153

Further proof of its effectiveness may be found in its long-continued use in certain applications such as television horizontal output and damper tubes which remained in current production up to 1963—a period of nearly 30 years. Quite apart from its use on tubes the octal base/socket was early adapted for use as an 8-pin plug-connector, being widely used as a wiring connector as well as a base for such renewable components as vibrators, electrolytic capacitors, and electro-mechanical relays.

The final American tube base development, wherein a separate cemented-on base shell was used, occurred with the production of the so-called 'Loktal' range of tubes by Sylvania in 1939. The loctal tubes, as they were later known, were notable for the first use of contact pins embedded directly in the bottom of the glass bulb—the so-called 'button base'. The use of a separate base shell was inherent in the loctal design, it being required to support a locating spigot as well as for shielding purposes. By making use of the metal spigot as a ground connection for the base shell all eight pins were consequently available for electrode connections thus avoiding the limitation of the single-ended octal design.

Tubes using Loktal bases (Circa 1940)

Unlike its octal predecessor the loctal base was fitted with a locking device from which the name of the series was derived. A groove near the tip of the spigot was designed to mate with an encircling spring clip located in the tube socket. In the author's opinion this lock-in feature was given undue prominence in contemporary advertisements which carried the implication that other, i.e., octal-based, tubes were liable to fall out of their sockets under certain conditions of use. Not so! Such advertising seemed to be a case of making a virtue out of necessity for without the lock-in feature the loctal tubes would have been much more likely to have fallen out of their sockets, for example, when used in mobile service. The comparative shortness of the pins coupled with their small diameter made it almost impossible to design a socket which could hold the tube firmly without some sort of locking device.

Compared with RCA's metal tubes the loctals suffered from the same disadvantage that affects all tubes having cemented-on bases; the base was liable to come adrift in service. With the loctals this problem was accentuated by the difficulty in removing a tube from its socket caused by the inbuilt locking device. To avoid loosening the base shell the recommended procedure was to lever up one edge of the shell before withdrawing the tube.

Hard on the heels of the loktals came RCA's 1.4-volt miniature types, released early in 1940. These tubes were the first to use a 7-pin 'glass button' base and, as in the case of the loktals, extensions of the tubes' element mounting rods provided the external contact pins; henceforth all new bases were simply developments of this idea. By the time the first indirectly-heated miniature tubes appeared America had become involved in World War II and consequently the development of tubes for military use took precedence over everything else. When a military demand arose for an indirectly-heated miniature type it was logical, or at least expedient, to use the existing 7-pin style which factories were already equipped to produce, rather than start afresh with a new design. The first of such wartime tubes were types 6C4, 6J6, and 6AG5 produced during 1942.

After the war the 7-pin base was standardised for all new T5½ miniature types produced for peacetime applications. It was not long, however, before the limitation in the number of base pins made itself felt; as three pins were needed for heater and cathode connections only four remained for other tube elements. Because the tubes were single ended they actually offered fewer external connections than did earlier types. This meant that some types of tubes such as duo-diode pentodes and triode-hexodes were automatically excluded from the range.

Next on the list of base developments came the 9-pin 'noval' range using slightly larger T6½ bulbs. In 1948 RCA released the first novals, types 12AU7 and 12AX7, which were both twin triodes featuring tapped heaters. No attempt was made to introduce a full range of noval-based tubes at this time, production being limited to those types which could not be accommodated on 7-pin bases. The so-called 'neo-noval' base was simply the existing noval style as fitted to tubes having larger (T9) bulbs.

In 1959 a larger version of the noval base known as 'novar' was developed for use on certain high power tubes, for example, types 6AY3 and 12CJ5, using the T12 size bulb. An almost identical European base, known as the 'magnoval', differed only in that the pins were 0.04 inches in diameter compared with 0.05 for the novar.

In 1961 GE introduced a 12-pin base which was used on a new series of their tubes known as 'Compactrons'. Some two years later RCA produced similar tubes using the same base which was referred to as 'decar'. This represented the final step in base development of American all-glass tubes.

Europe After 1929

In both Britain and the continent a standardised 5-pin base was somewhat slower in appearing than had been the case in America. This was partly due to the later development of all-electric receivers in Europe and partly because of the need for any standard to be mutually acceptable by the countries concerned. In view of the differences in later developments where British and continental practices sharply diverged it is surprising that a standardised European 5-pin base ever eventuated.

Originally France and Germany used two completely different styles of 5-pin bases but in 1929, apparently by common consent, those two countries together with Holland adopted a new style of 5-pin base. It was now possible to speak of a continental standard.[6] The new base, which can be described as a scaled-down version of an

The standardised European 5-pin base introduced in 1929.

Example of a British 5-pin valve having a side terminal for the sixth connection (1930).

existing French 5-pin type was constructed by using the existing standard European 4-pin base as a starting point and then placing an additional pin in the centre of the others.

Although no 6-pin base as such was initially developed in Europe, the demand for a sixth external connection, which arose with the advent of indirectly-heated output pentodes in 1932, was initially provided for by the addition of a terminal on the side of the existing 5-pin base.

By the end of 1928 it was apparent that British valve makers could no longer afford to delay the introduction of an industry standard in the matter of basing AC valves. Lack of standardisation was having the effect of retarding the development of mains-operated receivers. Up to this time individual valve makers had each gone their own way with the result that there were five different forms of AC valves on the market. Apart from the need for a standardised 5-pin base for AC valves there was also a lesser need for such a base in the case of directly-heated output pentodes. Presumably because of the existing standard in continental Europe the same type of 5-pin base was adopted as the standard of the British industry. Now it could be called a European standard.

First British usage of the new base was on directly-heated output pentodes and indirectly-heated triodes.[7] In the former case the new base was also used on certain valves which had previously been fitted with 4-pin bases having side-mounted terminals. This procedure had the unfortunate result that the same valve type became available with a choice of bases. It was a small price to pay, however, if it meant that there was now an industry standard.

As stated earlier there was never a European 6-pin base as such but a type of 6-pin base did come into use by certain manufacturers. Strictly speaking it was not a true base style but was a sort of backward development of the existing continental 7-pin standard formed by the simple expedient of omitting one pin. As far as can be ascertained, the only two tubes to use this base were Philips type E444 and E463; that is, unless one counts the Mullard equivalent of the E444, the type SD4. The Continental 7-pin base was introduced in 1934 being mainly used by Telefunken, Tungsram, and Philips-Valvo. Examples are: Philips KF2 and Telefunken BCH1.

Because 6-pin bases were never used on British valves a jump was made from five to seven pins when in 1933 the first 7-pin types appeared. One of the first valves to use the new base was the Marconi-Osram type MHD4, a review of which appeared in *Popular Wireless* for June 10, 1933. For the next six years the 7-pin base remained in current use, even after the introduction of octal types.

In 1934 another jump in sequence occurred with the arrival of the first 9-pin valves.[8] No other countries ever used 9 pins on bakelite-based tubes and even in the U.K.

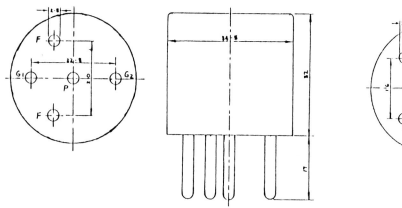

FRENCH BI-GRILLE 5-pin

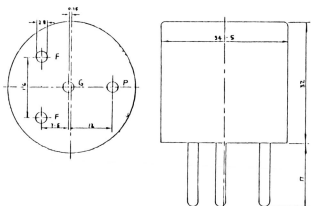

FRENCH RADIOLA 4-pin

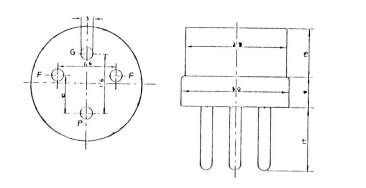

FRANCO-BRITISH 4-pin

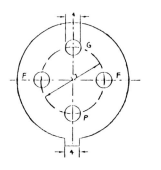
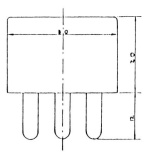

TELEFUNKEN 4-pin

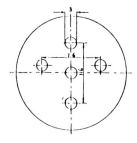

EUROPEAN STANDARD 5-pin

they were not common. Originally Mazda, as the largest maker, listed but two 9-pin types—a triode-pentode and a QPP double pentode. Apart from Hivac and Mullard no other manufacturers made any 9-pin types.

Another event in 1934, which at the time seemed to pass unnoticed, was the introduction of the continental side-contact base on to the British market by Mullard.[4] While its introduction on the continent could be regarded as an attempt at standardisation in that area, its appearance on the British scene only added to the growing confusion. The first side-contact valves marketed consisted of six types, two of which were rectifiers. All types carried a 200 mA heater rating and were intended for series-heater operation in AC/DC service, although three types having 13-volt heaters could also be used for car radio work.

From America use of the octal base spread first to Britain in 1937 and then to certain other European countries, notably Italy and France. The main effect of this importation was to increase the number of different bases in use rather than to render existing bases obsolete and for many years the 'battle of the bases' continued to bedevil the British industry. With two of the largest valve producers under American control it is perhaps surprising that the American influence did not make itself felt even earlier but, be that as it may, 1937 must be regarded as a landmark date in the history of British valve making.

Following M-O.V.'s lead Brimar, as the first British manufacturer to produce a comprehensive range of pre-octal American type valves, released a range of octals in 1938 which by the end of the year, had grown to include 21 different types.[10] Whether all those listed were actually of British manufacture is open to question as it is known that Brimar marketed many American-made tubes under their own label. By 1940 all major British makers, with the exception of Mazda, were producing at least some octal-based types with the score reading at that time: Brimar 47, Osram 37, Mullard 21.

Mazda's omission from the ranks stemmed from what can only be regarded as an anti-American attitude which led in 1937 to an attempt to persuade the leading British valve makers to join with them in producing a completely new series of valves which it was hoped would become an industry standard. The new valves were to be fitted with a modified version of the American octal base having a different arrangement of pin spacings and connections.

The hoped-for co-operation was not forthcoming because, for one thing, the proposal came rather late in the day. By this time Brimar and M-O.V. were already committed to the American standard, whilst Mullard had been making increasing use of the continental side-contact bases, leaving only Cossor uncommitted. So it was that, in the face of industry apathy if not actual opposition, Mazda decided to proceed alone—a decision which inevitably resulted in their becoming 'the odd man out'.

Early in 1938 the first Mazda octals were announced and

supplies became available later in the year. Even though they were used by two of the leading set makers, McMichael and Murphy, they had no real chance of dominating the market for in spite of having a respectable parentage the Mazda octal can only be described as a bastard. The only real justification for the introduction of a new base would have been on the basis of its acceptance by a majority of B.V.A. members, and this did not occur.

By 1938 the number of different bases in current use in the U.K. had reached fourteen, of which nine were of non-British origin. It should be explained that valves with American type bases were needed to service imported American receivers as well as for initial equipment of the increasing of British receivers using American type valves. Apart from this an export market existed for British-made American type valves. Even so there was a widespread feeling that there were too many bases in use. *Wireless World* was to comment editorially and rather wryly in 1938:

'The number of different valve bases is fortunately not yet equal to the number of valves, . . . If we have not yet reached the condition of a different base for every valve, we are approaching the state of every valve having different connections'.[11]

But by 1940 things had worsened, for the same journal was moved to remark:

'The evergrowing diversity of valve base connections in use in this country—there are now well over 200 distinct variations—has compelled us to modify our former method of presentation'.[12]

The main development on the continental scene was the introduction of side-contact bases by Philips and Telefunken during 1934. Tungsram, too, made side-contact tubes whilst Mullard also produced a limited number of types. Although most widely used and best known in its 8-contact form (Philips Cap P), the side-contact base was also made in a 5-contact form; the latter being used only on duo-diode detector tubes. First production consisted of 4-volt AC and 200 mA AC/DC types which were followed in 1938 by a range of 6.3-volt types. Their arrival signalled the end of the 4-volt era in Europe, or at least confirmed a trend which had been apparent since the introduction of the octal base.

Although Germany had been one of the first countries to use side-contact tubes, production of these was confined to 4-volt AC and 200 mA AC/DC types. The first German use of 6.3-volt heaters occurred in 1938 when Telefunken issued a range of all-metal tubes fitted with 8-pin bases. The base had some slight resemblance to the American octal but was fitted with 'waisted' pins which formed a means of locking the tube to its socket. Metal-glass versions of these tubes were made by Philips, Tungsram, and Valvo.

The final European pre-war development in tube bases occurred late in 1939 when Philips introduced their first all-glass tubes, types EF50 and EE50. These two types were broadly similar to the American loctal series but used nine contact pins.

Following the end of the war only one base of British origin appeared on the scene, and, as in an earlier case, not all manufacturers agreed to adopt it. The similarity extended even further as the same politics came into play. Once again it was Mazda who proposed a new base for what was intended to be an industry standard for miniature type valves and once again Brimar and M-O.V. refused to 'play ball'. This time, however, Mullard joined with Mazda in producing the B8A miniature, as they were called.

The base used on the British miniatures had eight contact pins and was fitted with a metal shell which gave the series some resemblance to the American loctals. In addition a small 'pimple' on the side of the base shell, in conjunction with a latch incorporated in the socket, formed a combined indexing and locking arrangement. The valves made by Mazda differed from Mullard in having a long guide pin located in the centre of the contact pin circle, but this did not affect the interchangeability of the two makes.

British Mazda octal base (right) compared with standard American type (left). Note difference in pin spacings and spigot diameter.

American standard. This difference did not affect the interchangeability of the two series. Examples of Philips and Mullard tubes in this series are types ECH21 and UBl21.

Brimar, Cossor (later Emitron), and Ferranti all produced exact counterparts of the most popular types of American loctals, using American type numbers. Marconi-Osram in 1947 produced a range of near-loctal valves which, although fitting the standard loctal socket, differed in other respects. The bases were of two-piece construction using an aluminium shell which was spun over the edge of a bottom disc which in turn carried the centre spigot. The bottom disc was made of die-cast alloy, except in the case of output valves and rectifiers when moulded bakelite was used instead. It may be mentioned that, however, that this rule was not invariably followed as variations have been sighted. As in the case of standard loctal types the same British base classification of B8B was used. Examples of valves in this range are types KT91, W81, and X81.

The first British-made miniature valves were either identical to, or patterned on, the American designs which also appeared in 1947; at first only as isolated specialised types.

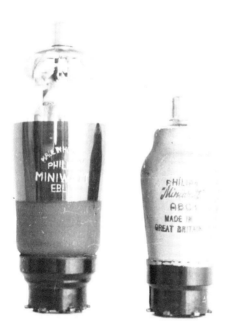

Examples of Continental side-contact bases, known by Philips as Cap P. c. 1938.

Other base styles appearing in post-war Europe were the American loctal and American 7-pin miniature. These were followed by the 'noval' and 'magnoval'. Philips and Mullard were early on the scene with a limited range of 'near loctals', the bases of which differed slightly from the

B10B Valveholders

McMurdo supply special valveholders for the new 10 pin (Decal) based valves type B10B, moulded in polypropylene and phenol formaldehyde. Available for printed circuits or for chassis mounting.

During the period of their currency most British firms made at least some B7G miniatures, as they were known, with Brimar producing the largest range. American type 7-pin miniature tubes were also produced in Holland and Germany from about 1949, and later in other European countries. At much the same time the design was also adopted in Japan as a post-war standard.

British-made versions of RCA's noval design first appeared in the U.K. in 1951 when Mullard introduced three types intended for television use. As in the case of the 7-pin miniatures, the noval design was soon taken up by Philips and Telefunken whence it grew to be the world's most standardised and widely produced type. At the time of writing production continues in some European countries as well as in Japan, Brazil, and Mexico.

The final European development was the introduction of a 10-pin base known as 'decal' or B10B in Great Britain. This base was used on only a very few multiple tubes which required more external connections than could be provided in the 9-pin noval series.

Tube and valve bases to 1940

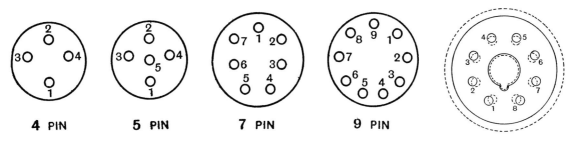

4 PIN   **5 PIN**   **7 PIN**   **9 PIN**

BRITISH

The illustration at the extreme right show the difference between the Mazda octal and the standard American octal (dotted outline).

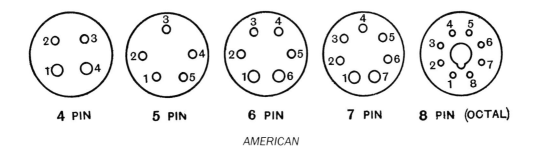

4 PIN   **5 PIN**   **6 PIN**   **7 PIN**   **8 PIN (OCTAL)**

AMERICAN

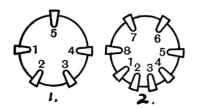   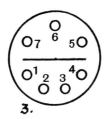   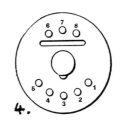   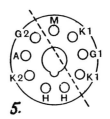

CONTINENTAL

    1. 5-pin side contact   *4. German octal (1939)*
    2. 8-pin side contact   *5. 9-pin 'All glass' (1939)*
    3. 7-pin standard

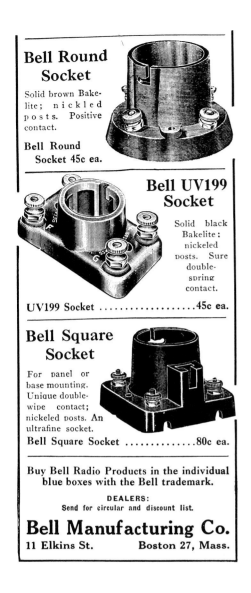

REFERENCES

1. See advt. of S.R. Mullard, *Wireless World,* July 10, 1920.

2. See, for example, *Wireless World,* Valve Data, May 1940, p. 252.

3. See, for example, *Philips Receiving Valve Catalogue,* 1926.

4. See, for example, advt. Edison Swan Electric Co. Ltd., *Wireless World & Electrical Review,* Dec. 27, 1923, p. ad. xi.

5. See advt. Cable Tube Corp., inside front cover, *Radio Craft,* June 1932.

6. A Telefunken receiver model T9 bearing a factory inspection date 21-10-28 used tubes having such bases.

7. Valves of Today, *Wireless World,* Oct. 2, 1929, pp. 376–377.

8. See *Wireless World Valve Data* supplement, Nov. 30, 1934.

9. Ibid.

10. See *Brimar Valve Catalogue,* No. P14/38.

11. See editorial *Wireless World,* Nov. 1938.

12. See editorial *Wireless World,* May 1940.

Chapter Twenty

Bulbs

Because the glass bulbs used in the making of radio tubes have varied considerably in size and shape over the years a word on this aspect of tube development is included here. In America, particularly, the fact that the electric lamp manufacturers initially played a major part in the large scale production of radio tubes resulted in the use of standardised lamp bulbs for this purpose. Existing standardised dimensions and their associated specifications were thus carried over into radio use and eventually became accepted as industry standards.

Briefly, the basic shapes were globular, tubular, straight-sided tapered and pear-shaped; they were designated 'G', 'T', 'S', and 'PS' respectively. Associated with these letters were two numerals which indicated the maximum bulb diameter expressed in eighths of an inch. For example, S-14 indicated a straight-sided tapered bulb having a nominal diameter of 1¾ inches while T-12 indicated a tubular bulb 1½ inches in diameter, and so on.

The true pear-shaped bulb was not normally used on receiving tubes though the description 'pear-shaped' has sometimes erroneously been applied to the 'S' style. The globular or spherical bulb, apart from its use on the early De Forest Audions, was not normally used on radio tubes, though there were one or two exceptions. For example, some Schickerling tubes made in 1924 had globular bulbs as did some Daven AC tubes marketed late in 1927. The most well-known tubes to use globular bulbs were those made by Western Electric for telephone use. Examples of other WE tubes with globular bulbs are types 205B, 216B, and VT2.

After its introduction on the first Radiotron/Cunningham tubes in 1920 the S-14 bulb became an industry standard for the next twelve years, it being used on all 5-volt battery tubes as well as on such early AC types as UX-226, UY-224, and UY-227. Tubular bulbs were preferred for use on dry-cell operated tubes such as types WD-11, WD-12, and UV/UX-199 and were even used on the first 2-volt types issued in 1930. In 1932 the so-called 'ST' bulbs were introduced and rapidly supplanted the earlier style. All such bulbs had a characteristic 'stepped' shape

with the upper section being of a smaller diameter than the main section. The designation 'ST' was derived from the combination of the 'S' and 'T' shapes.

With the introduction of 1.4-volt dry-cell battery tubes by Sylvania in August 1938 the then obsolete tubular bulb reappeared on the scene, following an ancient tradition for this class of tube. Later in 1938 when the first Hytron Bantam GT and Philco Loktal tubes were issued it was obvious that tubular bulbs had come to stay. Tubes had once again become tubular! The trend was continued as GT type tubes gradually replaced G types, and by the late 1950s ST bulbs had become obsolete.

On the European scene globular bulbs had first been used during World War I on British and French military tubes. After the war globular bulbs remained in common use up to 1924. As in the U.S., tubular bulbs were also quite common in the early days and with the arrival of the first dull-emitter valves during 1923–24 became the preferred shape with British valve makers. From about 1925 a straight-sided tapered bulb was used by most European manufacturers but such bulbs did not follow existing lamp bulb shapes and sizes. In no other countries did a national standard for radio use emerge as it had done in the U.S. Each manufacturer tended to use an individual style of bulb which in effect served as a sort of trade-mark and often made it possible to recognise a particular make by the shape of the bulb. This state of affairs existed up to the advent of miniaturisation following World War II. Only in those countries where American style tubes were made could there be said to be any standardisation of bulb shapes and sizes.

The American ST-style bulb came into use in Europe during 1934 and, as in the U.S., quickly supplanted the earlier shape. However, some manufacturers continued to issue certain types of tubes fitted with the older style bulbs for quite a long period, in some cases up to 1937.

Another aspect of bulb development was the change that took place, roughly within the first decade of tube manufacture, in the manufacturing technique used for sealing off after evacuation. Following electric lamp practice an

162

Outline Dimensions of RCA Radiotron
and Cunningham Radio Tube Types

This chart of tube dimensions is to be used in conjunction with the text.   The bulb reference number for each tube is given under its Characteristics.

The prefix letters of the bulb designation indicate the bulb shape; as S for "straight side," T for "tubular," ST for a combination of tubular and straight side, or "dome type." The suffix numbers of the bulb designations indicate the nominal maximum diameter of the bulb in eighths of inches, i.e., the diameter of the S-12 is 12 eighths, or 1½".

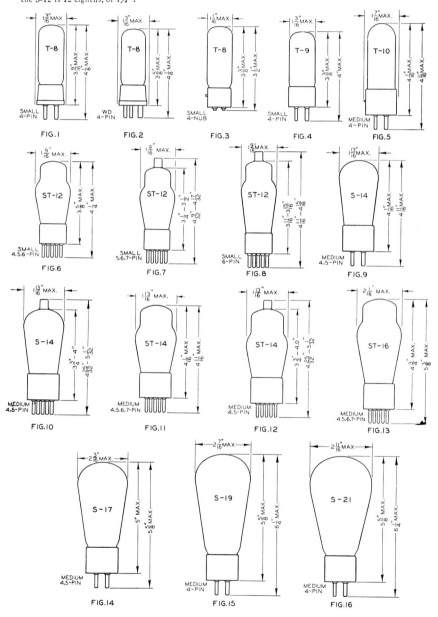

American bulb shapes and dimensions to 1933.

external seal-off point was located on the top of the bulb, except in the case of some double-ended tubes where it became necessary to locate the point elsewhere on the bulb surface.

Again following lamp-making practice the radio tube industry changed to the use of 'stem sealed' bulbs from 1924–25 onwards, though because it entailed the use of new machinery the change could not be made overnight. Partly because the presence of a tip seal was such a readily apparent feature which tended to look old fashioned once tipless bulbs had appeared, American manufacturers were the quickest to complete the changeover. To think the jaunty tip which is nowadays so admired by tube collectors so quickly became obsolete! A notable exception was to be found in the case of Western Electric tubes which retained their seal-off tips until the 1930s.

While standard sized tubes continued to use tipless bulbs thereafter this form of construction could not be used in the case of 'midget' tubes which appeared in the middle 1930s. Finally the advent of the first button-base miniature tubes in 1940 marked a return to tip sealing, a feature which remained inherent in the construction of all miniature types.

In the early days the bulbs of all tubes were completely clear, at least when they were new, but after a period of use they often became darkened due to evaporated filament material condensing on the inside walls. Sometimes enough of the tungsten filament material could accumulate in one place to cause a small silvery patch to appear. This is mentioned in order that it is not confused with the later gettering process which resulted in all or part of the bulb acquiring a silvery appearance.

Probably the earliest getter material used was red phosphorus and this imparted a pinkish tinge to the bulbs of tubes using it. With the advent of thoriated filaments during 1923 came the use of magnesium gettering. In tubes such as the 201-A a tiny pellet of magnesium was attached to each side of the plate structure and after firing the entire inner surface of the bulb became coated with condensed magnesium, imparting a mirror like appearance to

it. In the case of early oxide-coated filament tubes, such as types 112-A and 171-A, the practice was to place the getter pellet on one side only of the plate. Later still the getter material was attached to a tiny inverted cup or tray which enabled the vaporised material to be 'aimed' in a desired direction—usually towards one side of the lower part of the bulb.

Metallising

Throughout most of the history of tube production the outer bulb surface has normally been left in its natural state but there was a period when 'metallised' bulbs were used. Metallising consisted in spraying a coating of zinc on the outside of the bulb, the purpose of which was to form an electrical shield. For this reason it was not normally used on output tubes and rectifiers but there are cases where even these types were so treated.

Originally introduced in Germany by Telefunken late in 1929 metallising then spread to England where it was first used in 1931. In the same year Grigsby-Grunow (Majestic) took up the idea in the U.S. where they were the only company to make metallised tubes. In Canada the affiliated Rogers-Majestic Co. also adopted metallising in 1931 and continued to use it long after the demise of American Majestic.

Amongst European manufacturers Philips of Holland although not using the process until 1933 nevertheless probably produced more types of metallised tubes than any other company. Unlike others Philips were not content to leave the applied coating in its natural grey colour but enlivened its appearance with a gold coloured finish; later when 6.3-volt side-contact tubes were introduced in 1936 a red paint was used.

Spray shielding continued in use in the U.K. and Canada up to and during World War II when many military tubes were produced in this form. After the war Mullard continued with their spray-shielded octal-based Red E series which remained in current use until about 1950. Marconi-Osram also issued a few spray-shielded octal types in the early post-war years.

Chapter Twenty-One

Some American Independents

De Forest After 1922

Late in 1923 the De Forest Radio Telephone & Telegraph Co. moved from New York to Jersey City and production of a new range of Audions was commenced. By this time De Forest himself had severed connections with the company though he allowed the use of his name in advertising in such a manner as to make it seem that he was personally responsible for the production of De Forest Audions.

The first tubes known to have been produced at the new location were types DV1, DV2, DV6, and DV6A. The last two so closely resembled the earlier type 20 that it is now generally believed by historians that they were in fact the earlier tube disguised under a new type number. All four types were fitted with nickel plated Shaw bases but the last two were later issued with Isolantite bases.

Towards the end of 1924 the De Forest Company underwent yet another reorganisation which resulted in a name change to the De Forest Radio Company and from this time an increased range of tubes was produced. The first three issued by the new company, types DV2, DV3, and DV5,[1] were initially fitted with bakelite bases but during 1925 a change was made to the use of Isolantite as a base material.[2] For the next two years Isolantite bases were a distinctive, though not unique, feature of De Forest tubes and by 1927 no less than 20 different types had been produced. A large number of these were storage battery types carrying the standard 5-volt filament rating and even allowing for the fact that many tubes in the range were duplicated by being issued in two different base styles (UV and UX), it still left a lot more types than were produced by other manufacturers.

In this respect the De Forest Co. was following European practice where it was not uncommon for individual manufacturers to produce as many as five or six different types within a particular filament voltage grouping. And this was in the days before the introduction of 'power tubes'. The De Forest tubes were advertised under the rather curious name of 'Specialist Audions' and it was stated that the production of tubes having differing char-

acteristics was in line with European practice which favoured the use of tubes specially designed for particular functions. This was in contrast to American practice where general-purpose tubes were used in all stages.

An advertised feature of De Forest tubes during this period was the use of 'yttriated' filaments.[3] As yttria is an oxide of the metal yttrium it may be assumed that the tubes had oxide-coated filaments. Although only two types, DV2 and DV3, were specifically mentioned it seems reasonable to assume that others in the range were similarly constructed. The success or otherwise of this development remains a matter of speculation but as far as storage battery tubes were concerned it is obvious that the De Forest Co. marketed oxide-coated types ahead of other manufacturers. A likely explanation for the adoption of procedure would be that as De Forest tubes were not licensed by RCA the company was seeking to avoid the use of the patented thoriated filament.

Most of the Isolantite-based tubes were available in either short pin (DV) or long pin (DL) styles and both

(L.) De Forest DV1.
(R.) De Forest DV6A and carton.

carried De Forest patent numbers ink-stamped on their bases. In the case of earlier issues this marking was enclosed in a circular outline while later issues carried the marking within a rectangular outline. Type identification was by means of a paper sticker attached to the side of the

165

glass bulb though a solitary type, the DV3A, had its type number ink-stamped on the base in addition.

The majority of the DV and DL series were fitted with tubular bulbs and all types, without exception, were top sealed. As stem-sealed (tipless) bulbs had been adopted as far back as 1924 by RCA and other manufacturers, De Forest tubes in consequence had an 'old fashioned' look which was retained up to the end of 1927.

The last tubes to be made at Jersey City consisted of seven types which by now all conformed strictly to conventional standards and carried standard type numbers; it was a case of Goodbye 'Specialist Audions', Hello 'New Standard' Audions. Tubes in this category may be recognised by the use of the figure 4 as the first numeral in the type number coupled with the prefix D.

In 1928 the company was reformed again, for the last time as it happened, and moved to Passaic (also in New Jersey) where standard type tubes continued to be manufactured up until closure of the company in 1933. During this period a range of 26 different receiving tubes was produced all of which were standard types apart from three. The exceptions were: type 420A equivalent to the UX-120 but had a 0.06 amp filament; type 422A equivalent to the UX-222 but had a 0.05 amp filament; type 471A equivalent to the UX-171A but had a 0.5 amp filament.

In addition to receiving tubes a quite extensive range of transmitting tubes was manufactured at Passaic. These were all standard types using the RCA '800' system of type identification but with the figure '5' in place of the '8'. Included in the range was a type 510 which had a counterpart, type 410, in the receiving range. Although the two types were structurally different the 410 was also advertised as being specially constructed for transmitting use.

When in 1933 De Forest Radio was in final receivership its assets were purchased by RCA who then took over production of transmitting tubes in their newly formed transmitting tube division. So great was the mania still attached to the name De Forest that for several years afterwards many types were marketed under the tradename 'RCA-de Forest'.

De Forest Receiving Tubes 1923–1932

DV1	D-01A	D400A	401A	432
DV2	DL2	D401A	410	433
DV3	DL3	D402	412A	440
DV3A	DL4	D410	422	445
DV5	DL5	D412	422A	447
DV6	DL7	D416B	420	450
DV6A	DL9	D471	420A	451
DV7	DL14		424	471A
DV8	DL15		426	471B
DV9	DR		427	480
DV9R			430	481
			431	499

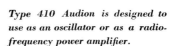
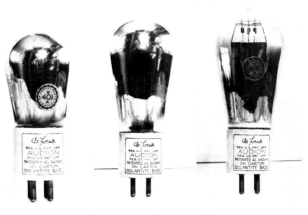

D401A   D402   D416A

De Forest Audions of 1931.

De Forest types 410 and 510. The 510 is a transmitting tube.

Arcturus

It must be admitted at the outset that Arcturus tubes have attracted more than their fair share of attention from tube collectors merely because of the attractive appearance of the blue glass bulbs used for the first six years or so of their production lifetime. Actually Arcturus were not the first blue tubes but due to the length of time blue glass was in use the words 'Blue' and 'Arcturus' became synonymous. The transparent blue glass was the same as that used on 'daylight blue' electric lamps and was considerably more expensive than ordinary clear glass, which was probably the reason for its eventual abandonment.

However, it was not just showy appearance that enabled Arcturus to gain and retain a place as one of the foremost independents of the day. The company was a pioneer producer of indirectly-heated AC tubes as well as being responsible for the early introduction of several new tube types over the years.

Advertisements announcing Arcturus tubes first appeared late in 1927,[4] so in the absence of anything to the contrary it is reasonable to assume that the company bearing the name was founded in that year. The Arcturus Radio Company, like so many of its contemporaries, was located in the city of Newark, New Jersey, but unlike others initially made only AC tubes. So it was that Arcturus, without the benefit of previous experience in the manufacture of battery tubes, embarked on the production of what was then an entirely new development—the indirectly-heated AC tube.

In 1927 the all-electric receiver was in its infancy and, although RCA had introduced their first i.d.h. tube during that same year, as yet there existed no industry standard in the matter of heater voltage and basing arrangements. Perhaps this was a good enough reason in itself why the first Arcturus tubes should have differed so very considerably from any others, but differ they did. Firstly an unusually high heater voltage of fifteen (15) was used, while the heater itself consisted of a thin rod or stick of carbon. The choice of such a high heater voltage was obviously connected with the use of carbon in place of the normally used tungsten wire heater, even though it has been suggested that the figure of 15 volts was chosen in order to make it convenient to obtain the heater supply from a toy transformer. Such a theory does not cut much ice with the author who believes that once the decision to use carbon had been made, 15 volts was found to be the most practical operating voltage. Further, it may be remarked that no other competing tube maker had found it desirable to use such a high voltage with tungsten wire heaters as suitable low-voltage stepdown transformers were readily available. As to the reason for using carbon in the first place, that is another matter. The company itself claimed to have elected to use carbon because it was less subject to burnouts than tungsten, and it is a fact that many early AC tubes suffered from burnt out heaters. Another reason may have been that at the time Arcturus was an unlicensed manufacturer and may have been seeking to avoid the use of a patented form of construction.

The heater rating of all types except one was 0.35 amps, giving a consumption of 5.25 watts, a figure that was high even by the standards of the day. In the case of the type A40 output tube the current was 0.4 amps and it is interesting to note that a comparable directly-heated power tube, type 171A, having otherwise identical characteristics could provide the same output for a filament consumption of 1.25 watts compared with the 6 watts required by the A40. With a performance like this who needed an indirectly-heated output tube?

The second and unique feature of the 15-volt tubes lay in the method of terminating the cathode connection; a standard UX type 4-pin base was used with the cathode tied internally to one heater prong. This enabled the tubes to be used to electrify existing battery-operated receivers without the need for a special harness as required when

forts as RCA's UY-224 did not appear until the following year. Initially all tubes were fitted with top sealed bulbs at a time when other manufacturers had turned to the use of stem exhausted (tipless) bulbs. In this respect Arcturus tubes looked old fashioned and the company obviously realised the fact as their advertisements of the period rather deceitfully pictorially represented them as being of tipless construction! Not until after 1929 were any Arcturus tubes produced in tipless form.

Because the original tubes used a private type numbering system which resulted in some confusion in later years when Arcturus produced standard types having identical numbers, the author has taken the precaution of adding the letter 'A' as a prefix to the early numbers as a means of differentiating between the two. This procedure is in line with that adopted by the various publishers of tube listings who were also confronted with the same difficulty.

By comparison with the McCullough-Kellogg tubes the Arcturus were little used in commercially built receivers of the period but, for the record, it must be mentioned that towards the end of 1928 the Sonora Phonograph Co. of New York marketed several models of electric phonographs and radio-phono combinations using the 15-volt tubes. Apart from the fact that they were branded Sonora and carried different type numbers the tubes were otherwise identical to Arcturus types. Other receiver manufacturers known to have used the tubes were Hammarlund-Roberts Inc. and C.R. Leutz Inc.

Towards the end of 1928 the first low-voltage AC tubes were advertised for sale, the initial release consisting of four types: 126, 126H, 127, and 071.[5] These were standard types with the exception of the 126H which was an indirectly-heated version of the UX-226 having the cathode tied internally to one side of the heater in the same manner as had been done in the case of the 15-volt types.

A new quick-heating type known as 'DETECTOR 127'

using other non-standard AC tubes having overhead or side-mounted heater terminations. At the same time the tubes were equally suited for use as initial equipment in all-electric receivers.

Although the permanently linked heater-cathode connection sometimes led to tricky biassing arrangements when used in this latter application, the tubes were intended for use in all stages as the range included a special detector, type A26. Even so, the main user, Sonora, elected to use a 5-prong tube with a separately connected cathode in the detector position.

Unlike other tube manufacturers Arcturus did not limit its production of non-standard tubes to one or two types. Between the years 1927 and 1929 no less than seven different types of 15-volt tubes were produced, all of which with one exception, were triodes. Included in the range was a high-mu voltage amplifier, another Arcturus 'first' and a type not produced by any other manufacturer until many years later. The inclusion of a screen-grid tube in 1928 was another indication of Arcturus' pioneering ef-

Arcturus AC28 and Sonora RA-1. These tubes had 15-volt carbon-heaters.

was announced early in 1929, and this was, seemingly, the first American tube to make use of a heater insulated from the cathode solely by means of a coating applied to the surface of the heater wire. For some reason this form of construction was not retained and for the next few years all Arcturus indirectly-heated tubes made use of a 2-bore solid insulator.

Early in 1929 the company underwent a reorganisation which resulted in a move to a new location at Elizabeth St., Newark, and a change of name to The Arcturus Radio Tube Co.[6] From this time the emphasis shifted to the production of standard type tubes, and by mid-1929 the first

Two versions of the 126.

Three versions of the 127.

battery-operated types had been issued. These were types 099 (UV & UX), 101A, 122, 012A.

It was during the years 1931 to 1933 that Arcturus tubes became most widely used by receiver manufacturers, two of the largest being Atwater Kent and Crosley. In the case of Crosley the tubes were hot-branded on the base.

'Crosley—Made by Arcturus Radio Tube Co'.

The following types are known to have been issued: 124, 127, 145, 180, and PZ.

In 1931 Arcturus claimed to have been the first manufacturer of the type 551 vari-mu screen-grid tube, as well as the first to produce a power pentode, type PZ. This claim is open to question as by mid-1931 several other manufacturers had announced similar tubes. It remains a fact, however, that both these types first became well known and widely used under the Arcturus brandname.

From a collector's point of view the type PZ is interesting in that apart from being one of the best-known early pentodes it was the first Arcturus tube to use a two-letter marking system which was subsequently used on types the company claimed to have pioneered.

By 1933 Arcturus appeared to be concentrating more on the replacement market and had introduced many types not previously made by them. Advertisements of the period listed a total of 60 types in current production, not including the 15-volt types which were now obsolete. The year 1933 also marks the general abandonment of the use of blue glass except in the case of Wunderlich types. It is pitiful to have to record that during the transitionary period certain types were produced with clear glass bulbs having the word BLUE marked on the bulb in blue paint!

Following the introduction of metal tubes by RCA in 1935 Arcturus brought out a range of metal-glass types under the name CORONET.[7] The Coronets, although resembling other MG tubes of the period, differed in both inward and outward appearance. Outwardly they were noticebly shorter than other makes and this was attributable to the use of a radically different type of electrode mounting in which the conventional stem seal was replaced by a novel annular seal. It was the resemblance of this annular seal to a coronet which rather obviously served as the inspiration for the name of the series.

Apart from producing Coronet types, which were the equivalents of metal tubes of the period, Arcturus also used the Coronet form of construction for the production of certain earlier 2.5-volt types. Because these peculiar hybrids were, of necessity, fitted with octal bases it was necessary to supply a conversion adaptor with each tube to allow it to be fitted into the corresponding receiver socket. Although this may seem an expensive and roundabout way of approaching the problem of maintaining a supply of earlier type tubes for replacement purposes it must have suited Arcturus' production methods at the time. Even so it was not long before the production of Coronets was discontinued and a return made to the use of conventional stem seal construction. The reason for this decision is not known; there could have been design weaknesses or the type of construction could have proved

169

too expensive to compete with MG tubes produced by other manufacturers. The last pre-war tubes produced were GT types in which Arcturus pioneered certain high-voltage heater types.

It is believed that the company ceased operations in 1941 as no advertisements have been discovered after that time and no traces exist of Arcturus tubes being made for the Armed Services during World War II. For a short period after the war a company by the name of Standard Arcturus Corp. located at 101 Sussex St., Newark, was advertising war assets surplus tubes. As this company used the Arcturus brandname and logo it may be surmised that there was some connection with pre-war Arcturus but nothing further is known to the author at this writing.

Arcturus Blue Glass Tubes

15-volt Types	Sonora Type		Arcturus Type
A22	DE1	Equivalent to	127
A26*	RA1	Equivalent to	A48
A28	RE1	Equivalent to	180
A30	RE2	Equivalent to	181
A32	SO1	Equivalent to	A40
A40	SO2	Equivalent to	150
A46*			
A48			

*Both A26 and A46 were listed as special detectors but it is not known if the A46 was ever issued.

'Letter' Designations		2.5-volt Types	6.3-volt Types
ARCTURUS	Equivalent	124	136A & 36A
AD	KR1 or 1V	127 & 27	137A & 37A
AE	none	127 Detector	138A & 38A
AF	82	145 & 45	139A & 39A
AG	83	46	6T5
GA	none	48	
PA	none	55	Wunderlich Auto
PZ	47	56	Battery Types
PZH	2A5	57	012A
		58	099
		59	101A
		551	120

Arcturus WUNDERLICH 'A' (L.) and 'A-Auto' (R.).

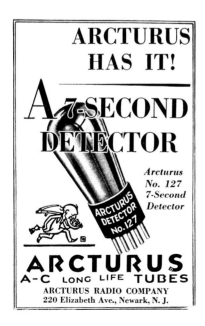

ARCTURUS HAS IT!

A 7-SECOND DETECTOR

Arcturus No. 127 7-Second Detector

ARCTURUS
A-C LONG LIFE TUBES
ARCTURUS RADIO COMPANY
220 Elizabeth Ave., Newark, N. J.

Made for the Crosley Radio Corp (1931).

Arcturus 2.5-volt tubes (1931).

OTHERS	2A6	122 & 22
071A	2B6	130
071H	Wunderlich A	131
110	(5-pin)	132
126 & 26	Wunderlich A	134
126 Detector	(6-pin)	
126H		
180 & 80		
181 & 81		
82		

Where a tube is listed under two type numbers, e.g., 180 & 80, the second number indicates a later production, usually 1933.

In the case of earlier non-standard types having type numbers which correspond with those of later standard type tubes, e.g., 48 and 48, there is no similarity in the tubes themselves. As mentioned in the text, the letter A has been added by the author to the type numbers of the earlier tubes in order to prevent confusion.

Ken-Rad

Amongst tube manufacturers the Ken-Rad Lamp & Tube Corp. of Owensboro, Kentucky, was unique in being located in the southern part of the United States, traditionally not an industrialised area. Ken-Rad tubes were first issued in 1926 under the name 'Archatron'. From this humble beginning grew one of the foremost independents who supplied the tube requirements of many of the largest receiver manufacturers.

During the tube proliferation battle, being waged in 1932 by many of the independent tube makers, Ken-Rad contributed their share of non-standard types. Whilst some of these differed only in carrying non-standard type numbers others were originated by Ken-Rad and had no counterparts amongst standard types. Of the latter some fell by the wayside whilst others eventually became standard types made by all manufacturers. An example of the latter is the type KR1, a small half-wave mercury vapour rectifier intended for car radio use. This tube was later issued by other makers in high vacuum form when it became known as type 1 or 1-V.

Cross Reference of Ken-Rad and Standard Types

Type	Equiv.	Type	Equiv.
KR1	1-V	KR28	84
KR5	6A4/LA	KR31	–
KR17	–	KR48	47
KR18	18	280M	80
KR20	–	281M	81
KR22	–	950	–
KR25	2A5	951	1B4

Of these the KR1, KR28, 280M, and 281M were mercury vapour rectifiers, production of which was soon discontinued. The type 950 was also made by National Union and Tung-Sol, while the 951 was issued by Raytheon under the type number 1B4-951. Apart from tubes issued

under the 'KR' prefix there were some which had originally allocated two-digit type numbers running from 90 to 98. It appears that these were experimental or sample types which if and when put into production were then given KR type numbers. Both the manufacture of non-standard tubes and the use of non-standard type numbers ceased by the end of 1934, following the introduction of the R.M.A. numbering system.

With the introduction of metal tubes in 1935 Ken-Rad became one of the first independents to produce them and this was followed by the production of G and GT types. During World War II Ken-Rad made a wide range of tubes for military use, including transmitting and miniature types. However, hardly had peacetime production been resumed when the company was taken over by General Electric. This occurred in 1946 when GE re-entered the field of receiving tube manufacture after an absence of some sixteen years. Tubes continued to be sold under the Ken-Rad name for the next three years or so at the same time as they were being sold under the GE name. Finally, when the Ken-Rad brand was withdrawn during the early 1950s it marked the end of yet another respected independent name.

National Union

In name National Union was a comparative late-comer in the industry as the company was not established until 1930. At this time a merger of four older companies—Magnatron, Marathon, Sonatron, and Televocal—resulted in the formation of the National Union Radio Corp. of Newark, N.J. National Union quickly grew to be one of the foremost names amongst independents of the day, specialising in the production of replacement tubes including many older non-standard types whose original manufac-

Types KR25 (L.) and KR5 (R.) non-standard output pentodes (1932).

turers were no longer in existence. In 1935 NU became one of the few independents to manufacture metal tubes, having previously made a range of MG types as a stop-gap measure. Amongst those companies making MG tubes NU was unique in being the only one to also make metal tubes.

Unlike other independents NU at no time attempted to introduce odd-ball types of tubes though, as noted above, the company did make replacements for many non-standard and obsolete types which would otherwise have been unobtainable.

During World War II NU became active in the development and manufacture of transmitting and special purpose tubes and by 1943 had established a second factory located in Lansdale, Pa. Following the war the company resumed the production of commercial receiving tubes before ceasing manufacture in the early 1950s.

Sylvania

The name Sylvania first appeared on radio tubes late in 1924 when three types were produced by a company known as Sylvania Products Co. of Emporium, Pa. In 1929 Sylvania merged with the Hygrade Lamp Corp. to form Hygrade-Sylvania Corp. which continued to issue tubes under the name Sylvania. In 1934 Sylvania became

Types 90 and 92. Note base markings 'sample tube.'

Say You Saw It in QST — It Identifies You and Helps QST   May 1938

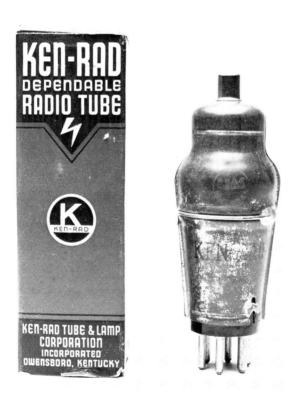

Type 85AS. It was made as a replacement for a Majestic spray-shielded tube.

one of the first independent receiving tube manufacturers to commence making transmitting tubes but it is understood that licensing difficulties with RCA prevented full exploitation of this field.

From an early date one of Sylvania's biggest customers had always been Philco and as Philco claimed in 1938 to be the world's largest receiver manufacturers it will be appreciated that Sylvania's tube output must have been very large indeed. Sylvania's close association with Philco was, in 1938, responsible for the launching of the 'Loktal' tube, an all-glass type intended to be their answer to RCA's much vaunted all-metal tube. Loktal tubes remained in current production until the late 1950s and in addition to being produced by other American manufacturers were also made by at least two British valve makers.

Sylvania celebrated its 50th anniversary in 1951, tracing its ancestry through its union with the Hygrade Lamp works which had been established in 1901. In 1963 Sylvania became a unit of General Telephone and at the time of writing remains the sole American producer of receiving tubes, having lived to see its erstwhile rival RCA bow out of this field in 1977.

172

Tung-Sol

Like many other independents Tung-Sol entered the receiving tube field by way of lamp manufacturing. The Tung Sol Lamp Works Inc. are known to have been making tubes as early as 1930, though this side of the business appears not to have been developed to the same extent as in the case of competing manufacturers. In the main Tung Sol stuck fairly close to the production of standard type tubes though in 1932, in common with others, did develop a few of their own design. For example, the TS-257 was a directly-heated output pentode intended for DC line operation.

In 1936 Tung-Sol embarked on the production of metal tubes and later also made G and GT types. During World War II the company made various types of receiving tubes for military use including the 717A (VT-269). The 717A was a Western Electric UHF pentode and the ones made by Tung-Sol carried the names of both companies. This particular tube was used in Scott receivers made in the immediate post-war years. Following the end of the war Tung-Sol made 7-pin miniature tubes for a short period before retiring from radio tube manufacturing.

Early National-Union tubes (1931).

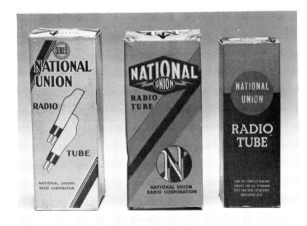

Carton styles 1930–1940.

Hytron

In a 1941 advertisement Hytron claimed to have been 'manufacturers of radio tubes since 1921', while in 1944 they proclaimed themselves as 'the oldest manufacturers of radio tubes'. As it is outside the scope of this brief review to assess the accuracy of these claims the reader is left to form his own conclusions.

Little information is available concerning the origins of Hytron but it is known that the Hytron Corp. of Salem, Mass. was manufacturing tubes in 1926. Not a great deal was heard of this company's activities until 1938 when an important new constructional development in tube manufacturing was introduced. At this time Hytron issued a series of dwarf sized octal-based tubes under the name 'Bantam'. These were the first GT tubes, the design of which proved so successful that it was soon taken up by all other manufacturers as well as being widely used in many other countries. Later in 1938 Hytron introduced the first American midget hearing-aid tubes, the 'Bantam Jr'. In 1941 the junior Bantams were followed by an even smaller tube known as the 'Super Bantam'. Also in 1938 Hytron commenced production of transmitting tubes and, over the years, introduced new types in their 'HY' series.

During World War II the company name was changed

173

Early Sylvania tubes (1931).

Philco tubes 24, 27, 35. Made by Sylvania.

Philco types 17 (L.), 47, 14 (R.) Made by Sylvania (1931).

174

to Hytron Radio & Electronics Corp., at which time there were factories located in four different cities. At this time Hytron became one of the first manufacturers of miniature tubes for military applications. Following the war the company remained active in the production of all current types of receiving and transmitting tubes. In 1952 Hytron became a unit of the Columbia Broadcasting System, after which time tubes were marketed under the name CBS-Hytron.

Raytheon

Amongst independents Raytheon must be counted as one of the oldest, even though the company initially produced only gaseous rectifying tubes. Prior to the formation of Raytheon a company by the name of the American Radio & Research Co. had developed and marketed cold-cathode gaseous rectifiers under their brandname Amrad. These rectifiers were half-wave types intended for transmitting use only and they continued to be sold until 1925 when the Amrad Corp. (as it was by then) was taken over by Crosley who discontinued production. At this time a new company by the name of the American Appliance Co. secured the Amrad patents and developed and marketed a new type of gaseous rectifier intended solely for receiving use.

In October 1925 the Raytheon Manufacturing Co. of Cambridge, Mass., was formed and for the next three years was engaged solely in the production of cold-cathode rectifiers. When RCA first granted tube manufacturing licenses in 1929 Raytheon became the first independent to be licensed and, thus equipped, embarked on the production of a range of standard tubes. Tubes produced at this

Tung-Sol 59 (L.) and 71A (R.). The centre tube is an F257 made for Fada.

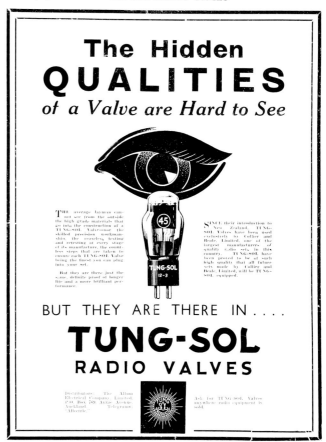

Tung-Sol TS280 (L.) and 485 (R.). The latter is a Sparton replacement.

time may be distinguished by the word Raytheon together with the type-prefix 'Ray', hot-branded on the bases.

Raytheon tubes to 1929

Ray-X	Ray-X	Ray-V	Ray	BA
200	222	199	224	BH
201A	226		227	
210	245	Gaseous Rectifiers		
240	250		B	
112	280		BA	
120	281		BH	
171A	199		BR	

With the exception of three types, X-201A, X-199, V199 and the gaseous rectifiers, all these tubes featured Raytheon's unique type of stem press which had a star shaped cross-section. This feature was extensively advertised as 'Four Pillar Construction'. The additional surface edges provided by this type of press allowed the use of extra support rods thus enabling a sturdier and more rigid assembly of the tube elements in the days before the advent of ST (domed) bulbs with their accompanying mica spacers. A characteristic of the earliest 4-pillar Raytheons was the extremely heavy plate structure used in output tubes and rectifiers. Such tubes were further distinguished by having the word Raytheon embossed in raised letters on the outer sides of their plates.

Towards the middle of 1929 Raytheon became associated with the National Carbon Co. (makers of Eveready batteries) who were apparently looking for an additional line of merchandise to offset falling sales of radio batteries caused by the advent of 'all-electric' radios. National Carbon became sole distributors of Raytheon which were then marketed under the name 'Eveready Raytheon'. At the same time an option to purchase the Raytheon Mfg. Co. was secured but as events turned out the option was never exercised.

Hytron type 47 and carton (L.). CBS-Hytron carton (1952).

Raytheon's edge over competing manufacturers in respect of the rigidity of the four-pillar construction was effectively removed by the introduction of ST bulbs throughout the industry in 1932. This development resulted in tubes having a greatly increased rigidity of their electrode structure due to the use of top mica spacers. For the next year or so Raytheon continued to use their four-pillar construction in conjunction with the ST bulbs but in an industry where every half cent counted this was obviously a wasteful procedure and from 1934 onwards the four-pillar feature was quietly dropped.

Towards the end of 1933 connections with National Carbon were severed and the company was reorganised as the Raytheon Production Corp. of Newton, Mass., and at the same time the brandname reverted to plain Raytheon. At this period Raytheon introduced several new types of receiving tubes, many of which became industry standards, and at the same time the development of new types of gaseous rectifiers was continued. In 1935 Raytheon became one of the first independent manufacturers of metal tubes. Manufacture of transmitting tubes was commenced in 1936 with Raytheon later introducing many new types in their 'RK' range of amateur transmitting tubes.

Following the end of World War II Raytheon made a brief attempt to regain their former position in the receiving tube field but apart from introducing the 'Bantal' series of octal-based tubes in 1948 made little impression in this area. Soon afterwards production of receiving tubes ceased though at the time of its 40th anniversary in 1965 the company was still advertising a line of foreign-made tubes under its once proud all-American Raytheon label.

Cardon Sparton

The Sparks-Withington Co. (Sparton) of Jackson, Mich., was probably the only large radio manufacturer to

Hytron Bantams (1938).

176

Early Raytheon 4-pillar tubes.

Raytheon Ray-X171A, 201A, 226. The centre tube was not of 4-pillar construction.

two makes of tubes were not directly interchangeable but either type could be used in a particular 'run' of receivers by using the appropriate style of 'harness' for the heater connections. The heater ratings and operating characteristics of both types were identical. Cardon later made tubes fitted with standard UY bases, though they still had non-standard heater ratings.

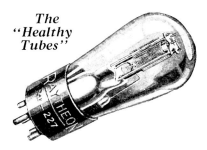

undertake extensive production of receivers using non-standard AC tubes. The first of such Sparton receivers appeared in 1927 before the Radiotron UY-227 AC tube had become an industry standard. The tubes fitted to these early Sparton sets were either a double-ended type made by Kellogg or a single-ended type made by Cardon. The Cardon tubes had elongated bakelite UX bases which in addition to the usual four base pins carried two small side-mounted contact pins located on opposite sides of the base near the top edge. The extra-long base was needed to allow clearance for the two side pins when the tube was inserted into a UV-type socket; a somewhat surprising requirement in view of the fact that UV sockets were obsolete by 1927.

Because of their different forms of construction the

Little is known of the origins of Cardon but it seems likely to have been a tube-making subsidiary of Sparton as both companies were located in Jackson, Mich. In the event the name Cardon disappeared after 1930 by which time Sparton had turned to the use of standard type tubes.

Because of the large numbers of early-type Sparton receivers which had been produced the continuing demand for replacement tubes after the demise of Cardon resulted in some other tube makers producing certain types. For example National Union, Tung-Sol, and Vox made the 5-pin types 484 and 485.

Amongst the many odd-ball tubes made by Sparton were such types as the C484A, which had a heater rating of 3 volts, 1.6 amps and was intended for use in 32-volt DC receivers, and the C686 which had a 3-volt, 0.25-amp filament. The latter was a battery-operated tube fitted with a 5-pin UY base having only four connections made to it.

Changes in carton styles 1929–1934.

IN RECEPTION FROM YOUR PRESENT
RADIO RECEIVER WITH NEW

EVEREADY
RAYTHEON 4-PILLAR TUBES

This particular odd-ball was intended for the 'battery-fication' of existing stocks of AC receivers having 5-pin sockets, an expedient which saved having to develop separate chassis for battery sets.

THE inevitable jolts and jars of shipment and handling can't budge the elements in an Eveready Raytheon Tube by as much as a thousandth of an inch. Their accurate spacing, which assures maximum performance, is immune to these common hazards.

The 4-Pillar construction, which gives Eveready Raytheon Tubes theirremarkablestrength,

is patented and exclusive. With no other tube can you get all its advantages. If you examine the illustration at the bottom of this page, you will see the superiority of this construction.

This is especially important in receiving tubes which have large and heavy elements — tubes such as the 224 screen-grid, the 280 rectifier, and power tubes used for push-pull audio amplification, requiring perfectly uniform characteristics.

People everywhere, using Eveready Raytheons in their receivers, report increased distance, more power, better tone and quicker action. To get the most from your receiver, put a new Eveready Raytheon in each socket. Your dealer has them in all types — including the famous B-H tube for "B" power units.

NATIONAL CARBON CO., INC.

General Offices:
NEW YORK, N. Y.
Branches: Chicago, Kansas City,
New York, San Francisco

UCC

*Unit of Union Carbide
and Carbon Corporation*

Cardon-Sparton Non-Standard Tubes

C-171	3V, 1.3A	Output Tube, replaced by C-181
C-182	5V, 1.9A	Output Tube, similar to standard 71A
C-182A	5V, 0.8A	Output Tube, replaced by C-482A
C-182B	5V, 1.2A	Output Tube, replaced by C-482B
C-183	5V, 1.25A	Output Tube, side-pin type
C-373	3V, 1.3A	side-pin type
C-401	3V, 1.3A	side-pin type
C-484	3V, 1.3A	replaced by C-485
C-484A	3V, 1.6A	for 32 V. DC line operation
C-686	3V, 0.25A	replaced by C-486

4-PILLAR TUBES
Showing the exclusive, patented Eveready Raytheon 4-Pillar construction. Notice the sturdy four-cornered glass stem. the four rigid supports, and the stiff mica sheet bracing the top.

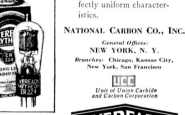

EVEREADY
RAYTHEON

Trade Marks

Say You Saw It in *QST* — It Identifies You and Helps *QST*

QST FOR NOVEMBER, 1929

4-PILLAR SCREEN-GRID
Eveready Raytheon Screen-Grid Tube, ER 224. The weight of the four large elements in this type of tube makes the exclusive Eveready Raytheon 4-Pillar construction vitally important.

PILLARS OF THE LAW

When the radio sets in the New York Police cars were equipped with Eveready Raytheon Valves, it was because of their special four-pillar bracing of the delicate electrodes.

Eveready Raytheon

Standard
Telephones and Cables (Asia) Limited

It was found that these four pillars (instead of the usual two) prevented any chance whatever of the highly sensitive filament, grid and plate, being displaced through the shocks of driving; ensuring faultless reception under every condition called for in the suppression of crime. To the Patrol-Car Police these two extra pillars are vital, and only Raytheons have them. To YOU it means definitely clearer reception and longer life, and once you've heard Raytheons nothing else will satisfy you.

Head Office: P.O. Box 638, Wellington.   Box 897, Auckland

Majestic

The company which produced Majestic tubes started life as the Grigsby-Grunow-Hinds Co., making A and B eliminators under the brandname Majestic. In common with many other eliminators of the day the Majestic 'Super B' used a Raytheon type BH rectifier, but later this was changed to a similar tube made by the QRS Music Co. of Chicago. The QRS tube as used by Majestic was not identified by a type number, being simply marked Majestic Super Power; it was the first tube of any sort to carry the Majestic brandname.

Grisby-Grunow-Hinds, like others in the industry during the late 1920s, were desirous of embarking on receiver manufacture but were prevented from doing so by RCA's then extant policy of refusing to grant further manufacturing licenses. Like others, too, G-G-H found a way around this difficulty by buying out an existing license holder, in this case the Pfanstiel Co. of Chicago. With the acquisition of Pfanstiel in 1928 the name Hinds was dropped from the company title which then became the Grigsby-Grunow Co., this name being retained for the remainder of the company's existence.

Originally tubes for Majestic receivers were purchased from outside suppliers but in 1930 Grigsby-Grunow set up its own tube factory, an achievement which made them the only independent receiver manufacturer to make their own tubes. Tube production was limited to only those types needed to equip Majestic receivers and because of this the number of different types produced initially was quite small. For example, the first production consisted of but four types—G-24, G-27, G-45, and G-80.

In spite of being a late-comer Majestic was, in 1931, one of the first two tube manufacturers to produce the type 551 variable-mu screen-grid tube and was also the first receiver manufacturer to market a model using the new tube. Also in 1931 Majestic became the first and only American manufacturer to produce spray-shielded tubes, a feature which in itself became something of a Majestic trademark. The idea of providing certain types of tubes with metallic-coated bulbs had originated in Germany in 1929, whence it had spread to the U.K. and the U.S. The spray-shielding process obviated the need for a separate metal shield-can which would otherwise have been required for certain types of tubes. In practice the metallic coating was grounded via the cathode connection or else by means of an additional base pin. A further Majestic innovation in 1932 was the production and use of the

Sparton C-482-B 5-volt output tube.

Sparton 686, battery triode. The fifth pin is unused.

Sparton C181. Heater connections are to the side pins.

Sparton C401. Heater connections are to the side pins.

world's first duo-diode detector tubes, types G-2-S and G-4-S, which for several years remained the only such American tubes in existence.

Although concentrating mainly on the production of mains-powered receivers Majestic did make one or two models of battery-operated sets and car radios, plus the necessary tubes to equip them. Even though the production lifespan of Majestic tubes was only a little over four years, the number of different types produced during this period was surprisingly large when it is realised that production of new types was geared strictly to receiver needs. In spite of this there were many special types produced which had no exact counterparts among standard American tubes of the period. For example, when the first Majestic 6.3-volt automative tubes appeared they differed in having a 0.4-amp heater rating instead of the standard 0.3-amp. Then there was the matter of the type numbering; while most Majestic tubes were standard types (apart from the spray-shielded ones) and carried standard type numbers, certain types carried the suffix 'A' which indicated a tube in an entirely different grouping. Thus the type 58-S was a 2.5-volt tube while the 58AS was a 6.3-volt type. Needless to say, such a system was completely out of keeping with standard American practice, and indeed, world practice. The suffix 'S' appearing in any type number indicated that the particular tube was spray shielded, though a few later types were not so identified.

When a study is made of the manner in which many of the Majestic special types differed from standard types one is forced to the conclusion that Majestic had been playing the 'non-standard' game for the same reasons as others— to make it impossible, or at least very difficult, to use standard tubes for replacements in Majestic's receivers, thus effectively keeping the replacement business in Majestic's hands. By the time production had ceased in 1934 over 50 different types of tubes had been made, though it should be noted that many of these differed only in the matter of having clear or spray-shielded bulbs.

Majestic gaseous rectifier made by QRS Music Co. (1927).

Because of the large number of Majestic receivers in existence following the demise of Grigsby-Grunow there existed for some years afterwards a sufficiently large demand for replacement tubes to make it worthwhile for certain independent tube makers to provide the needed replacements. Thus Ken-Rad, National Union, and Raytheon all produced replacements for the various non-standard Majestic tubes, though in the case of spray-shielded types it was necessary to use a close-fitting tube shield as no metallic coating was provided on the replacements.

The following is a listing of all known Majestic tubes:

G-2-S	G-36	G-56-S	G-89
G-4-S	G-37	G-57-S	G-1A6
G-24	G-38	G-58-S	G-2A5
G-24-S	G-42	G57-AS	G-2A7-S
G-25-S	G-43	G-58-AS	G-6A7-S
G-27	G-45	G-59	G-6C7*
G-27-S	G-47	G-59-B	G-6D7*
G-30	G-50	G-75	G-6E7*
G-32	G-51	G-80	G-6F7*
G-33	G-51-S	G-81	G-6Y5*
G-34	G-53	G-82	G-6Z5
G-35	G-55-S	G-84	G-25Z5
G-35-S	G-56	G-85	

*Spray-shielded type not identified as such by the use of the suffix S in the type number.

Some of the first Majestic tubes (1930).

Typical Majestic tubes. Note the use of a large-size (S-14) bulb on the type G-30.

Make your
Radio
young again

Majestic Super A.C. Valves
will add

POWER
TONE GREATER
VOLUME
and Keener Selectivity to
ANY Radio Receiver

Majestic

VALVES
'For Better Reception'
From Leading Radio Dealers
Everywhere

REFERENCES

1. See advt. *Radio News*, December 1924, pp. 892–893.
2. See, for example, advt. *Radio in Australia & New Zealand*, May 27, 1925, p. 184.
3. See advt. *Radio in Australia & New Zealand*, July 22, 1925, p. 341.
4. See advt. *Radio News*, November 1929, p. 447.
5. See advt. *Radio News*, December 1928, p. 592.
6. See advt. *Radio News*, April 1929, p. 960.
7. The Latest in Tube Developments, *Radio Craft*, March 1939, p. 524.

Later Majestic spray-shielded tubes.

Majestic 'spray-shielded' tubes. The suffix 'A' indicated 6.3-volt heaters.

Chapter Twenty-Two

Canadian and Australian Tube Manufacture

Canadian

Information on the origins of radio tube manufacturing in Canada is surprisingly meagre. Because of this the full story will have to await the time when some sufficiently motivated native son takes the trouble to research and write it. Leaving aside the independent efforts of Edward S. Rogers, whose work has at least received some recognition, it appears that the first Canadian tube manufacturer was the Canadian General Electric Co. (CGE). At much the same time another firm by the name of the Radio Valve Co. of Canada Ltd. was also offering apparently identical tubes (valves)! Two other firms—Canadian Westinghouse and the Canadian Marconi Co. were also active in the radio tube field at an early date.

Just how many of these firms actually manufactured tubes is open to question but it seems unlikely that as many as four separate factories were in existence, at least in the early days. The products of all four companies initially carried the word Radiotron in addition to the individual company names. Canadian GE continued to use the word Radiotron for as long as tubes were manufactured. Westinghouse, on the other hand, discontinued its use sometime in the 1930s.

Marconi commenced using the RVC logo sometime in the late 1920s, after which time the Radio Valve Co. ceased to issue tubes under their own name. Tubes issued after this time were sold under the name style—Marconi RVC Radiotron. Later still, apparently after World War II, Marconi adopted a new logo—CMC—to replace the earlier RVC.

Because of their joint use of the word Radiotron it is obvious that there must have been some sort of trading arrangement between the companies involved. By the same token it is also obvious that there must have been some connection with RCA, if only in the matter of using American patents and designs.

The first Canadian-made tubes offered for sale were the Radiotron types UV-200 and UV-201. This followed the same pattern as in the U.S. from which it may be assumed

Two early Canadian cartons with an American RCA (centre).

that the date of issue would have been in 1921. In external appearance these two tubes were indistinguishable from American-made Radiotrons apart from being marked with a list of patent dates in place of the license clause.

Although the majority of Canadian Radiotrons were

Northern Electric 208-A (L.). Canadian Radiotron 201-A (R.). Note patent markings on base.

identical to their American-made counterparts a few exceptions may be mentioned. For example, there were some developments of the standard 201-A type tube which were not made by RCA. These were the types 01-B (0.125-amp filament) and the 01-C (0.06-amp filament). A third type in the same series, known as UX-121B, was a power output tube with a 0.125-amp filament. Two examples of variants amongst AC tubes were the UY-227A and the later 227-A.

Apart from the above companies Western Electric's Canadian Subsidiary, the Northern Electric Co. Ltd., produced Western Electric type tubes at least as far back as 1930 and probably earlier. Apart from carrying the name Northern Electric Co. these tubes may be recognised by the use of the prefix 'R' in their type numbers. Thus the 211-E was marked R211-E and so on.

Rogers

The first, and so far as can be ascertained the only, independent Canadian manufacturer* of vacuum tubes commenced business in 1925 under the name Standard Radio Mfg. Corp. Ltd. The founder, Edward S. Rogers,

Canadian battery tubes not having corresponding RCA equivalents.

1, 2, 4 Canadian cartons of the 1930s. 3, American RCA carton.

*Not counting the short visit of the American 'refugee', Elmar B. Myers, in 1923.

184

Canadian Westinghouse and Sparton AC tubes.

was an early Canadian amateur radio operator who commenced manufacture of AC-operated receivers which were sold under the name 'Rogers Batteryless'. Right from the start Rogers made his own tubes to equip the receivers, or it might be more correct to say that the receivers were designed around the tubes. Whichever way it was, the fact remains that Rogers himself deserves to be recognised as a pioneer in the production of both AC tubes and light-socket receivers; in fact it has been claimed his company was the first in Canada to market such receivers.

Rogers had early realised that the future of household radios lay in mains operation and with this in mind had acquired the Canadian rights to the American McCullough AC tube. The first Rogers tubes, types R32 and R20, closely resembled the McCullough types 401 and 403 having the same distinctive bullet-shaped bulbs fitted with overhead heater connections. The first single-ended version, type R30, followed a year or so later and used the same shaped bulb but was now fitted with the new standard American style 5-pin UY base. For the next few years tube production was limited to a small range of standard American-type AC tubes as needed to equip the Rogers receivers then in production.

In 1929 the Standard Radio Mfg. Corp. became associated with the Grigsby Co. of Chicago and a new company known as the Rogers Majestic Corp. Ltd. was formed. From this union came the American influence which was to affect both receiver and tube designs for many years after the collapse of the American company. Sometime later, around 1932, a subsidiary company—Rogers Radio Tubes Ltd.—was set up to handle tube production. However, a Rogers tube chart dated 1938–39 carries the name Canadian Radio Corp. Ltd., indicating another change in the company name style.

As far as the American influence on tube design was concerned the most obvious effect was the adoption of the 'spray-shielding' process which characterised many of the

Majestic tubes during their short production life span. Rogers took up the idea of spray shielding even more enthusiastically than Grisby-Grunow, even producing spray-shielded output tubes and rectifiers! Originally the design of Rogers tubes closely followed Majestic practice in which the metallic coating was connected to the cathode pin of the tube but, following the demise of Grigsby-Grunow, Rogers tubes evolved along somewhat different lines. From about 1934 the metallic coating was extended to cover the bakelite base, and grounding was achieved by means of a contact clip which pressed against the base of the tube when it was inserted into the receiver chassis. At

this time, too, the distinctive Rogers corrugated grid caps were introduced and it is interesting to note that these were later also used on Rogers octal-based tubes.

The next change apparent in Rogers tubes occurred with the production of octal-based types in 1937, after which time the bare zinc coating was covered with black spray paint. These black octal-based tubes were referred to as 'metal sprayed' to distinguish them from the earlier 'spray-shielded' types and in addition they carried the suffix 'M' in their type numbers. The 'M' series was Rogers' response to the American production of all-metal tubes, though apart from their black colour and octal bases the Rogers tubes had little resemblance to the metal ones. Even the grid caps did not belong, being the older large size as used on pre-octal tubes.

Whilst the design of Rogers tubes in general remained firmly based on American practice there were many which had no counterparts in the standard U.S. range, particularly in the case of certain types issued around 1934–35. Also

Rogers 'Spray-Shielded' AC tubes c. 1934. Note shielding covering bases.

Rogers AC tubes c. 1931.

Rogers AC20 power output tube.

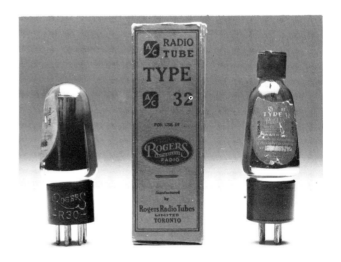

Rogers R30 (L.) and AC32 (R.). Note similarity to American McCullough.

185

Rogers 'spray-shielded' AC tubes c. 1934. Note corrugated grid caps.

Rogers 'Metal Spray' tubes c. 1937.

Rogers 'Metal Spray' tubes. Note corrugated grid caps.

Canadian tube cartons of the 1940s.

during the late 1930s the number of different types in production increased enormously so that by 1939 there were over 133 listed. Of course much of this increase simply reflected the situation existing in the U.S. where proliferation had been going on for years, but even so one is forced to the conclusion that the continuing new production of special Rogers types had no justification other than that it ensured an effective means of securing subsequent renewal business.

During World War II Rogers-Majestic, in common with other Canadian manufacturers, made tubes for the British and Canadian armed forces, many of which were standard commercial types that had been assigned military type numbers. In addition Rogers also made the equivalents of certain British commercial types being used for military applications. For example, some types in the Mullard Red E octal-based range were manufactured by Rogers using their metal spray technique. Such tubes although of necessity having the same electrical characteristics as those made by Mullard, were of different appearance, being fitted with Rogers' standard black painted tubular bulbs. Examples are: VR53 = EF39 and VR55 = EBC33.

Not long after the end of the war the company producing Rogers tubes and receivers, Rogers-Majestic Electronics Ltd., was taken over by Philips of Holland who were by then established in the U.S. under the name of North American Philips Inc. Tubes continued to be sold under the Rogers name by Philips Electrical Industries of Canada Ltd. with some types being issued under Philips' own name.

Rogers A.C. Tubes to Approx. 1932

R20	R200	R245	AC551
R30	R224	R247	AC51S
R32	R24S	R280	
R100	R227	R210	

186

Receiving valves are known to have been manufactured in Australia as early as 1920 though there was very little real activity before 1933. As the largest radio organisation in the Commonwealth it is not surprising to find that Amalgamated Wireless (Australasia)* Ltd. (A.W.A.) should have been the first company to commence valve manufacture. A.W.A. had been founded in 1913 to take over the Australian interests of the Marconi Co. and the German Telefunken Co., hence the use of the word Amalgamated in the company name. As an indication of its strong links with the Marconi Co. A.W.A. made use of the same telegraphic and cable code word 'Expanse' and for several years thereafter also used the word as a trade-

AWA99 (L.) compared with an American UV199 (R.).

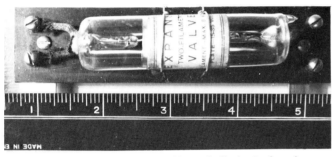

Expanse 'two-filament' valve. Note similarity to American 'Audiotron.'

Expanse 'B' two-filament valve. Serial numbers were die-stamped on anodes.

mark on all their Australian-made apparatus, including valves.

The first valve to carry the Expanse label was a double-ended, double-filament type which looked to be identical to the American AudioTron. As A.W.A. never claimed to have made this original Expanse valve it seems reasonable to assume that it was in fact an AudioTron. In 1920 the company patented a somewhat similar type of valve known as the Expanse 'B'.[1] This valve differed from the AudioTron design in two respects: a floating glass pinch was used at each end of the assembly in place of the usual flat stem press, and ebonite (hard rubber) end caps were cemented

*The word 'Australasia is an archaic and ill-defined term denoting Australia, New Zealand, and the Pacific Islands.

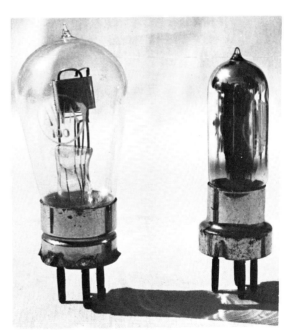

AWA100 (L.) and AWA33 (R.).

to each end of the bulb to protect the lead-out wires. These valves may be positively identified by the word Expanse die-stamped on the tubular aluminium anode.

In 1924 as the result of an agreement made with RCA a manufacturing license was obtained to enable selected types of American Radiotron tubes to be made in Australia. For the next few years all Australian-made valves were sold under the name AWA, used as a prefix to the type numbers, thus—AWA33. The first two such valves were marketed in 1925; they were the AWA99 which was equivalent to the original style UV 199 except for having a nickel plated base, and the AWA33 which was the same valve fitted with a Franco-British style 4-pin base. Other early AWA valves were types 99X, 101A, 101X, which were the equivalents of types UX-199, UV-201A, and UX-201A respectively.

Throughout the 1920s and early 1930s Australian production accounted for only a small proportion of the valves sold by AWA. In 1927, for example, only four types were locally made while 32 types were imported. In 1932 a decision was made to expand the company's valve making activities and in that year a separate company known as the Amalgamated Wireless Valve Co. Pty. Ltd. (AWV) was formed.[2] It was at that time that the American name Radiotron was adopted for use on the Australian-made valves and it is interesting to note that shortly afterwards the use of this name on American tubes was discontinued by RCA.

The first Australian Radiotron was the ubiquitous type 80 rectifier; it was followed in September 1933 by types 57, 58, and 2A5. Over the years the number of different

Australian-made STC valve SY prefix = Sydney.

types produced grew steadily and by 1939 Australia was largely self-sufficient in respect of the most commonly used receiving valves.

The manufacture of transmitting valves began in 1936 and was greatly expanded during World War II when a peak production of 175,000 valves per month was reached. Of this figure transmitting valves accounted for between 5% and 10% of the total. Included in AWA's wartime production were some highly specialised types such as klystrons and cavity magnetrons used in radar equipment.

Production of the first Australian-made miniature valves occurred in 1946 and during this year four 1.4-volt battery types were released. The first 6.3-volt AC miniatures followed in 1948 and by 1952 the first 9-pin noval type was in production. For a short period during the early post-war years certain British-made Osram valves, such as types X65M and KT61 were sold in Australia under the Radiotron name. One Osram 9-pin miniature type, the X79, was actually made by AWV and sold under the type number 6AE8.

Following the lead of American and British manufacturers AWV eventually turned to Japan for the supply of many types of receiving valves and during the late 1970s Australian production was phased out.

In 1931 it was announced that Philips intended to set up a valve manufacturing operation in Australia 'early next year'[3] but, in the event, it was 1936 before this occurred.[4] The Australian factory was originally located at Camperdown, N.S.W., but in 1946 it was moved to Hendon in South Australia. During the late 1930s a limited range of American type valves plus certain 6.3-volt side-contact continental valves were produced in the Australian factory.

By 1948 a range of 74 Australian-made valves was being offered and it is interesting to note that only six European types were included in the total.[5] Manufacture of miniature valves commenced in the early 1950s when certain American type 7-pin, 1.4-volt battery types were produced. These were followed by 6.3-volt AC types using the same B7G base style. By 1958 quite a large range of European type 9-pin noval miniatures was in production,

AWV Radiotrons c. 1943
6P6 (L.)   AV11 (R.)

these being marketed under American type numbers. At this time Philips also produced several different types of valves for the Australian Post Office for use in telephone repeater service. These ranged from the type 18004, a replacement for the WE type (4)102-D to types 18046, a noval-based pentode. Production of receiving valves was phased out during the late 1970s.

S.T.C.

The only other known Australian valve manufacturer was the firm of Standard Telephones & Cables Ltd.* This company had originally been established as Western Electric Co. (Australasia) Ltd., becoming S.T.C. in 1925. In 1939 a small valve manufacturing operation was set up in Sydney to supply certain requirements of the Australian Post Office. Valves produced in Australia were distinguished by the letters 'SY' (for Sydney) used as a prefix to their type numbers. Due to local considerations it was decided to use the British S.T.C. type numbering system,

rather than the original WE, as a basis for valve identification. For example, the Western Electric type 101-D, made in England as type 4101-D, became SY4101D when made in Australia.

During World War II S.T.C. produced large quantities of military type valves for the Australian armed forces. These were mainly of Western Electric or British S.T.C. design though one Australian designed valve, a 350-watt triode type T610, was developed locally. Amongst valves made during the war were several radar types including the famous British-designed pulsed magnetron NT98, and VT90 micropup.

One final Australian valve remains to be mentioned. In June 1923 an announcement appeared indicating that an Australian-designed valve was to be marketed under the name 'G & R'.[6] This valve had been developed by A.J. Garrod and S. Radcliff, both of Sydney, and had been patented by them in January 1923.[7]

A contempory illustration of the valve shows it as having an axial filament surrounded by a coarse ladder grid followed by a widely-spaced box-like anode. Judged by the standards of the day such a design was obviously inefficient and it is not surprising to find that the G & R valve was not a commercial success.

*The information concerning S.T.C.'s valve production was abstracted from *Some Notes on the Manufacture of Electronic Valves by Standard Telephones & Cables, Sydney*, dated Oct. 1, 1974, authored by K.S. Brown.

A group of Australian-made Radiotrons c. 1935.

Australian G & R valve patented Jan. 1923.

(L.) Australian-made Radiotron 6AR7GT (1953). (R.) Radiotrons 6K7GT and 6K8GT made in England by Brimar c. 1955.

REFERENCES

1. Australian Patent No. 17769 of Sept. 2, 1920.
2. J. McDonald, The History of the Receiving Valve, *Radiotronics*, Vol. 22, No. 12, p. 188.
3. See announcement *Wireless Weekly*, Nov. 15, 1931, p. 41.
4. Refer *Philips Data Book*, 1948, p. 3.
5. Ibid., p. 3.
6. Radio Discovers Australian Scientists, *The Australian Wireless Review*, June 1923.
7. Australian Patent No. 10811/23, filed Jan. 24, 1923.

Chapter Twenty-Three

The British Electrical Companies

Ediswan

Undoubtedly the honour of being the world's first manufacturer of radio valves belongs to company known at the time as the Edison & Swan United Electric Co. This company had been formed in 1883 by a merger between Edison's British company, the Edison Electric Light Co., and the Swan Electric Lighting Co. In 1889 J.A. Fleming requested Ediswan to make for him some experimental lamps which would allow him to study the Edison effect at first hand. At this time there was no thought of any practical use for these lamps, Fleming's work being a continuation of his earlier studies of the blackening in use of carbon-filament lamps.

In 1904 Fleming again approached Ediswan, this time with a request for twelve 12-volt carbon-filament lamps each containing a metal sleeve surrounding the filament. These 'lamps' may justly be called the world's first radio valves. Acting on Fleming's suggestion they were put to work by the Marconi Co. as detector diodes in receivers produced by the company. From this time on until the formation of the Marconi-Osram Valve Co. in 1919 all valves used by Marconi's were made by Ediswan.

During World War I Ediswan became one of the several lamp-making companies who made 'R' type valves for the British government for military purposes. After the war Ediswan, in company with these same makers, used the R design as a basis for their first post-war valve production. Besides this Ediswan had by the early 1920s initiated production of their 'ES' series which ran from the type ES1 of 1920 to the ES6 of 1926. It seems likely that the R type was renamed the ES1 as the two appear to be identical. An interesting feature of their construction was the use of a cruciform or star shaped stem seal in place of the conventional flat pinch.

Another item of interest is that up to about 1923 some valves bore the marking 'Royal Ediswan' in the same way as did the electric lamps made by the company. It may be mentioned for the benefit of non-British readers that the word 'Royal' used in this manner signified that the Edison Swan Co. had supplied lamps to the Royal Household,

originally to Queen Alexandra (wife of Edward VII) in 1913. This entitled the company to apply for a Royal Warrant permitting them to use the words 'By Appointment to H.M. Queen Alexandra, purveyors of Electric Lamps and Fittings' in their advertising. This Royal Appointment carried on throughout the reign of Edward VII and in turn the company was re-appointed by King George V and King George VI; the appointment finally lapsing with the death of the latter in 1952. By this time lamps were no longer being marketed under the Ediswan brandname.

Concerning the use of the word 'Royal' on Ediswan valves it may safely be assumed that this could not have

Royal Ediswan valves c. 1922. Note cruciform stem seal on the R type (L.).

occurred before 1913 and thus any valve so marked must have been made after this date. It is known that Ediswan valves continued to carry the word Royal up to the time the type AR was issued in 1922 but the use ceased abruptly thereafter. Because of this sudden cessation of use of the word Royal on radio valves it may be assumed that it had never been authorised in the first place and that someone had finally awakened to the fact and done something about it. After all it was most unlikely that valves

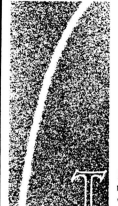
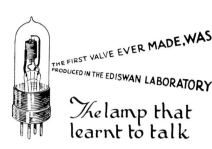
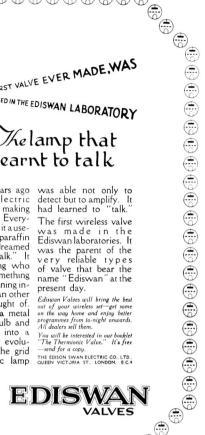
were ever supplied to any Royal Household in the way that lamps were.

Production of Ediswan valves during the 1920s followed the general trend throughout the industry with dull-emitters appearing in 1923, power output types in 1924, specialised HF and LF types in 1925, definite 2-, 4-, and 6-volt groupings in 1927, screen-grid types in 1928 and pentodes in 1929.

In 1927, however, the winds of change blew strong for it was in this year that Ediswan was merged with B.T-H. and Met-Vick to become a unit of a new organisation known as Associated Electrical Industries Ltd. (AEI). Under the new setup a policy of rationalisation in valve manufacture resulted in receiving-valve production being concentrated under the name 'Mazda'. This same name had previously been in use for lamps made by B.T-H. and it continued to be so used. Previously, as independent companies, B.T-H., Ediswan, and Cosmos had each produced and marketed valves under their respective brand-names. Commencing in 1928 the name Cosmos was withdrawn while by the end of 1929 the name Ediswan had been completely replaced by Mazda. However, the name

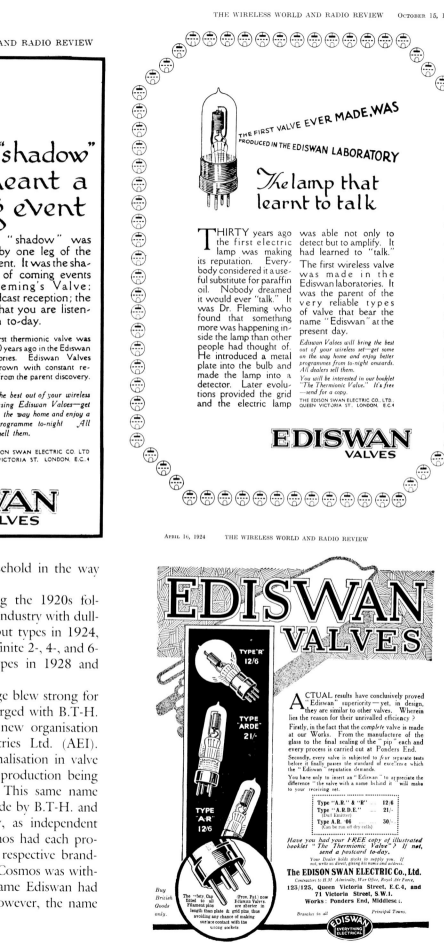

Ediswan was retained for use on non-receiving valves as well as being used on valves sold in certain countries where the name Mazda could not be used due to copyright restrictions.

Following the merger Mazda grew to be one of the foremost British valve manufacturers and one of the most British in outlook, in spite of the American origins and connections of two of the AEI units. The company's story is continued under the title Mazda.

Ediswan Valves to 1929

Type	Approx. Date First Issued	Type	Approx. Date First Issued
R	1916	PV1	
ES1	1919	PV2	
ES2	1921	PV3	
ES4	1921	PV4	
ES5	1922	PV5	All 1925
ES220	1927	PV6	
		PV5DE	
AR	1922	PV6DE	
AR.06	1923	PV8DE	
AR.DE	1923		
AR.DE(HF)	1925	RC210	
AR.DE(LF)	1925	HF210	
AR.06(HF)	1925	LF210	2-volt group 1926–27
		PV215	
MI41	1928	PV225	
MI41RC	1928	RC410	
5E1225	1928	HF410	
5E415	1928	LF410	4-volt group 1926–27
		LF410A	
HV235	1928	PV425	
		RC610	
GP2	1926	HF610	
DR2	1926	LF610	6-volt group 1926–27
RC2	1926	PV610	
		PV625	
SG215	1928	PV625A	

Two versions of the Ediswan PV2.

Four versions of the Ediswan 'AR.'

SG410	1928
SG610	1928

Notes–the prefix 'AR' is supposed to indicate 'Amateur Receiving'.
> The types MI41 were the first Ediswan indirectly-heated AC mains valves.
> Type HV235 was the only mains rectifier valve.
> Type 5E225 & 5E415 were Ediswan's first 'Five Electrode' pentode output valves.
> Types 'PV' were Power (output) Valves.

Another old-established and prominent electrical manufacturer, also a maker of electric lamps, the British Thompson-Houston Co. was similarly called upon to use its lamp-making expertise and facilities to produce radio valves during World War I. As in the case of the other companies B.T.-H. continued making valves after the war and marketed them under the B.T.-H. brand. In addition B.T-H was one of the first of the electric companies to produce and market radio receivers which they sold under the American brandname 'Radiola'.

B.T-H. had been formed in 1896 taking its name from an American company, the Thompson-Houston Electric Co., which later became the General Electric Co. (GE). Initially the American connection had a strong influence on B.T-H.'s valve making techniques which is evident from the similarity in the construction of most of the early valves produced. Such valves may be distinguished by the vertically-mounted planar electrodes used in conjunction with inverted vee filaments. One type, the B4, even carried the same filament rating as the American type 201-A although being fitted with a British type base. Furthermore, at least three of the early valves—types B3, B4, B6—are known to have been available with American type UV bases.

During their production lifetime, which ended in 1928, B.T-H. valves were perhaps somewhat less popular than other makes and, in the early days at least, were not as well known nor as widely used. This was no reflection on the valves themselves but may be explained by the fact that the company was mainly concerned with the production of heavy electrical equipment and as a result the radio side of the business remained relatively unimportant. Be that as it may the fact that B.T-H. had lagged somewhat in valve development can be gauged by referring to the *Wireless World* Valve Data published in August 1927 wherein B.T-H. was the only major manufacturer not listing at least one screen-grid valve nor any indirectly-heated AC types. However, it is only fair to mention that with the formation of AEI in 1927 B.T-H., as one of the three constituent companies, was the first to phase out the manufacture of receiving valves and this factor undoubtedly accounted for the company's poor showing at this time. By the end of 1928 the production of receiving valves under the B.T-H. name had ceased entirely.

Towards the end of 1928, presumably as the first step in a policy of rationalisation resulting from the formation of AEI, the name B.T.-H. was withdrawn and replaced by the name Mazda. This particular brandname had long been used for electric lamps made in the U.S. by GE and Westinghouse; now it was to be used on radio valves made in England as well as for valves made in France by French Thompson-Houston.

In September 1928 a new range of 16 types of valves

B.T.H. types B3, B4, B5.

bearing the Mazda brandname was advertised by B.T-H. All were battery triodes carrying the then usual 2-, 4-, and 6-volt filament ratings and were stated to be made at the company's Coventry factory. Shortly after this several indirectly-heated AC valves made by Met-Vick, and formerly marketed under that company's Cosmos name, were added to the Mazda range.

Towards the end of 1929 the first advertisements linking the names Ediswan and Mazda appeared and from then on any reference to B.T-H. was discontinued. The phasing out of the Cosmos and B.T-H. names had been completed by the end of 1929, after which time the name Mazda remained in sole use for receiving valves and cathode-ray tubes sold on the home market while the name Ediswan was reserved for use on industrial, special-purpose, and transmitting valves. In the case of valves exported to certain countries where the name Mazda could not be used due to copyright restrictions the name Ediswan was used instead. In February 1930 the new AEI logo was featured in Mazda advertisements for the first time and remained in use throughout the 1930s and 1940s.

Throughout the 1930s Mazda grew to be one of the foremost names on the British market with Mazda valves being used by many of the leading set makers. An event which, perhaps more than anything else, was responsible for bringing the name Mazda into the limelight was the introduction of an entirely new range of valves in 1938. In doing this Mazda, as sponsor of the new valves had hoped for the co-operation of other B.V.A. members in making the new design an industry standard to be taken up by all members to the exclusion of foreign designs. Perhaps Mazda had reckoned without the foreign connections of other manufacturers but, whatever the reason was, the fact remains that no such co-operation was forthcoming and Mazda was consequently forced to go it alone.

B.T.-H Mazda

Whilst the concept of an industry standard was obviously praiseworthy in principle the suggestion really came

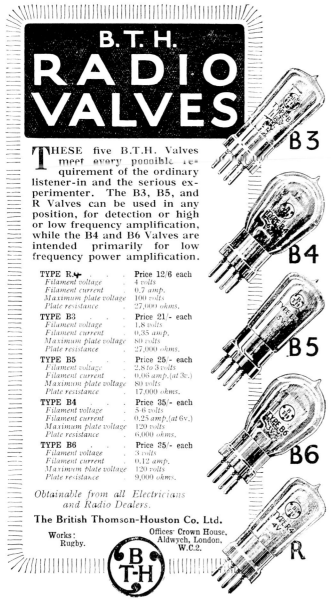

B.T.H. RADIO VALVES

THESE five B.T.H. Valves meet every possible requirement of the ordinary listener-in and the serious experimenter. The B3, B5, and R Valves can be used in any position, for detection or high or low frequency amplification, while the B4 and B6 Valves are intended primarily for low frequency power amplification.

TYPE R. . . Price 12/6 each
Filament voltage . 4 volts
Filament current . 0.7 amp.
Maximum plate voltage . 100 volts
Plate resistance . 27,000 ohms.

TYPE B3 . . Price 21/- each
Filament voltage . 1.8 volts
Filament current . 0.35 amp.
Maximum plate voltage . 80 volts
Plate resistance . 27,000 ohms.

TYPE B5 . . Price 25/- each
Filament voltage . 2.8 to 3 volts
Filament current . 0.06 amp. (at 3v.)
Maximum plate voltage . 80 volts
Plate resistance . 17,000 ohms.

TYPE B4 . . Price 35/- each
Filament voltage . 5-6 volts
Filament current . 0.25 amp. (at 6v.)
Maximum plate voltage . 120 volts
Plate resistance . 6,000 ohms.

TYPE B6 . . Price 35/- each
Filament voltage . 3 volts
Filament current . 0.12 amp.
Maximum plate voltage . 120 volts
Plate resistance . 9,000 ohms.

Obtainable from all Electricians and Radio Dealers.

The British Thomson-Houston Co. Ltd.

Works: Rugby. Offices: Crown House, Aldwych, London, W.C.2.

Cossor as the major uncommitted B.V.A. member and it is understood that they were prepared to co-operate in the proposed scheme provided unanimity amongst other

B. T-H Valves, 1915–1928			
R	1916–1924	B8	1925
R4	1924	B11	1927
B2	1926	B12	1928
B3	1924	B22	1927
B4	1924	B23	1927
B4H	1925	B210H	1927
B5	1924	B215P	1927
B5H	1925	PX650	1028
B7	1925	RH1	1927

New Series 1928		
2 volt	4 volt	6 volt
RC210	RC407	RC607
HF210	HF407	HF607
GP210	GP407	GP607
LF215	LF407	LF607
P227	P415	P615
SG207		

members could be achieved. With Brimar, M-O.V., and Mullard already committed to their respective policies it is not surprising that unanimity was not achieved, at which time it might have been thought that the scheme would have collapsed through lack of support. Not so! Having initiated the designs for the proposed new range Mazda proceeded to go it alone.

In May 1938 the first two types in a new range of 2-volt battery valves were advertised for sale and by the end of the year a limited range in the 4-volt AC and 200 mA AC/DC series was available. Apart from output valves and rectifiers these valves were noticeably smaller than any existing British designs, though no smaller than the continental designed Red E series marketed at almost the same time by Mullard.

The feature that set the Mazda valves apart was the use of a non-standard type of octal base which differed slightly from the American style and was not interchangeable with it. Indeed so similar was the Mazda octal to the American that to a casual observer the two appeared identical. The adoption of a 'near octal' base was criticised at the time and in retrospect it must be admitted that the criticism was justified. All that the new base succeeded in doing was to gain for Mazda the dubious distinction of being the only valve maker in the world to produce a range of valves having a type of base not used by any other manufacturer.

Before the production of valves using the so-called 'British octal' base (officially shortened to B.O.) was finally discontinued, a few odd types appeared during and just after World War II. These included 6.3-volt versions of the SP41 and VP41 known as SP61 and VP61, as well as types 6F32, V453, U22. In addition an extremely short-

too late for it to have had much chance of succeeding for by 1938 most of the major valve makers were already committed to other designs. Furthermore the introduction of yet another range of valves at the time could be, and was, criticised on the grounds that it would only add to the growing proliferation and confusion already existing in the industry.

By 1938 there were already three disparate groupings of valve design origins apparent on the British scene—indigenous, American and continental. For example, Mullard had introduced a range of continental style side-contact valves as early as 1934, whilst in 1937 M-O.V. had marketed a range patterned on the American octal-based G series; Brimar, too, were turning increasingly to the production of American type valves and by 1938 had also marketed a range of octal-based types. This left only lived range of 1.4-volt battery types—SP141, FC141, H141, Pen141—was marketed briefly in 1947–48. In view of Mazda's attachment to their 'baby' it is somewhat surprising to find that by 1949 quite a lot of valves had been issued using the formerly despised American-style octal base. The writer is unable to offer any explanation for this apparent change of heart though the thought occurs that Mazda may have eventually become tired of being the odd man out.

Following the end of World War II, with the prospect of miniaturisation looming large on the horizon, Mazda apparently felt that the time was ripe to repeat their earlier effort and attempt to introduce another exclusively British range of valves which would hopefully form a post-war standard for the industry. This time, however, Mazda found a solitary collaborator in Mullard who, together with their parent company in Holland, were anxious to get production of miniature type valves under way. On this occasion Mullard's willingness to join in was probably influenced by the fact that Philips' ability to carry out developmental work must have been hampered by wartime conditions. Thus it was in their own interests to co-operate rather than compete on this occasion.

The first British miniature valves were announced by Mazda and Mullard in December 1946. Whilst the products of these two makers mostly had identical characteristics and were interchangeable in their basing arrangements the bases themselves differed in detail. Both makes were fitted with a metal-shell skirt which carried a locating/latching device, but the Mazda differed in having an elongated guide pin positioned at the pin circle centre. This type of base became known as B8A and the valves themselves were referred to as B8A miniatures. The Mullard valves were actually identical to a range produced by Philips in Holland and also by Telefunken and Valvo in Germany, the Philips-Mullard being referred to as 'Rimlock' types.

With the introduction of the B8A series history repeated itself in that British valve makers were still divided in their loyalties and once again a proposed new industry standard failed to gain a majority acceptance. Mazda and Mullard remained the only two firms making the B8A miniatures whilst the remaining manufacturers opted for the American 7-pin design, known in the U.K. as B7G. Although committed to the B8A design Mazda nevertheless did produce some B7G types, including a range of 1.4-volt battery valves which were identical to their American counterparts.

In common with the remaining valve makers, Mazda eventually concentrated on production of miniature types in the American 9-pin noval series, known in Britain as B9G. After 1960, as a result of a merger between Associated Electrical Industries Ltd. and Thorn Electrical Industries Ltd., manufacture of Ediswan-Mazda receiving valves and picture tubes was merged with Brimar; both brands

then being produced by a new company known as Thorn-AEI Radio Valves & Tubes Ltd.

Cosmos

One further old-established electrical manufacturer who became involved in valve making as a result of lamp-making activities was the Metropolitan-Vickers Electrical Co. Ltd. This firm had its origin in the union of two other companies—a lamp factory which had been established in 1908 by a German named Julius Pintsch, and the British Westinghouse Electrical & Mfg. Co. Ltd. which had been established in 1889. In 1917 the British Westinghouse operation was taken over by Vickers Ltd. and at the same time the German owned lamp factory also passed into British hands and became known as the Cosmos Lamp Works Ltd. This led in 1919 to the formation of the Metropolitan-Vickers Electrical Co. Ltd. and in 1924 a subsidiary known as Metro-Vick Supplies Ltd. was formed to handle the distribution of radio products. In 1928 a further merger occurred when Met-Vick joined with B.T-H. and Ediswan to form Associated Electrical Industries Ltd.

Met-Vick first became involved in valve manufacture

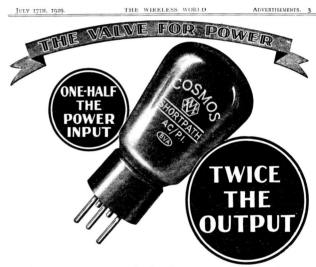

195

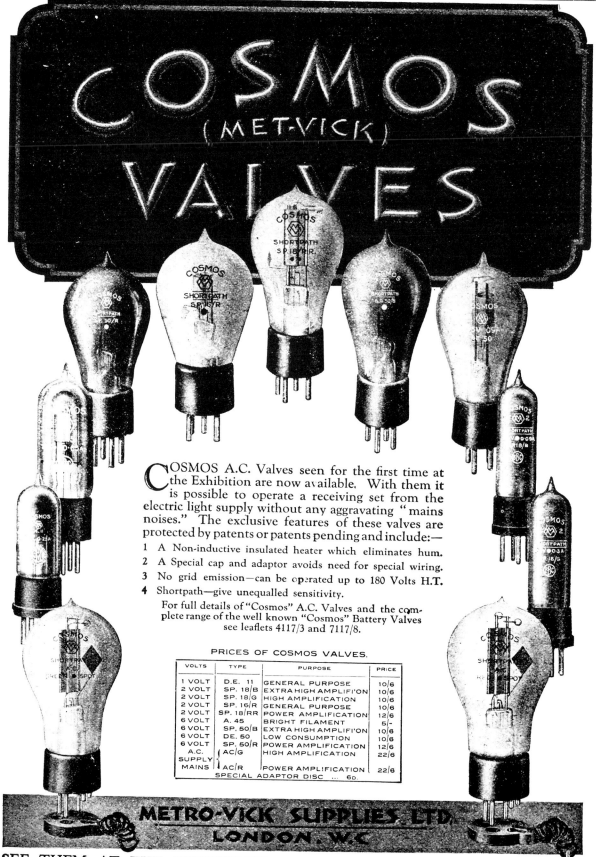

COSMOS (MET-VICK) VALVES

COSMOS A.C. Valves seen for the first time at the Exhibition are now available. With them it is possible to operate a receiving set from the electric light supply without any aggravating "mains noises." The exclusive features of these valves are protected by patents or patents pending and include:—

1 A Non-inductive insulated heater which eliminates hum.
2 A Special cap and adaptor avoids need for special wiring.
3 No grid emission—can be operated up to 180 Volts H.T.
4 Shortpath—give unequalled sensitivity.

For full details of "Cosmos" A.C. Valves and the complete range of the well known "Cosmos" Battery Valves see leaflets 4117/3 and 7117/8.

PRICES OF COSMOS VALVES.

VOLTS	TYPE	PURPOSE	PRICE
1 VOLT	D.E. 11	GENERAL PURPOSE	10/6
2 VOLT	SP. 18/B	EXTRA HIGH AMPLIFI'ON	10/6
2 VOLT	SP. 18/G	HIGH AMPLIFICATION	10/6
2 VOLT	SP. 16/R	GENERAL PURPOSE	10/6
2 VOLT	SP. 18/RR	POWER AMPLIFICATION	12/6
6 VOLT	A. 45	BRIGHT FILAMENT	5/-
6 VOLT	SP. 50/B	EXTRA HIGH AMPLIFI'ON	10/6
6 VOLT	DE. 50	LOW CONSUMPTION	10/6
6 VOLT	SP. 50/R	POWER AMPLIFICATION	12/6
A.C. SUPPLY MAINS	AC/G	HIGH AMPLIFICATION	22/6
	AC/R	POWER AMPLIFICATION	22/6
SPECIAL ADAPTOR DISC ... 6D.			

METRO-VICK SUPPLIES, LTD. LONDON, W.C.

SEE THEM AT THE EXHIBITION   :   :   :   STANDS Nos. 155-156

during the 1914–18 war when the lamp factory was taken over by the British government. Developmental work on R type valves was initiated in 1915 which resulted in production being achieved in the following year.[1]

After the war Met-Vick was early on the scene with the production of radio receivers and the necessary valves to equip them. Both these items were marketed under the brandname 'Cosmos', a name which had first been used for electric lamps. Three types of valve were produced initially, two dull emitters, types D.E.11 and S.P.18, and a bright emitter type A.45.[2] The latter was descended from the standard wartime R type and had the usual filament rating of 4 volts 0.65 amps. With its tubular bulb and vertical electrode assembly the A.45 resembled such better-known makes as the Mullard ORA or the Ediswan AR.

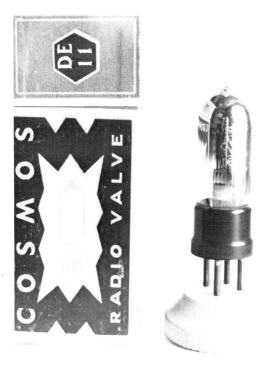

Cosmos DE11. Note limegetter on pinch.

Of the dull emitters the D.E.11 is particularly interesting because it was, apart from the Mullard Wecovalve, the only British-made valve of the period to make use of an oxide-coated filament intended to operate from a single dry cell. The significance of this feature makes a closer investigation into the origin of the D.E.11 desirable because the particular type of filament employed and the use of a chemical getter were covered by Westinghouse patents.

When it is recalled that Met-Vick had descended from British Westinghouse, and thus could be expected to have had access to the American parent company's patents and manufacturing techniques, it becomes apparent that the Cosmos D.E.11 was, to all intents and purposes, simply a British-made version of the Westinghouse WD-11 which differed only in the type of base fitted to it. The following tabulation is offered in support of the author's contention. At the same time it also serves to refute a published statement that the D.E.11 was of British design.*

Points of Similarity Between D.E.11 and WD-11

1. Use of an oxide-coated filament.
2. Use of chemical getter (visible as a white paste applied to the sides of the pinch).
3. Identical style of electrode structure.
4. Identical ratings and characteristics.
5. Similarity of the type numbers.

Regarding 1, it is worth bearing in mind that the only other British-made valve of the period to use an oxide-coated filament, the Mullard Wecovalve, was also of American design.

The first Cosmos valve to show signs of independent British design was the type S.P.18 which appeared early in 1925.[3] The letters 'S.P.' in the type number stood for 'Short Path' and indicated that the electrode spacing was closer than that in common use. The Short Path design is credited to Met-Vick's chief valve design engineer, E. Yeoman Robinson, a man whose name was to become well known a little later on for a highly efficient form of indirectly-heated cathode.

By 1926 the Cosmos range had been increased to six types with the addition of the first power output valve, type S.P.55R, while the S.P.18 was now produced in three different versions. At this time a scheme of colour coding (an idea which was already in use by other makers) was introduced for the purpose of indicating the suitability of a given valve for a particular application. In practice this took the form of a small paint spot applied adjacent to the type number marked on the bulb, while the type number itself also incorporated a coded suffix R, B, or G indicating the colours red, blue, or green. Red indicated an output valve, blue a resistance-coupled type and green a general purpose type.

The first Cosmos indirectly-heated AC valves, types AC/G and AC/R appeared in September 1929[4] and their release must be regarded as a landmark in the development of this class of valve because they were the first in the world to make use of a new and revolutionary design of heater-cathode insulation, details of which are given in another chapter.

Towards the end of 1928 a screen-grid valve, the AC/S,[5] was announced and early in 1929 three more triodes including two output valves were added to the range, making a total of six types. All these Short Path AC valves were indirectly-heated which made the two output valves

*See Gerald F.J. Tyne, *Saga of the Vacuum Tube*, p. 373.

unique among their British contemporaries at a time when such types were always directly-heated.

Because at the time of their introduction in 1927 there existed no British standard in the matter of bases for AC valves Met-Vick devised an ingenious type of 5-pin base which, together with an adaptor, allowed Cosmos valves to be used in the normal 4-pin sockets. As in the case of the American Kellogg AC tubes the idea was to allow the electrification of existing battery-fed receivers without the necessity of making changes in wiring. At the same time Met-Vick also offered special 5-pin sockets which allowed the new valves to be used as initial equipment without the need for any adaptors.[6]

In spite of being early on the scene with AC valves Met-Vick appeared to lag in the production of HT rectifiers, for until 1928 no such valves were listed in the Cosmos range. However, as the *Wireless World* Show Report for 1927 mentioned two Cosmos rectifiers (of unspecified type numbers) it would seem that Met-Vick initially produced rectifiers only for use in their own HT battery eliminators. Cosmos rectifying valves were first listed in the 1928 *Wireless World* valve data published in September of that year.

Following the formation of AEI in 1928 the brandname Cosmos was gradually phased out although advertisements for Cosmos valves continued to appear until at least July 1929 by which time the new AEI brandname Mazda had become well established.

Marconi-Osram

In view of the increasing importance of the thermionic valve in both receiving and transmitting aspects of radio communication, as evidenced by its military applications during World War I, the Marconi Co. apparently decided to become more directly involved in valve making after the war. Prior to this time Marconi valves had been made by the Edison Swan Electric Co. but in October 1919 an arrangement was entered into with the General Electric Co. (GEC) which resulted in the formation of a new jointly owned company known as the Marconi-Osram Valve Co. (M-O.V.). In 1920 the name was changed to the M-O. Valve Co.

As one of the foremost electric lamp manufacturers GEC had, in common with others in the same field, first gained experience in valve making during the war when they supplied valves made to military specifications for the British government. These valves were the standardised 'R' type and its variations which all carried the company's 'Osram' trade-mark in addition to the appropriate military markings.

After 1919 all Marconi valves, both transmitting and receiving types, were made at GEC's Hammersmith factory. At the same time GEC was free to market valves separately under the Osram name but for some reason did not initially do so, probably because there was practically no retail market in existence at the time. The large quantities of war surplus available from 'disposals' sources was adequate to cater for what little demand there was. Even after 1922, when GEC became one of the founding fathers of the British Broadcasting Company and had commenced making receivers under the 'Gecophone' brandname, the company did not advertise valves under the Osram name until the end of 1925. Up to this time all valves made by M-O.V. bore the inscription Marconi Valve Made at the Osram Lamp Works, but after October 1925 the existing arrangement was altered and GEC commenced marketing valves under the Osram* brandname. This brand was already in use for electric lamps and continued to be so used after its extension to include valves. From this time GEC and Marconi's each separately promoted their own brandnames until 1929 when the latter company relinquished its interest in the manufacture and sale of domestic radio receivers and associated equipment.

In December 1929 a policy decision resulted in the dis-

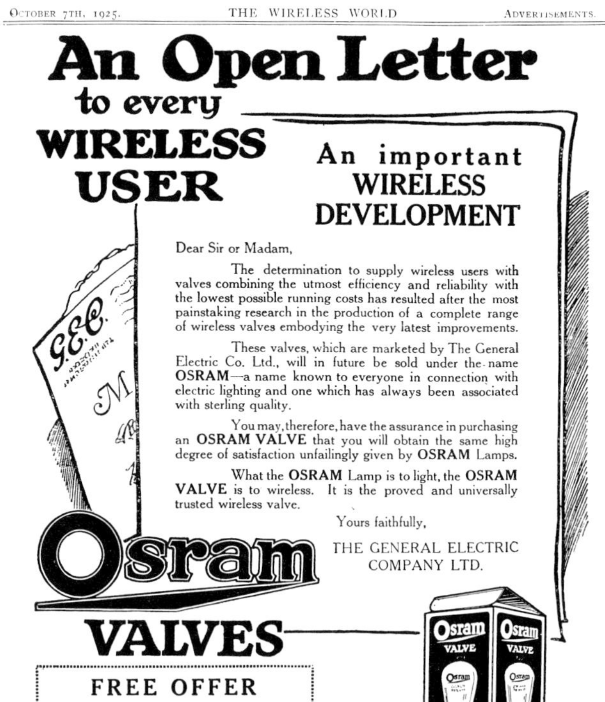

OCTOBER 7TH, 1925.
THE WIRELESS WORLD
ADVERTISEMENTS.
An Open Letter to every WIRELESS USER
An important WIRELESS DEVELOPMENT
Dear Sir or Madam,
The determination to supply wireless users with valves combining the utmost efficiency and reliability with the lowest possible running costs has resulted after the most painstaking research in the production of a complete range of wireless valves embodying the very latest improvements.
These valves, which are marketed by The General Electric Co. Ltd., will in future be sold under the name OSRAM—a name known to everyone in connection with electric lighting and one which has always been associated with sterling quality.
You may, therefore, have the assurance in purchasing an OSRAM VALVE that you will obtain the same high degree of satisfaction unfailingly given by OSRAM Lamps.
What the OSRAM Lamp is to light, the OSRAM VALVE is to wireless. It is the proved and universally trusted wireless valve.
Yours faithfully,
THE GENERAL ELECTRIC COMPANY LTD.
Osram
VALVES
FREE OFFER
THE KEY TO PERFECT WIRELESS RECEPTION
An extremely useful and novel indicator card showing at a glance the right type of valve for any working condition will be sent post free on application to Publicity Dept., The General Electric Co. Ltd., Magnet House, Kingsway, London, W.C. 2.
Name
Address
Osram VALVE
Worth its weight in gold
Sold by all leading Wireless Dealers, Electrical Contractors and Stores.
Advt. of The General Electric Co. Ltd., Magnet House, Kingsway, London, W.C 2
In answering this advertisement it is desirable to mention "The Wireless World."

*In the case of valves exported to certain countries where the name Osram could not be used due to copyright restrictions such valves were sold under the name Gecovalve.

posal of the wholly owned Marconiphone Co., as well as Marconi's interest in the M-O. Valve Co., to the Gramophone Co. (HMV). At the time HMV was half-owned by RCA and it is known that a certain gentleman by the name of David Sarnoff was largely responsible for HMV's acquiring these assets. Under the terms of the takeover agreement Marconi's were to refrain from trading in the so-called 'entertainment' field for a period of twenty years, that is until 1949.[7] The existing arrangement with GEC in regard to valve manufacture was carried on by HMV and valves continued to be produced under both the Osram and Marconi brandnames. The fact that valves carrying the world-famous Marconi name were now being made and distributed by a company with which Marconi's had no connection may occasion some surprise but it is nevertheless quite true. Even more surprising is the fact that in addition to relinquishing the Marconiphone trademark Marconi's also ceded the 'personal signature' trademark

The 'personal signature' trade-mark used by the Marconi Co. until 1930.

'G. Marconi'. Here too the hand of the astute Mr. Sarnoff can be seen.

Apart from the existing Osram and Marconi brand-names the name HMV was also used briefly on valves fitted to HMV receivers during the early 1930s. Incidentally, it is interesting to note that some time later the famous 'Little Nipper' (listening dog) trademark was also used on valves made on the other side of the Atlantic and sold under the RCA Victor and Canadian Victor labels.

Reverting now to the period just prior to the establishment of M-O.V., mention must be made of some of the earliest valves which carried the Marconi trademark. Captain H.J. Round of the Marconi Co. was responsible for the design of a unique type of triode first produced in 1916. Initially two versions were issued, types V.24 and Q, the latter being a detector (referred to in the language of the day as a rectifier). A third type known as QX was added after the end of the war. All three were special low-capacity types having their electrode connections brought out to widely spaced contact points mounted directly on the bulb surface. The filament rating was 5 volts at 0.75 amps for the V.24 and QX, and for the type Q 0.4 amps.

The M-O.V. Co. was the first British manufacturer to develop dull-emitter valves having thoriated filaments, their L.T.1 being marketed as early as 1921,[8] some two years before the first American type had appeared. The L.T.1 carried a filament rating of 1.8 V, 0.06 A and was intended to operate from a single 2-volt lead-acid cell (ac-

Wireless World JULY 10, 1920.

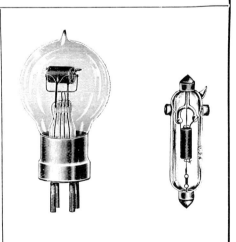

cumulator). To what extent this early design was successful is difficult to estimate but it is known that the valve later underwent some modification after which it became known as type D.E.R. In its later form it was being advertised up to 1925.

In view of the original work done on thoriated filaments by General Electric in America it is surprising that British development was sufficiently far advanced to enable the marketing of a dull-emitter valve at this early date.

Other early dull emitters were types DEQ, DEV, DE2, DE3, DE5, DE7, and FE3. Of these the DE3 which had a filament rating of 2.8 V, 0.06 A was the first British thoriated-filament valve intended for dry-cell working.

Marconi DE3, DE5, DE6 early dull emitter types.

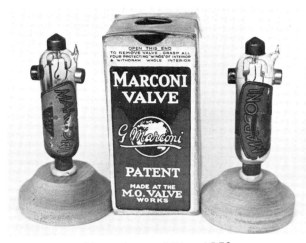

Marconi types DEV and DEQ.

A word concerning the prefix 'DE' used in the type numbers of M-O.V. valves made during the 1920s. As may be surmised, these letters stood for Dull Emitter; they were introduced in 1923 and discontinued in 1928. Some of the last valves to carry the DE prefix were such types as the DEH210 and DEL610 which after 1928 became known as H210 and L610, respectively. In the case

of certain early transmitting valves which also carried the DE prefix in their type numbers the use was retained for a much longer period. Valves so marked were being issued up to the 1950s, an example being type DET28.

The year 1924 saw the introduction of the first power output valves, starting with the LS1 and continuing to the LS6A of 1929. The letters 'LS' incorporated in their type

'Little Nipper' in three countries: Canada, Gr. Britain, U.S.A.

numbers indicated that such valves were intended for loud-speaker working. The company was a pioneer in the production of high efficiency output triodes and their PX4 and PX25 were world leaders, the former being released some four years ahead of RCA's type 2A3.

Early in 1927 the first British indirectly-heated AC valves were produced by M-O.V.; those under the Marconi label being first advertised in February of that year.[9] Two types were available, known as KH1 and KL1, but unfortunately their design was not entirely satisfactory and it is known that replacements were later made for M-O.V. by Met-Vick. Towards the end of 1928 a completely new range of directly-heated AC valves was marketed, a move which can be taken as an indication that the company's experience with indirectly-heated types had been less than encouraging. The first three issues in the new range consisted of a low-mu and a high-mu triode plus an output triode, types HL.8, H.8, and P.8 respectively.[10] These valves had short thick filaments rated at 0.8 volts, 0.8 amps and were known as the 'Point 8' series, the name rather obviously being derived from the filament rating. In 1929 a screen-grid, type S.8, and an output pentode, type PT.8 and a special detector, type D.8 were added to the range. The D.8 differed from the others in having an extra thick filament rated at 1.6 amps, the doubling of the current obviously being an attempt to further increase the thermal inertia and thus reduce the hum level.

Towards the end of 1929 the first valves in a completely new range of 4-volt indirectly-heated types appeared and by 1931 the range had been extended to include a vari-mu RF pentode and two output pentodes. The following year saw the production of the first valves designed for series-heater operation on DC mains. These valves had a uniform heater rating of 16 volts, 0.25 amps but it should be noted that this rating was not an agreed industry standard and only two other makers, Cossor and Lissen, produced valves with the same heater ratings. Two years later such valves were rendered obsolete by the introduction of the first British AC/DC types which appeared in 1934. This new range used the standard American 300 mA heater rating but here again even this rating was not accepted as an industry standard, Ferranti and Cossor being the only other British manufacturers to adopt it.

In 1933 M-O.V. were responsible for the production of the world's first 'all-metal' valves which were marketed under the name 'Catkin'. However, very few types were produced and by 1936 they were no longer being manufactured.

The next development was M-O.V.'s decision in 1937 to standardise on the production of American type octal-based glass valves, a move which initiated a trend in the industry for by 1940 most of the leading valve makers had followed suit.

Following the end of World War II M-O.V. became the first British manufacturer to produce American-style 7-pin

(B7G) miniature valves which were marketed in 1947. At the same time a separate range based on the American loctal design was also put into production.

In 1946 the Marconi Co. was acquired by the English Electric Co., though it continued to operate as before. The change of ownership, incidentally, occurred three years before the 20-year marketing agreement between Marconi's and E.M.I. was due to expire in 1949, though whether the latter event had any bearing on the matter is not known. It seems unlikely, however, that Marconi's would have chosen to re-enter the fields of domestic radio receiver or valve production after such a long absence. Although the English Electric Co. became active in the production of transmitting and special-purpose valves they did not produce receiving types. Their closest association with the entertainment side of the industry came when they made a brief incursion into the manufacture of metal-cone picture tubes during the 1950s. The E.E.V. Co. was the only British producer of this class of picture tube.

By comparison E.M.I. remained deeply involved in the entertainment side of the industry and not only retained their interest in M-O.V. but, in 1949, expanded in this area by purchasing the valve-making division of A.C. Cossor Ltd. In 1946 Cossor's had reorganised this division, following an agreement made with the American firm of Sylvania, when a new company known as Electronic Tubes Ltd. had been established.

Under E.M.I.'s ownership production of valves and tubes was continued with marketing being done under the brandname 'Emitron'. In 1957 E.T.L. was sold to Mullard Ltd. who used the factory to increase their production of picture tubes. Prior to this, in July 1956, E.M.I. had disposed of its half-share of M-O.V. to GEC who thus became sole owners of the valve company. Production of receiving valves under the GEC and Osram brandnames continued until the late 1970s.

Standard Telephones and Cables Ltd.

The American firm of Western Electric opened a British office in 1883, known as the Western Electric Co. Ltd., to handle sales of telephone equipment. With the advent of broadcasting the parent company commenced to manufacture a limited range of broadcast receiving apparatus some of which was sold in the U.K. When the British Broadcasting Company was established in 1922 British WE was one of the six founding members. However, because one of the main objects of the B.B. Co. was to encourage the formation of a British radio manufacturing industry by prohibiting the importation of foreign apparatus one may be pardoned for thinking that British WE was suffering from a self-inflicted wound at that time. In spite of this the company remained active in the transmitting field, presumably because transmitting apparatus was unaffected by the ban.

It was the company's initial lack of manufacturing facilities that resulted in the first British valve production being carried out by Mullard. During 1923–24 the American-designed 215A 'peanut' valve was being offered for sale by Mullard under the name 'Wecovalve' and by British WE under the type number 4215A, the four-digit number indicating section 4000 in the British catalogue.

When I.T. & T. acquired the International Western Electric Co. in 1925 this firm became the International Standard Electric Co. (ISEC) and this in turn resulted in British WE becoming Standard Telephones & Cables Ltd. (STC).* A similar change of identity occurred in other British countries where WE had previously been established. For example, the Australian and New Zealand branches became Standard Telephones & Cables A/sia Ltd. Rather obviously it was as a result of the word 'Standard' appearing in the American company's corporate title that the same word was used in the re-naming of the British company.

*It should be noted that the correct company logogram consists of the three letters STC only without the ampersand. The spoken contraction is *not* ST and C.

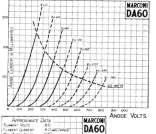

Under its new name the British company continued to follow the same pattern of activities as before but with the growth of broadcasting as a new medium of entertainment the company entered the field of receiver production as well as commencing valve manufacture. The first valves produced were marketed under the tradename Standard and consisted of two versions of the peanut valve which had originally been made by Mullard. These were now known as types G125 and H125; the letters G and H indicating General Purpose and High Frequency, respectively. Normally both types were fitted with the standard British 4-pin type of base but were also available with the original WE style base, in which case the suffix A was added to the type numbers. By 1926 the first British-designed valves were being offered for sale, though initially only two types, the P425 and P612, were available.[11] In 1927 the range had been increased to ten but due to variations in base styles there were actually only seven different types in the range.

In January 1926 an arrangement was entered into with the Birmingham Small Arms Co. (BSA) whereby STC were to supply receivers and valves which were to be jointly marketed by STC and a new company named BSA Radio Ltd.[12] The valves used in the BSA receivers were branded BSA-STANDARD and carried the same type numbers as the normal Standard Valves. This was a short-lived venture which apparently did not mix with BSA's other activities as within the space of two years it came to an end.

For some years after this STC's activities in the field of receiver and valve manufacture appear to have been in a very low key as no mention of either occurs in the *Wireless World* Radio Show reports for the years 1926 to 1931. However, with the acquisition of Brandes Ltd. and the establishment of Kolster-Brandes Ltd. this company then became, for several years, the System's main British receiver manufacturer although receivers under the Standard brandname were still being produced in 1932.[13] At this time STC also commenced receiver manufacture on behalf of

British Philco, and in this connection it is interesting to note that the Philco receivers were initially equipped with American-made valves.[14]

By comparison with other manufacturers STC were much slower in introducing indirectly-heated AC valves and even as late as the middle of 1932 had none on the market. For this reason it had been necessary to turn to outside suppliers to obtain the valves needed to equip Kolster-Brandes receivers. For example, the K-B model 279 of 1931 used a mixture of Mazda and Mullard valves in conjunction with a Philips rectifier.

Towards the end of 1932 the first release of AC valves under the newly introduced 'Micromesh' brandname was made.[15] Initially only four types were offered—a detector triode, an output triode, and two rectifiers, all of which were indirectly-heated types. Not a very auspicious beginning, considering the lateness of the day but the limited range of types was apparently sufficient to supply the company's own receiver needs for the small 3-valve sets which were then in production.

The valves themselves, however, caused something of a sensation in technical circles at the time of their release due to their phenomenal performance figures. Using the standard British 4V, 1A heater rating the Micromesh detector boasted a mutual conductance of 8 mA/V, while the figure for the PA1 output triode was no less than 12.6 mA/V (12600 micromhos) using the same heater rating! In 1932 such figures were almost unbelievable and it is a

Standard Valves
P425   4239A   P425A/4002A

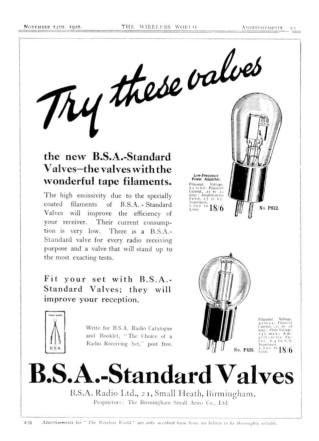

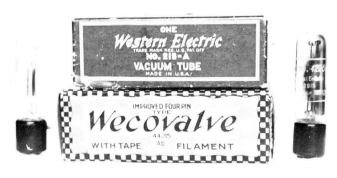

Standard telephones and cables. Wecovalve (R.) compared with a Western Electric 215-A (L.).

matter of record that no comparable valves issued by any other maker ever achieved such efficiencies. To coin a phrase, however, thereby hangs a tale.

It must be said that i-h output triodes as a species have never been an unqualified success, regardless of their country of origin, and the PA1 was no exception. It was, perhaps, too good for its own good and never again did any subsequent Micromesh valves exhibit such high values of mutual conductance for valves of the same type.

STC versions of WE's types 101D and 205D.

The two rectifiers, types R1 and R2, warrant mention not so much because they were among the earliest indirectly-heated types but because as rectifiers they constituted half the entire range of the initial release of Micromesh valves!

The omission of a screen-grid valve from the initial release is rather surprising, considering the date and the fact that such valves were in the limelight at the time. However, something must have been in the pipeline for this deficiency was soon made up. In November 1932 the first two Micromesh SG types, the SGA1 and VSG1 (the latter a vari-mu type) were added to the range.

The first power pentode, type PenA1, was also available by the end of 1932 and at the same time the first 2-volt battery types—HLB1, PB1, and PenB1—were also marketed. By the end of 1933 the first RF pentodes, types 8A1 and 9A1, became available and by this time the Micromesh range consisted of 17 types.

A reorganisation of STC's valve manufacturing activities in 1934 resulted in the phasing out of the Micromesh label and the introduction of what was to become one of the best-known brandnames in the industry—Brimar.[16] At the same time this move signalled a shift towards the production of American-type valves, a trend that was to be accentuated as time went by.

Although American type valves appear to have been made as early as 1933 these were not initially marketed separately in the U.K. The first release of American types under the Brimar label consisted of a range of six types intended for AC/DC service. These valves were of hybrid construction which, while having identical characteristics to equivalent American types, differed in two respects. The heater rating was the European standard 200 mA, compared with the American standard 300 mA and the valves were fitted with British type 7-pin bases. The first six issues comprised types 15D1, 8D2, 9D2, 11D3, 7D3, and 1D5 and were referred to as 'low slope universal types'.[17]

Early Brimar valves c. 1935.

It appears that the decision to embark on the production of American type valves in the U.K. resulted from the need of a European source to equip receivers made not only in the 'System's' British factory (Kolster-Brandes) but also those made in certain other European countries.[18] In addition the recently established British Philco factory provided Brimar with a further outlet for American types.

Because the American parent company itself had no receiving tube manufacturing facilities in the U.S. it seems likely that Brimar must have drawn on some other American source for the know-how needed to enable the production of American type valves to commence. In this connection it is interesting to note that at one period around 1938, certain octal-based valves sold under the Brimar label were actually of American manufacture although this fact was not indicated. Similarly, American-made valves produced during and shortly after World War II are known to have carried the imprint Brimar Made in U.S.A. In the latter case the issuing of valves so marked was probably an attempt to tide over wartime and post-war shortages. At this time too Brimar, in common with some other British valve makers, re-branded and issued certain American war surplus metal valves which in some cases continued to be listed for several years after the end of the war. Examples of such valves listed in Brimar catalogues are 12A6, 12SJ7, 12SK7, 12SR7. Incidentally, the earliest example of an American-made tube to be sold under the Brimar label was the 0Z4 gaeous rectifier, a type made only by Raytheon and first available in the U.K. from about 1937.

The production of American type valves had, by 1938, been expanded to include a range of 21 octal-based types, referred to as 'International Octal', and by 1940 had been further expanded to include a newly introduced range of 14 loctal types. A feature of the 1940 listings was an increase in the number of earlier American type valves being offered, many of which were in effect duplicated by being listed under two slightly different type numbers. An example of this is provided by the type 78/78E, which in the 1937–38 Brimar Valve Manual was the only one so listed. By 1940, however, there were nine such listings, examples being 47/47E and 42/42E. The types carrying the suffix E had identical ratings to standard American types but had marginal differences in characteristics; so marginal in fact as to cause one to ponder on the wisdom of such apparently unnecessary duplication.

As the production of tubes carrying the suffix E in their type numbers had been originated by American Philco it is logical to assume that Brimar's production of similar types had been in response to a specific demand. Rather obviously that demand could have come from only one source—British Philco. The origin of American Philco's use of the suffix E is believed to be that tubes so marked were intended for use in export model receivers.

Following the end of World War II Brimar continued the production of both octal- and loctal-based valves as, apart from replacement use, such types were still needed for initial equipment purposes. It was at this time that Brimar also introduced the American GT (Bantam) octal-based series to the British market and as in the land of their origin they gradually superseded the older G types. Brimar was also one of the first manufacturers to intro-

A group of Brimar valves c. 1938.

206

duce the American 7-pin (B7G) miniature series which by 1951 consisted of a range of 32 types. Not all of these were strictly replicas of American designs as five types —9D6, 8D5, 8D3, R10, R12—had no direct American equivalents.

It was during the late 1950s and early 1960s that the winds of change blew strong in the British radio industry and many were the mergers taking place during this period. At this time, too, STC moved further away from the entertainment side of the industry by disposing of the Brimar Valve Division to a newly established firm known as Thorn-AEI Radio Valves & Tubes Ltd.[19] This company took over the production of receiving valves and picture tubes under the Brimar and Mazda labels, leaving AEI and STC to continue separately with the production of transmitting and special purpose valves under their respective brandnames as before.

It seems likely that the circumstances which brought about STC's withdrawal from receiving valve manufacture were, as in the case of other valve makers, not solely attributable to economic conditions but were due also to the increasing impact being made by transistors. And, speaking of solid-state devices, it may be mentioned that STC had for many years been active in the production of selenium rectifiers (which were marketed under the name SenTerCel) long before the company commenced to manufacture transistors.

Throughout its existence STC had, until 1970, discreetly soft-pedalled its American parentage but from this time a new logo incorporating the letters ITT-STC in conjunction proclaimed the connection.

REFERENCES

1. Letter from J.H. Ludlow (former Met-Vick engineer) to the author.
2. See 1924 Met-Vick catalogue, p. 4.
3. Valves tested, *Wireless World*, March 11, 1925, pp. 153–154.
4. See advt. *Wireless World*, Sept. 21, 1927, ad. 23.
5. The Trend of Progress, *Wireless World*, Oct. 3, 1928, p. 466.
6. See, for example, advt. *Wireless World*, Oct. 5, 1927, ad. 17.
7. W.J. Baker, *A History of the Marconi Co.*, p. 200.
8. M. Thompson and A.C. Bartlett, Thermionic Valves with Dull Emitting Filaments, *Wireless World and Radio Review*, April 23, 1924, p. 107.
9. See advt. *Wireless World*, Feb. 9, 1927, p. ad. 2.
10. Trend of Progress, *Wireless World*, Oct. 3, 1928, p. 465.
11. See advt. *Wireless World*, Nov. 24, 1926, ad. 23.
12. See advt. *Wireless World*, Jan. 6, 1926, ads. 16–17.
13. See advt. Standard sets, *Wireless & Gramophone Trader*, Oct. 8, 1928, ad. 15.
14. Announcement *Wireless & Gramophone Trader*, Sept. 24, 1932, p. 412.
15. Standard Micromesh A.C. Valves, *Wireless World*, Aug. 5, 1932, pp. 102–103.
16. Refer *Wireless World* Valve Supplement, Nov. 1934.
17. J.S. Jammer & L.M. Clements, Radio Broadcast Receivers.
18. *Electrical Communication*, Oct. 1934. Reprinted in *Radio Engineering*, Dec. 1934, pp. 16–20.
19. News of Industry, *Wireless World*, Nov. 1961, p. 600.

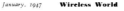

Chapter Twenty-Four

Some British Independents

Early Days

In spite of the fact that the market was flooded with large quantities of 'disposals' valves following the end of World War I, a few small firms were soon on the scene offering their own productions. For example, the Sullivan

SULLIVAN
IMPROVED THREE ELECTRODE THERMIONIC VALVE
(FOR RECEPTION)

An extremely efficient hard receiving valve, conforming approximately to the characteristics given below, and having a high value of voltage amplification and long life.

It will be observed that with an anode potential of **50 volts** and with a filament potential of **3·5 volts**, the straight steep portion of the characteristic falls across the zero grid potential ordinate, ensuring that with these values and with the grid connection made to the negative side of the filament circuit, the valve functions well as an amplifier or rectifies efficiently with a leaky grid condenser.

Suitably connected the valve oscillates readily with the above voltages.

In addition to its electrical qualities the valve possesses great mechanical strength, the electrodes being constructed and supported in such a manner as to render it specially suitable to withstand rough usage.

All valves sent at purchaser's risk.

PRICE—EACH
14/-
POST FREE.

Sole Agents for Lancashire, Cheshire and Yorkshire— **Messrs. FREDERICK TAYLOR & CO.**
60, Long Millgate, **MANCHESTER.**

H. W. SULLIVAN, WINCHESTER HOUSE, LONDON, E.C.2, ENGLAND
Works :—" LIVERPOOL HOUSE," MIDDLESEX STREET, LONDON, E.1
Telegrams : "Deadbeat, Avenue, London."   Telephone : Office—London Wall 3518   Works—Avenue 4871

MARCH 19, 1921   THE WIRELESS WORLD

'Improved Three Electrode Valve' was being advertised as early as March 1921, and the RMR 'Improved Pattern Valve' in September of the same year. The latter valve was unique in having its anode made in the form of an inverted bowl while the grid was made in a tapered spiral shape matching the contour of the anode. Such a form of construction was obviously an attempt to avoid infringing the patented tubular construction of the R type valve.

In 1922 the Economic Electric Co. produced a valve under the name 'Xtraudion' which had its anode in the form of an inverted channel or trough. During the following year, 1923, a further two companies entered the field; the Penton Engineering Co. offered a valve identified as type H.E.4 which required only 0.15 amps at 4 volts, the same company offered a similar though unidentified type in 1924; Phillips Valves Ltd. of Southall, Middlesex, advertised a valve which was available in two versions, a single-filament type at 12/6 and a double-filament type at 15/-. The latter type had a switch on the underside of the base to allow the second filament to be brought into use after the first had failed. The Phillips valves are interesting because they appear to have been the first to use moulded composition bases, and also because the double-filament valve was the first British-made type of its kind. Incidentally, it should be noted that in spite of the similarity in the spelling of the names there was no connection with the Dutch firm of Philips.

The year 1924 saw the emergence of four more names— G.W.I., Radion, Louden, and Thorpe. The G.W.I. 'Plate-less Valve' was unique in that the anode consisted of a metallic coating applied to the inner surface of a small-diameter tubular bulb. Two types were available known as G.1 and A.1.

The Radion on the other hand was of the conventional R type but its filament required 0.25 amps instead of the normal 0.75. Two versions were available, known as A2 and D4. The Thorpe K1 was a bright emitter consuming 0.42 amps of filament current while the type K4 by the same firm was a double-grid type. The fourth make to appear in 1924 was the Louden, a product of the Fellows

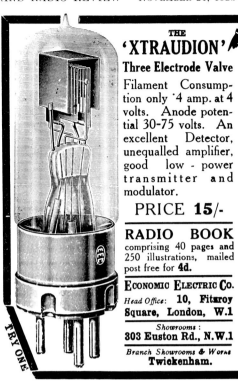
Magneto Co. of London. Filament consumption was 0.4 amps at 4.9 volts and two versions were offered known as 'Plain' and 'Blue'.

Four of the brands so far mentioned—Penton, Phillips, Louden, and Thorpe were of unusual construction and had one common feature, their anodes were formed from a closely-wound spiral of wire. Apart from this one common feature there was little other similarity between the four makes so it seems unlikely that the manufacturers were connected. To the writer's knowledge the use of wire spiral anodes was unique to the manufacturers mentioned. Only Louden made any claim of superiority for the use of a wire spiral anode:

'. . . the filament enjoys great length of life because the harmful charges which otherwise continuously bombard it are forced through the spiral anode out of harm's way'. [The world's first ion trap?!]

Only two new names appeared in 1925, Burndept and Nelson-Multi. The latter was unique in Great Britain and probably the entire world in that it had three filaments which could be selected independently or else two placed in parallel by means of a switch located on the underside

THE WIRELESS WORLD

DECEMBER 15TH, 1926.

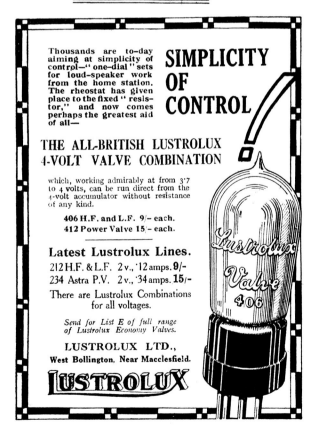

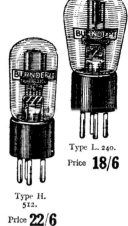
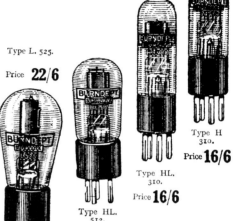

of the base. However, this design was soon abandoned and the Nelson Electric Co. turned to the manufacture of conventional single-filament valves in 1926. Burndept valves were made by an old-established receiver and parts manufacturer, Burndept Ltd., but the company discontinued valve manufacture after it was re-organised in 1927.

A third name, Cleartron, had appeared on the British scene in 1925 but apparently too late for inclusion in the *Wireless World* Valve Data published in September of that year. A recently established American company, the Cleartron Vacuum Tube Co. of New York, set up a factory in Birmingham to produce British-made Cleartron valves which were first advertised in September 1925. Of the six types offered two bore American type numbers—CT199 and CT201A, while a third the CT25 appeared to be identical to the CT201A apart from being fitted with a British type base. Apparently the parent company 'folded' in the 1929 crash which in turn resulted in the closure of the British operation at much the same time.

Several new brandnames appeared in 1926 but only three are thought to be those of actual manufacturers—Lustrovox, Neutron, and Octron. Of the remaining names, Amplion and Benjamin (incidentally both well known in the field of radio components) were being ap-

to have been derived from the shape of the base. A completely new range of valves was introduced in 1929, at which time the use of octagonal bases was discontinued though from then on little more was heard of the company. In 1932 a compnay by the name of Clarion Radio Valve Co. was operating from the same address and advertising valves under the name Clarion.

The year 1927 saw six new brands of valves being advertised, all of which were listed in the *Wireless World* Valve Data for that year; they were A.P. (Aneloy), C.A.C., Mellodyne, Midland, Quikko, and Voltron. In 1928 the growth rate had slowed to the extent that only one new name appeared, P.R. (Peter Russel), but the company was apparently only a distributor.

Although there were two new brands being offered in 1929, Eton and Four-in-One, the year was a turning point in that it marked the end of the annual crop of new names. Only seven were added between 1929 and 1935—Clarion, Pix, '362', Ever Ready, Graham Farish, Hivac, and Lissen. Of these only Hivac became of any importance and it is treated separately. Apart from the names mentioned above there were several others which had come and gone on the British market during the years before 1939, e.g., E.T.A., Dario, Metal, Triotron, etc., but these were of foreign origin and are not included for that reason. In addition there were such foreign firms as Fotos, Ostar-Ganz, Loewe, and Tungsram who made valves in England for varying lengths of time. Of these only Tungsram was successful in maintaining its British operation, the company surviving into the 1950s.

Hivac

The name Hivac first appeared in 1932 when the recently formed High Vacuum Valve Co. marketed a range of ten 2-volt battery valves. The company was unique in that while it was entirely British it was not a member of

plied to valves made for the two brandname owners by Met-Vick who were also selling identical types under their own Cosmos brand. Valves sold under the name S.T. were made for S.T. Ltd. by Mullard, the letters S.T. representing the name of the firm's proprietor, John Scott Taggart. In the case of Six-Sixty valves the name had actually been in use prior to 1926 but did not become well known before then. In that year The Electron Co. concluded an arrangement with Mullard to supply valves to be sold under the company's Six-Sixty brandname.

Valves under the Neutron brandname first appeared in December 1925 when two types, identified as Red Spot and Blue Spot were advertised as being made and guaranteed by Neutron Ltd. By the end of 1926 six types, including a power output valve, were being offered. In the following year, 1927, the company was reorganised as Neutron (1927) Ltd., after which time valves were no longer being advertised. Octron valves were announced by the H.S. Electric Co., Birmingham in October 1927 when three types were being offered. By mid-1927 the name of the firm had been changed to Octron Ltd. when five types of valves were available. Octron valves were fitted with distinctive octagonal-shaped bases which served to prevent their rolling off the edge when placed on a table or bench. Additionally the brandname seems rather obviously

211

the British Valve Makers Association and apparently did not seek membership as it was established on the basis producing high quality valves which were sold at half the ruling B.V.A. prices.

As a non-ring producer Hivac was thus unable to enter the initial-equipment market and had to be content with selling replacement valves and catering to the needs of home constructors. In any case Hivac did not make mains valves until 1934 and strangely never made any form of frequency changer. It would be interesting to learn the reason for the omission of such an essential type of valve when all other commonly used types were included in the Hivac range.

It was in 1935 that the first of the valves that were to become a Hivac speciality appeared. These were a series of tiny 2-volt valves intended primarily for hearing-aid application and were given the name of 'midgets'. Hivac eventually gave up production of standard sized valves entirely in favour of midgets and later miniatures.

The name Hivac was also associated with the production of a specialised type of output tetrode known as the Hivac-Harries valve. This valve used the principle of 'critical distance' spacing of the screen and anode, a feature which enabled it to be used in place of a conventional output pentode. The first of such valves was marketed late in 1935 and they soon replaced pentodes in the Hivac range.

For the record, mention may be made of a unique 'all-purpose' valve, type A.15, which was an adaptation of the Harries design fitted with five independent grids each connected to a separate base pin. Depending on the manner in which the grids were connected into the circuit the valve could function as an RF or IF amplifier, a frequency changer, a detector or output amplifier. To assist users a diagram of a 5-valve superhet receiver was included with each valve. The A.15 was fitted with an American-style octal base and had a metal top cap of 'non-complementary' dimensions to which No. 1 grid was connected. The heater

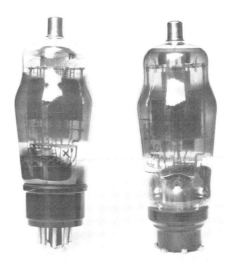

Hivac A 15 (L.) and AC/TZ (R.).

rating was 15 V, 0.3 A, a figure which virtually limited the valve's application to use in AC/DC receivers though the circuit diagram supplied showed parallel heater operation from a 15-volt winding of a mains transformer. Any such transformer, being strictly a non-standard type, would not have been readily available and this factor in itself would have been quite sufficient to prevent general acceptance of the A.15, a fact of which its manufacturer seemed completely unaware.

Another unique Hivac valve was the type AC/TZ, which consisted of a triode combined with an output tetrode. At the time of its appearance, late in 1938, such a combination had never been produced in any other country. The AC/TZ seems to have been specially made at the behest of Pye Ltd. for use as a combined line oscillator-cum-output valve in television receivers. This valve was also unique in being the only British-designed type to be fitted with a continental style side-contact base. This, too, was obviously a requirement of Pye Ltd. who were using a series of Mullard side-contact valves in their model 817 receiver at the time.

Both the A.15 and the AC/TZ remain something of

Hivac QP240 double pentode (1935).

mystery valves in that neither was ever listed in *Wireless World* or Brans' *Vade Mecum*. Their rarity, coupled with their odd-ball design, should serve to make them a collector's delight.

During World War II the company name was changed to Hivac Ltd., and in 1944 ownership passed into the hands of the Automatic Telephone & Electric Co. (ATE) who had held a controlling interest since 1939. Although the manufacture of ordinary receiving valves was not resumed after the war, the company continued to make special midget and miniature types as well as miniature indicating lamps.

Ever Ready

The Ever Ready Co. (Great Britain) Ltd. was a comparative latecomer to the radio scene although the company was an old-established battery manufacturer. Little information is available concerning the valve marketing activities of this firm but it seems that valves bearing the name Ever Ready were intended mainly for initial equipment for a line of receivers marketed in 1935. By this time a radio division under the name Ever Ready Radio Ltd. was in existence.

Ever Ready valves were first listed in the pages of the *Wireless World* Valve Data in 1935 and it is understood that in the same year Ever Ready purchased the Six-Sixty Radio Co. from Mullard, presumably in order to secure a source of supply for valves to equip their receivers. In view of this action it is somewhat surprising to find Mazda valves being used in a 1936 model Ever Ready receiver (model 5008), when equivalent Ever Ready valves were in

Ever Ready K30C made by Mullard c. 1937.

existence. Just how many types of valves, if any, were actually made by Ever Ready is not known but it seems that most, if not all, were made by Mullard. Ever Ready valves were also used in some models of Pye and Lissen receivers sold during the late 1930s.

Valves under the Ever Ready name were no longer listed in the *Wireless World* Valve Data after World War II though a company by the name of Ever Ready Radio Valves Ltd. was in existence and receivers using Ever Ready valves (made by Mullard) were being marketed until at least the late 1950s.

Lissen

Lissen Ltd., an old-established components and accessories manufacturer, first issued valves under the Lissen brandname in 1929 when a range of eight 2-volt battery types was marketed. These particular valves were actually made by B.T-H and in view of the date of their introduction, September 1929, it seems likely that they were stock which had been made redundant by the formation of AEI when the manufacture of B.T-H receiving valves was discontinued. During 1930–31 Lissen marketed two models of HT battery eliminators and it is known that the rectifier used in these units was a Lissen battery triode connected in half-wave mode with the grid and plate strapped.

Lissen valves were first listed in the 1930 *Wireless World* Valve Data when there were 32 types available of which 29 were battery-operated types, one was a general purpose

Lissen SG215 and B2 (1933).

AC triode while the remaining two were rectifiers. By the end of 1933, with the addition of a range of 16-V, 0.25-A DC mains valves the total number of types being offered had risen to over 40. Because many of these valves bore the same type numbers and had the same characteristics as those made by certain other companies such as Mazda and M-O.V. it seems likely that some at least were not of Lissen's own manufacture. From 1934 onwards Lissen Ltd. turned increasingly to the manufacture of complete receivers and the number of different types of valves being offered was drastically reduced. By 1938 there were only 15 Lissen valves listed in *Wireless World*'s Valve Data and thereafter the name Lissen was not included.

Not much is known of Lissen's own manufacture of valves but it can be said that the valves themselves were quite different in external appearance from those of other British makers. It seems likely that, during the years 1930–34 at least, Lissen were actually making their own valves. An involved agreement concluded in 1935 between Mullard, Pye, and Ever Ready seems to have been responsible for the disappearance of valves branded Lissen.

Ferranti

The firm of Ferranti was established in 1896 when Sebastian Z. de Ferranti set up as a manufacturer of electrical machinery. By 1905 the firm had become a registered company known as Ferranti Ltd. In 1926 the manufacture of a limited range of high quality radio components was commenced while in the same year a New York sales office was opened. During 1930–31 a line of receiver kitsets was introduced, while early in 1931 the first complete Ferranti receivers were marketed. Initially Osram valves were used to equip the receivers but shortly afterwards the company commenced to make their own valves.

Initial valve production consisted of but three types—a general-purpose triode, an output triode, and a full-wave rectifier—respectively known as D.4, P.4, R.5. They were 4-volt AC types, apart from the rectifier which carried a 5-volt filament rating.

When the first Ferranti superhet receiver was marketed towards the middle of 1932 it was a seven-valve model using three vari-mu screen-grid valves, but as Ferranti's had no such valves in production at the time they were forced to rely on an outside supplier to fill the gap. So it was that this receiver used Osram type VMS4 vari-mu valves while the remainder were Ferranti. Not until the following year was there an 'all-Ferranti' superhet, the range of valves having by this time been increased to include all currently needed types.

In June 1933 Ferranti became the first British valve maker to market a heptode (pentagrid) frequency changer, type VHT4, which closely resembled current American types apart from having a 4-volt heater and British 7-pin base. Apart from this solitary 'first' Ferranti remained slower than others in releasing new types of valves; for example, at this time they had neither made nor used output pentodes, and not until 1934 was the first of such types added to the range. In this case the delayed production appears to reflect what was then a commonly-held dislike for the breed during the early years of its existence.

Somewhat surprisingly, or so it now seems, Ferranti embarked on the production of battery valves during 1934 and a limited range of 2-volt types was issued over the next year or so. Even allowing for the greater popularity of battery-operated receivers in the U.K. at this time, 1934 still seems to be rather late in the day for any manufacturer to start making battery valves.

In 1935 Ferranti's were apparently again unable to keep production of new valve types abreast of receiver trends as once again they had to turn to GEC, this time to supply the frequency changer for use in their first AC/DC receiver. Similarly another AC/DC receiver, model 513Am of 1938, made use of a mixture of Mazda and Mullard valves, which seems surprising in view of the fact that there were no less than 27 different types of Ferranti valves listed in 1936. However, when it is realised that, according to the 1938 *Wireless World* Valve Data, there were by then only five Ferranti valves listed this helps to explain the situation, as there had obviously been a drastic cutback in the number of different types in production. Even so *Wireless World*'s figures cannot have been quite up-to-date as there were additional Ferranti valves in use in receivers which had been reviewed in the pages of the very same journal during the preceding few months; fur-

Ferranti PT4D and LP4 (1935).

thermore, Ferranti's were advertising some of these valves at this time.

In common with several other British manufacturers, Ferranti's had by 1938 turned to the production of American type octal-based valves and the first Ferranti receiver to use them (model 515B) was reviewed in *Wireless World* for December of that year. Following the end of World War II Ferranti's, again in common with others, continued using octals during the immediate post-war years before turning to loctals, and later still, to miniature types.

By this time, however, there was an increasing amount of 'label swapping' becoming apparent within the industry which makes it difficult, even pointless, to try to determine just who made what, and when it happened. From this time onwards Ferranti's turned increasingly to the production of industrial and special-purpose valves before ceasing manufacture of receiving types entirely in the late 1950s.

Ekco

The firm of E.K. Cole Ltd. commenced business in 1926 by making HT battery eliminators which were sold under the name of EKCO. By the end of 1928 Ekco had become one of the very first British manufacturers of mains-operated receivers. Progress continued steadily through the 1930s during which period Ekco became one of the leading receiver manufacturers. In 1936 the company com-

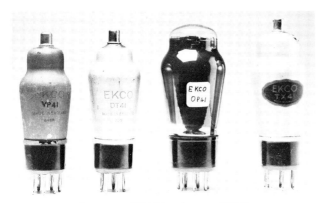

A group of EKCO valves c. 1937.

menced making a limited range of valves to equip certain models of their receivers. *En passant* it may be remarked that 1936 seems rather late in the day to have embarked on valve production, in fact Ekco was the last company to do so.

Very little is known of Ekco's valve-making activities, which is not surprising in view of the fact that valves were made for a short period of less than three years. Production was confined mainly to 4-volt AC types with a few 200 mA AC/DC types being included. No battery type valves were made, Ekco being content to turn to Mullard to supply their requirements in this area. Ekco was one of the few receiver manufacturers to make their own valves, a fact that does not seem to be widely known. Valve production ceased shortly after the outbreak of World War II when the company became fully engaged in the production of military radio equipment.

The following is a listing of Ekco valves known to have been used in pre war Ekco receivers.

TX41	= TH4B	OP42	= PenA4
VP41	= VP4B	DO42	= Pen4DD
DT41	= TDD4	R41	= DW4/350
2D41	= 2D4A	VPU1	= VP13C
T41	= 354V	DTU1	= TDD13C
OP41	= PenB4	6D2	= TV4

The Mullard equivalents shown to the right of the Ekco type numbers are included purely as a matter of interest to enable readers to obtain an idea of the functions of the various types.

Cossor

Undoubtedly the oldest-established independent, though not the first actual valve maker, was one A.C. Cossor who commenced business in 1896 with the manufacture of Crookes tubes. This was followed in 1902 by the production of cathode-ray tubes and X-ray tubes, it being later claimed that Cossor was the first person in England to make such devices. In 1908 a private company was formed to handle the increased business which by then included the manufacture of specialised incandescent lamps for medical and other purposes.

At this time Cossor also began making wireless components, supplying the Marconi Co. and the Admiralty. During World War I Cossor's experience in this field led to their manufacturing complete receivers for military purposes. In common with several other companies Cossor first gained experience in valve manufacturing during the war when production of White valves was undertaken followed by the production of standard R type valves.*

*The information in these two paragraphs was taken from a publication entitled *Half a Century of Progress* produced by A.C. Cossor Ltd. in 1947.

Cossor 'Tin Hat' valves (1922–1925).

After the war Cossor continued to make and market R type valves until 1922. By this time the Marconi Co. was on the warpath in the matter of infringements of the French patents which they owned in the U.K. Because of this Cossor deemed it prudent to develop a non-infringing type of valve and in 1922 their first independent design appeared. Cossor's approach was to modify the structure of the electrodes to get away from the cylindrical formation on which the French patent was based. In practice this was achieved by using an arch-shaped filament over which was fitted a grid of inverted 'U' shape while the anode took the form of a dome with two flat sides.

These early Cossor valves earned for themselves the sobriquet 'tin hat', a name derived from the helmet-shaped appearance of their anodes. The words tin hat themselves had originally been used by World War I British troops as a light-hearted reference to their steel helmets. The first two tin-hat valves issued were types P.1 and P.2, both were bright emitters carrying filament ratings of 6 volts, 0.75 amps.

Cossor was the first British manufacturer to introduce a system of colour coding valves as an indication of their suitability for different applications. In this code red, blue, and green indicated RF amplifier, RCC amplifier, output valve respectively.

In November 1923 the first Cossor dull-emitter was advertised under the name 'Wuncell'; a name obviously derived from the valve's ability to operate from a single cell, in this case a 2-volt accumulator. By February 1924 two types of Wuncell, identified as P.3 and P.4., were being offered for sale. Later in the same year three more Wuncell types were announced which were unique in being able to be operated either from a 2-volt supply or from a 4- to 6-volt supply. A small resistor inside the valve base was wired in series with the filament and could be shorted out by means of a contact screw on the side of the base. The type numbers of these three valves were originally listed as W.1, W.2, and W.3 but appear to have been changed to WR1, WR2, and WR3 a short time later.

The stated purpose of the production of the Wuncell series was to allow the owners of sets using bright-emitter valves to change to dull-emitters one at a time while continuing to use any remaining older valves and the original battery. Presumably it also saved Cossor's having to produce valves in a range of three different filament voltages.

In 1926 a range of three new valves was introduced under the name 'Point One'. The filament rating was 1.8-V, 0.1-A, from which the name of the series was derived. These were quickly superseded by a completely new range of low-consumption valves which were available in 2-, 4-, and 6-volt versions. All carried a uniform 0.1-amp filament rating and were still known as Point One types. They were the first Cossor valves to use 'M' filaments, the shape of which conveniently matched the contour of the characteristic helmet-shaped anodes which remained in use until 1931.

The earlier system of colour coding was carried on in a different form by the use of a coloured paper band encircling the bulb close to where it joined the base. Imprinted on the band were the maker's name, filament rating, anode

217

voltage, function code letters, and a serial number—everything but the type number! Not only was the valve's function indicated by its label colour, viz., red = HF & detector, blue = RCC, black = LF, green = output, but these letters were also included on the already overburdened label. Altogether a most comprehensive system of marking, subject only to the criticism that the label could come unstuck! After about 1931 the paper band labels were replaced by small diamond shaped stickers which for several years remained the only means of identification used by Cossors.

Production of the first indirectly-heated AC valves occurred in 1928 when a range of four types having their heater connections taken to two terminals mounted on a bakelite top cap were marketed. The construction of these valves was broadly similar to that used on the American McCullough and Sovereign and was not used by any other British valve maker. The double-ended valves were superseded in the following year by a similar range fitted with standard 5-pin bases.

Two 'world's firsts' claimed by Cossor were the production of an RF pentode, type MS/PenA, in May 1930 and a battery type vari-mu screen-grid valve, the 220VSG, in December 1931.

From the earliest days Cossor's radio activities were not confined to valve making as during the late 1920s the production of kitset receivers was commenced. Although many of the components were made by the company the sale of kitsets obviously also helped to sell more valves. Production of 'Melody Maker' kitsets continued until the early 1930s by which time a separate factory had been established for the purpose of manufacturing complete receivers under the Cossor brandname.

Between 1926 and 1928 a substantial shareholding in the company was acquired by GEC Ltd. though Cossor remained a private company until the death of the major shareholder and managing director, W.R. Bullimore, in 1927. Early in 1938 the company was taken over by Ismay Industries Ltd. but continued to trade under the Cossor name.

After a distinguished wartime effort in radar manufacture one of Cossor's first post-war moves was to enter into an agreement with the American firm of Sylvania Products Inc. which led to the establishment of a new company known as Electric Tubes Ltd. By this time there were six companies within the Cossor group but in 1949 Cossor ceased valve manufacture by disposing of their interest in Electronic Tubes Ltd. to E.M.I. Ltd. who then used their own brandname Emitron. Production of radio, radar, and television by Cossor continued until 1961 when the radar division was taken over by the American firm of Raytheon.

Mullard

One of the first independent valve makers was a former World War I officer, Capt. S.R. Mullard, who had been making radio components for a year or two prior to commencing valve manufacture. In 1920 the first Mullard valves were being advertised for sale by S.R. Mullard of

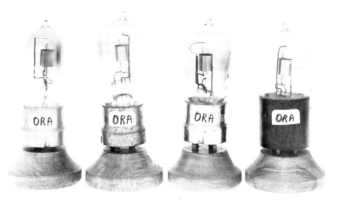

Four versions of the Mullard ORA.

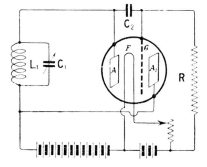

Carton for Negatron valve.

Oscillator circuit using Negatron valve.

Polar Negatron valve made for the Radio Communication Co. by Mullard 1923.

71 Standen Rd., London.[1] Two types were offered, the standard R type at 22/6 plus another identified as K type which sold for 35/-. Unfortunately detailed information on the K type is lacking but a contemporary illustration shows it to have a tubular style bulb of smallish diameter resembling the later ORA type.[2] No explanation can be offered for the large discrepancy in the prices of the two types; it can only be assumed that the performance of the K type was superior in some way, possibly in regard to filament efficiency.

At the end of 1922 the Mullard Radio Valve Co. Ltd. was established and although the manufacture of components was continued, valve manufacture became the main activity from this time on. It may perhaps be argued that with the formation of a limited-liability company Mullard was no longer strictly an independent producer because of the two factors which led to its inception. These were firstly, assistance given by the Admiralty who were seeking a source of commercial manufacture for its own design of high-power silica transmitting valves and, secondly, financial participation by the newly formed Radio Communications Co. who, as a rival of Marconi's, were seeking an independent source of supply for radio valves.

Mention of the Radio Communication Co., manufacturers of 'Polar' brand equipment, makes it convenient to comment briefly on an unusual type of valve known as the Polar Negatron. This Mullard-made valve was designed by John Scott Taggart for use in a special oscillator circuit devised to avoid using Marconi-held patents. The valve itself had two plates and a single grid, its name being

derived from the negative-resistance characteristic obtained.

Apart from these two assured markets for its products Mullard's early took steps to capture a share of the burgeoning retail market that was developing in Britain and certain Empire countries. Following production of the R and K types came the famous ORA which was first advertised in 1922. The ORA was an improved version of the R, which it eventually superseded, and appears to have been developed from the K type as it had the same tubular style of bulb. The designation ORA was derived from the initial letters of the words Oscillator, Rectifier, Amplifier which indicated the three basic functions. In this connection it may be mentioned that the word rectifier refers to signal-frequency rectification or detection, not power rectification.

The next production was of an American-designed valve which was made for a short period during 1923–25 to the specifications of the Western Electric Co. Ltd. These were known as Wecovalves, the name being formed from the initial letters of the company's title. The valve itself was simply a British-made version of the American type 215A peanut tube. As in the U.S. it was one of the first valves to have an oxide-coated filament designed to operate from a single dry cell. Wecovalves were made with two types of base, the standard British 4-pin as well as the WE special 215A type. Adaptors were also available to enable the use of American based valves in British standard sockets.

By 1925 there were over thirty different types of Mullard valves on the market, including several power output

types and one four-electrode (double-grid) type. From all appearances Mullard's position in the marketplace seemed quite strong, yet it could not have been such a strong position that the company could afford to turn down an offer made in 1924 by a foreign manufacturer to purchase a half-interest.

So, although Mullard had made a brave start as an independent and had survived a patent infringement action brought against them in 1922 by the Marconi Co., they allowed the Dutch firm of Philips to acquire a half-interest while the other half remained in the hands of the Radio Communications Co. In August 1925 a public announcement was made that 'an outstanding collaboration' had been accomplished between 'the world-renowned manufacturers of Mullard valves and Philips Glowlampworks Ltd., the famous lamp and valve makers in Holland'.[3]

Included in the agreement was a clause to the effect that Philips would henceforth cease to market 'all imported foreign valves into Great Britain, Northern Ireland and the Irish Free State'. The word 'foreign' in this connection would read better if it were 'Philips', as obviously Philips had no control over the importation of other foreign valves. It should also be mentioned that rectifiers were exempt from the terms of the agreement and Philips continued to import and market these under their own brandname. As a result of this policy certain types of rectifiers were sold in apparent competition with similar or identical types made by Mullard.

In 1926, by what must have been both a fortuitous and fortunate occurrence Philips were enabled to secure full control of Mullard's when the Radio Communication Co. was taken over by the Marconi Co. As Marconi's already

Mullard 'R' c. 1922.

Mullard 'RA' c. 1922.

had their own valve-making arrangements they disposed of R.C.C.'s holding in Mullard, possibly without realising that by so doing they were enabling a foreign interest to gain control of a British company. Thus it was that in 1927 Mullard's became wholly owned by Philips, a move which was an early step along the road to Philips becoming a multinational.

Following Philips' entry in August 1925 the name of the firm was changed to the Mullard Wireless Service Co., and henceforth Philips' designs were used for all new productions. The first valve to be issued under the new set up was a small power output type designated PM4. It was the first Mullard valve to carry the 'PM' prefix in its type number. Rather obviously the letters PM stood for Philips-Mullard though it was sometimes stated in Mullard's advertisements that they stood for 'Pure Music'. Incidentally, no valves were ever issued carrying the words Philips-Mullard, in spite of an illustration appearing in an early advertisement. Apart from the initial announcement, Philips were at pains to conceal their ownership of Mullard in order that Mullard valves could be considered as being all-British. The PM prefix remained in use on battery valves for nearly a decade and was also used for a short time on American type AC valves, e.g., PM224, sold during the early 1930s.

Of the major valve makers Mullard was the last to market indirectly-heated valves, a fact which appeared to reflect their dependence on research and development carried out by the parent company in Holland. Continental development of mains-operated tubes was somewhat slower than in both American and Britain, possibly because of the extensive use of direct-current mains in some countries. Be that as it may, the first Mullard i.h. valves were

not marketed until 1929. Prior to this, two types had been used in a Dutch-built receiver marketed in Britain towards the end of 1928, a short time before manufacture was commenced there. These two valves, a screen-grid tetrode S4V, and a triode 154V, were 4-volt types fitted with 4-pin bases having side terminals to which the cathodes were connected. By comparison the first valves offered for general sale were fitted with standard 5-pin bases. In September 1929 *Wireless World* mentioned the availability of five i.h. types—S4V, 104V, 154V, 164V, 354V. By 1931 the first vari-mu screen-grid and the first i.h. O/P pentode had been added to the range.

For several years Philips and Mullard rectifying valves were sold separately under their respective brandnames but after about 1931 Philips radio type rectifiers were restricted to the equipping of Philips receivers whilst non-radio types, e.g., battery charger rectifiers, continued to be marketed as before. In this connection it may be mentioned that Philips Lamps Ltd., as a foreign owned British company were excluded from membership of the B.V.A. On the other hand Mullard remained a B.V.A. member in spite of their foreign ownership.

During the 1930s Mullard went from strength to strength, becoming one of the receiver industry's largest valve suppliers. With their continental connections they were in a position of being the first valve makers in Britain to exploit such developments as the pentode output valve (1928), the RF pentode (1933), and the octode frequency changer (1934). In addition Mullard introduced side-contact valves, beginning with car radio and 200 mA AC/DC types in 1934 and continuing with 6.3-volt AC types in 1938. These were followed in 1939 by the Red E range of octal-based valves. Also in 1939 Mullard introduced the first 9-pin 'all-glass' valves, types EF50 and EE50. These were intended for television work but the advent of World War II prevented this use. Instead the EF50 was put to good use in radar receivers and such was the demand that Mullard could not produce all that were needed. Because of this arrangements were made with Sylvania to undertake manufacture in the U.S.

With the resumption of television broadcasting after the war a vast new market opened up which called for the large-scale production of miniature valves as well as pic-

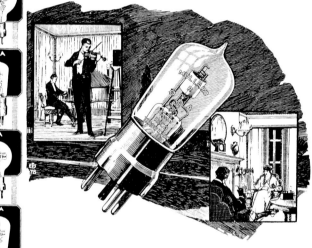

ture tubes. In 1949 the company name was changed to Mullard Electronic Products Ltd. and in 1951 another change was made, this time to Mullard Ltd. By 1954 Mullard could account for over half the total annual sales of vales and picture tubes in the U.K.

Mullard Valves 1920–1925

A	c. 1920	PA	1923	DFA0	1924
F	1920	S.3	1925	DFA1	
K	1920	S.5	1927	DFA2	
R	1920	S.6		DFA3	
RA	1923	D.06HF		DFA4	
ORA	1922	D.06LF		DFA6	
ORA-A		D.3HF	1925	DFA7	
ORA-B	1923	D.3LF		DFA8	
DF-ORA	1924	D.3Det		DFA9	
LF-ORA	1924	D.6		DG	1925
1-volt ORA	1924	PA.2	1923		
Wecovalve A	1923				
Wecovalve B	1923				

British Tungsram*

In 1928 an Hungarian-based lamp and valve maker, having factories in several European countries, established a British factory under the name of Tungsram Elec-

---

*Although not strictly a British independent company, British Tungsram is included here for the sake of convenience.

---

tric Lamp Works (GB) Ltd. By October of that year the first valves from this factory were on the market—a few 2-volt battery triodes being the entire offering. Four years later, in 1932, Tungsram could boast of an extensive range amounting to 43 different types. A Tungsram specialty was the production of American type valves and in 1931 Tungsram was the only company offering a full range of American type directly-heated AC valves as well as their equivalents of types UX-222 and UY-224. The policy of producing American type valves was carried on continuously from this time and in 1937 Tungsram became one of the first makers to offer octal-based types.

Because of their foreign ownership Tungsram were denied entry into the B.V.A. but in spite of this were able to supply valves as as initial equipment to several smaller receiver manufacturers. Apart from making a large range of British type valves Tungsram also produced continental side-contact types in all ranges except 4-volt.

In 1952 British Tungsram was taken over by Philips, the factory continuing valve manufacture until 1956.

REFERENCES

1. See advt. *Wireless World*, July 1920, p. ad. V.
2. W.R. Whale, Transatlantic Tests, *Wireless World*, Apr. 2, 1921, pp. 16–19.
3. Announcement, *Wireless World*, Aug. 26, 1925, p. ad. 8.

British Valves

Brandname	Manufacturer or Distributor	Date of mfr.
Aneloy	Aneloy Products Ltd.	1927
Amplion	Graham Amplion Ltd.	1926
Beriton	Merchant Mfrs. Co. Ltd.	1927
Benjamin	Benjamin Electric Ltd.	1926
Brimar*	Standard Telephones & Cables Ltd.	1934
Brivaron	British Valve & Access. Mfg. Co. Ltd.	?
BSA-Standard	Birmingham Small Arms Co. Ltd.	1926–27
B.T-H.*	British Thompson-Houston Co. Ltd.	1916–1928
Burndept	Burndept Wireless Ltd.	1925–27
C.A.C.	C.A.C. Valve Distributing Co.	1927
Clarion	Clarion Radio Valve Co.	1932–36
Clearbell	?	?
Cleartron	Cleartron Radio Ltd.	1925–29
Cosmos	Metropolitan-Vickers Ltd.	1923–28
Cossor*	A.C. Cossor Ltd.	1922–1949
Dextraudion	Economic Electric Co.	1925
Ediswan*	Edison Swan Electric Co. Ltd.	1917 on
Ekco	E.K. Cole Ltd.	1936–39
Eton	Eton Glass Battery Co.,	1929
Ever Ready*	Ever Ready Co. (Great Britain) Ltd.	1933–on
Ferranti*	Ferranti	1932–on

Four-in-One	Quadruple Valve Co.	1929
Gecovalve*	M.O. Valve Co. and G.E.C. Ltd.	1925–on
Graham Farish	Graham Farish Ltd.	1935–37
G.W.I.	G.W.I. Ltd.	1924
His Master's Voice	The Gramophone Co. Ltd.	? –
Hivac	High Vacuum Valve Co. Ltd.	1933–on
Lissen	Lissen Ltd.	1929–1939
Loewe-Audion	Audion Radio Co.	1926
Louden	Fellows Magneto Co. Ltd.	1924
Lumos	?	?
Lustralux	Lustralux Ltd.	1926–27
Lustravox	Lustralux Ltd.	1926–27
Marconi*	various, see text	–
Marconiphone*	various, see text	–
Mazda*	Edison Swan Electric Co. Ltd.	1928–on
Mellodyne	North London Radio Valve Co.	1929
Micromesh*	Standard Telephones & Cables Ltd.	1932–34
Midland	Midland Valves Ltd.	1927
Mullard*	Mullard Wireless Service Co. Ltd.	1922–on
Nelson Multi	Nelson Electric Co. Ltd.	1925
Neutron	Neutron Ltd.	192?
Octron	H.S. Electric Ltd.	1926–29
Osram*	M.O. Valve Co. and G.E.C. Ltd.	1916–on
Penton	Penton Engineering Co.	1923–26
Phillips	Phillips Valves Ltd.	1923
Pix	British Pix Co. Ltd.	1932–34
P.R.	Peter Russell Ltd.	1928–29
Puratone	Rubon Ltd.	1931
Pyramid	?	?
Quikko	J.W. Picavant Co. Ltd.	1927
Radion	Radions Ltd.	1924–25
Six-Sixty*	The Electron Co. Ltd.	
S.T.	S.T. Ltd.	
Standard*	Standard Telephones & Cables Ltd.	
Thorpe	Bower Electric Co. Ltd.	
Tungsram	Tungsram Electric Lamp Works (G.B.) Ltd.	
Vita	?	
Voltron	Voltron Co.	
Wecovalve	see text	
Xtraudion	Economic Electric Co.	
362	The 362 Radio Valve Co.	
660-Electron	see Six Sixty	

*Indicates member British Valvemakers Assn. (formed in 1924).

In cases where the name of the manufacturer or distributor has changed the original name is listed.

Continental Brands Sold in Great Britain, 1920–1930

Brandname	Importer	Origin	Date
Aravalve	?	Holland	1925
Beam	Lester & Marquis	?	c. 1925
Dario	Impex Electrical Ltd.	Austria	1928–1939
ETA	Electrical Trading Assn. Ltd.	France	1931–32
Fama	?	Holland	c. 1924
Fotos*	Concertron Radio & Elec. Ltd.	France	1929–1932
Frelat	Continental Radio Import Co.	Holland	1925–28
Iris	Anglo-Franconia Ltd.	France	c. 1925
Loewe-Audion	Audio Radio Co.	Germany	1926
Metal	John Rae Ltd.	France	1927–28
Microlux	?	France	1924–28
Ostar Ganz	Eugen Forbat	Austria	1933–39
Philips	Philips Lamps Ltd.	Holland	1928
Radio Micro	Impex Electrical Ltd.	France	1928
Radio Record	?	Hungary	c. 1929
Radio Vicco	Radioland Ltd.	France	c. 1926
Siemens	Siemens Bros. Ltd.	Germany	1928
Stal	Lester & Co.	?	1928
Sutra	C.A.S.E. of Paris, London	France	1927
Triotron	Triotron Radio Ltd.	Austria	1931–39
Vatea	Abbey Radio	Hungary	1930

*Fotos valves were also made in England for a short period.

Chapter Twenty-Five

Philips

Because of the important position now held in the world of electronics by the Dutch based firm of N.V. Philips a brief outline of the company's history is included here. In 1891 Frederick Philips and his son Dr. G.L.F. Philips established a lamp factory in the then small country town of Eindhoven; later a second son, Dr. Anton Philips, also joined the company.

By 1903 Philips had become the fourth largest European manufacturer of electric lamps.[1]

According to legend Philips got into the making of radio tubes quite by chance. In 1918 a young Dutch radio enthusiast, Hanso Idzerda, who shortly afterwards became famous for the establishment of a broadcasting station located at The Hague, was seeking to interest someone in the manufacture of radio tubes. Mr Idzerda approached Philips who, not surprisingly, displayed little interest in the suggestion. In spite of this Idzerda was able to persuade someone within the Philips organisation to make small quantities of tubes in accordance with his requirements.[2] From such beginnings grew one of the world's largest producers of radio tubes and one of to-day's multinational electronics companies.

The original tubes made to Idzerda's specifications were being sold by his company, Nederlandse Radio Industrie, as early as 1918 and were the first ever made by Philips. These tubes were identified by the first three letters of the inventor's name, IDZ.[3] A strong American influence is apparent in the design of Idzerda's tubes in that they were of double-ended construction and used the same type of candelabra screw base as used on the De Forest Audions. Furthermore, the electrode structure was almost identical to that used in the De Forest 'double wing' Audion; that is, two small square plates and two zig-zag wire grids together with a horseshoe filament.

Not long afterwards Philips themselves entered the field of radio tube manufacture using the Idzerda design as a starting point. The first tube to be issued was known as Philips Ideezet and was marketed in April 1918.[4] Later versions of the tube were known as types A, B, C, the latter with sub-divisions C1 and C2.

226

Philips Tubes to 1925

1918–20	Philips-Idzerda IDZ (Ideezet, double-ended)
1920–21	C1 (soft), C2 (hard), formerly IDZ
1920	D1 (soft), D2 (hard)
1922	D3, D4, D5
1923	E Last stage audio
1923	Q Double-grid tetrode
1923–24	D6 formerly Q
1924	B2 First 'Miniwatt' triode
1924	B6 First 'Miniwatt' tetrode

1925–26

1-volt Group	2-volt Group	3-volt Group	4-volt Group
A106	A241	A306	A410
A109	B2	A310	A406
		A341	A441
A141	5-volt		B406
B105	C509		

Note: In the early type numbering system used up to 1925 any figures following the initial letter were expressed in Roman numerals but late in 1925 a change was made to modern numerals. For example, type DII became D2, and so on. To avoid confusion the author has avoided the use of Romal numerals in the above list.

THE THOUSANDTH TRIUMPH!

FROM the midst of a thousand triumphs in modern radio ONE stands out as a blazing beacon — the Philips "Miniwatt" Valve.
When you hold in your hand one of these products of the Philips Laboratories you see on its brilliant surface seven letters spelling the word P-H-I-L-I-P-S — each of which is at once both a promise and a faithful guarantee of unequalled performance and long life.
Philips "Miniwatts," correctly used, ensure
Increased Volume —— Purer Tone.
Greatly reduced "A" Battery Costs—
—Decreased "B" Battery consumption.
Our Technical Department exists to advise you.

ASK YOUR DEALER

PHILIPS
"MINIWATTS"
Advertisement of
Philips Lamps (N.Z.) Ltd., Radio Dept., Hope Gibbons Bldg., Courtenay Place, Wellington.

The first Miniwatt types carried a filament rating of 1.6 volts and consumed only 0.15 amps.[5] They used an early form of oxide-coated filaments in conjunction with a gettering process and were the forerunner of an enormous range of battery tubes, mostly in the 4-volt class. In common with most other European tube makers Philips did not go through an intermediate step of using thoriated filaments on receiving tubes, presumably in order to avoid having to pay patent royalties.

In 1925 a new numbering system was introduced in which various characteristics and ratings were encoded, and this system remained in use for the next ten years. In it the first letter indicated the filament amperage, the first numeral indicated filament voltage while the following numerals, running from 3 to 38, indicated the amplification factor.

Philips Type Numbering System 1925–1935

First Letter	First Numeral	Remaining Numerals
A = up to 0.1 A.	1 = 1.5 V.	Amplification factor
B = up to 0.2 A.	2 = 2.0 V.	in steps of 1.
C = up to 0.3 A.	3 = 3.0 V.	
D = up to 0.5 A.	4 = 4.0 V.	
E = up to 1.5 A.	5 = 5.0 V.	
F = up to 2.0 A.	6 = 6.0 V.	
	7 = 7.5 V.	

Example:

```
              A615
0.1A.     6 V.     15
```

This system was adequate in the case of triodes but following the introduction of pentodes and screen-grid tubes whose amplification factors numerically exceeded two figures the system was modified as under:

41,45 = double-grid tetrode	46,56 = RF pentode
42,52 = screen-grid tetrode	47,58 = mixer hexode
43,53 = output pentode	49,59 = vari-mu hexodes
44,54 = diode-tetrode 'Binode'	
45,55 = vari-mu tetrode 'Selectode'	

Rectifying tubes were not included in the above system and were identified by means of a three or four letter number, e.g., 506, 1561.

Quite apart from any type numbering system, the need early arose for a means of quickly and positively identifying the type of base used on a particular tube. As early as 1924 Philips had produced tubes which differed only in the type of base that was fitted. Originally these differences were identified by a change in type number; for example, the type D2 had a Franco-British base, the D3 a German base, and the D4 an American UV base. From 1925 onwards a separate base coding was introduced though this was marked only on tube cartons, apart from being used in catalogues and price lists. It served as a quick and easy means of identifying stocks and ordering

supplies in countries where a particular tube was available in alternative base styles. After the introduction of bakelite bases in 1926 additional information indicating the base diameter was incorporated in the coding—thus A34 indicated a Franco-British base having a diameter of 34 mm. The 'diameter' code fell into disuse following World War II; in fact by 1945 or so the need for a separate base code no longer existed.

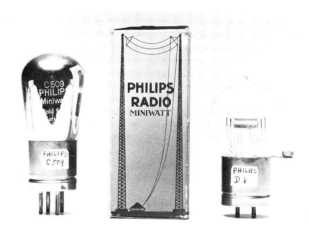

Two Philips tubes of the 1925 era.

Early bakelite-based Philips tubes 1926.

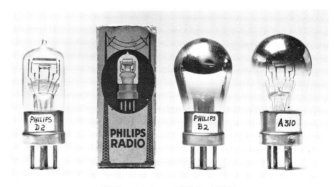

Philips tubes 1924–1925.

227

Philips Tube Caps (Bases) 1924–1939

A = 4-pin standard European (originally Franco-British)
B* = 6-pin continental
C* = 7-pin continental
D = 5-pin French, used on bi-grille tetrodes
E* = 7-pin American 'medium 7-pin'
F = 4-nub American 'UV-199'
G = 4-pin American (originally 'UX')
H = 3-pin Philips special
J = 6-pin American
K = 8-pin American octal
M* = 7-pin British
N = 5-pin American (originally 'UY')
O = 5-pin European
P = 8-contact European side-contact
T = 9-pin Continental 'all-glass'
U = ? used on type B2043 pentode only?
V = 5-contact European side-contact
W = 5-pin special
X = Acorn
Y = 8-pin continental (orig. used for German metal tubes)

*Notes regarding earlier usage.

B was originally used for German (Telefunken) 4-pin base
C was originally used for American UV base
E was originally used for French Radiola 4-pin 'Y' base
M was originally used for American 'WD11' base

N.B. Strictly speaking the description 'European' is applicable to only two styles of base—Philips caps A and O—as these were the only ones which were accepted as a standard in all European countries including Great Britain.

The first Philips indirectly-heated AC tubes 1928–1929.

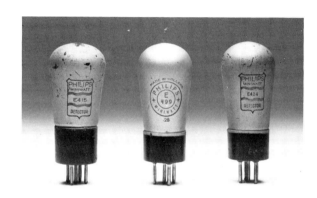

Philips 4-volt triodes—'Golden Series' 1934.

To continue with the narrative: As inventors of the pentode output tube Philips were naturally in a position to be first to market it which they proceeded to do in 1928.[6] It was in this same year that the first Philips screen-grid tubes appeared, while in 1929 the first indirectly-heated AC tubes were marketed. It should be noted that all the above-mentioned types had earlier been used in Philips receivers before they were released for general sale. For example, the model 2501 receiver, a mains-operated type of the 1927–28 season used two types of indirectly-heated tubes, types C142 (screen-grid) and F142 (triode) in addition to a directly-heated pentode, type D143.

Presumably in order to secure effective market penetration in the face of tariffs or other restrictions Philips soon commenced tube production in other countries by the acquisition of existing concerns. For example, in Britain by the acquisition of Mullard in 1925–27, and in Germany by the acquisition of Radio Rohre Fabrik (RRF) in 1924, after which time the firm became known as Valvo Werke GMBH.

When Philips commenced to issue tubes with metallised coatings in 1933 the hitherto rather drab appearance of similar tubes produced by competing manufacturers was enlivened by Philips' use of a gold coloured finish. These tubes were known as the 'Golden Range' when they were first introduced and the gold colour scheme remained in use for all metallised tubes issued in the 4-V AC, 0.2-A AC/DC and 2-volt battery ranges.

The year 1934 was marked by two events—the release of the first tubes fitted with a novel, though not particularly practical, side-contact base, and the introduction of a new 'European' type numbering system. This system came about as a result of an agreement between Philips and Telefunken concluded in 1934. Although referred to as the continental or European system it was, apart from its use by the two companies concerned, little used in other European countries, at least in the pre-war years. It was of course used by Philips-owned companies such as Valvo in Germany and Mullard in Great Britain, though in the latter case Mullard continued to use their own British style numbering alongside the new system, which was used only for side-contact valves.

The new system was in the form of a basic alphanumeric code which indicated the following details:

1. Filament/heater voltage, or current in the case AC/DC tubes.
2. Generic tube type or types in the case of multiple tubes.
3. Sequence of issue. Originally a single digit number but extended to include information on type of base and structural grouping.

First Numeral	Example	Second or Third Numeral	Example
A = 4.0 V	AL4	A = single diode	EA76
B = 180 mA AC/DC	B2006	B = double diode	EB91
C = 200 mA AC/DC	CL4	C = triode	EC31
D = 1.4 V batt.	DK91	D = O/P triode	AD1
E = 6.3 V AC	EF9	E = tetrode	VEL11
F = 13 V auto.	FZ1	F = V/A pentode	AF3
G = 5.0 V rect.	GZ32	H = hexode, heptode	AH1
H = 150 mA AC/DC	HL90	K = octode	DK91
K = 2.0 V batt.	KL4	L = O/P pentode	EL41
P = 300 mA AC/DC	PL84	M = magic eye	EM1
T = 7.4 V		N = thyratron	EN31
U = 100 mA AC/DC	UL41	P = sec. emiss.	EEP1
V = 50 mA AC/DC	VCL11	Q = nonode	**FQ80**
X = 0.6 A AC/DC	XL36	W = HW gas rect.	
L = 450 mA AC/DC	LFL200	X = FW gas rect.	AX50
Y = 450 mA AC/DC	YF183	Y = HW vac. rect.	EY88
		Z = FW vac. rect.	EZ40

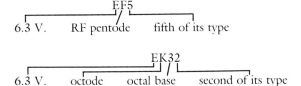

In case where two or more separate assemblies were contained within a single envelope the appropriate code letters were placed in conjunction thus: EBF2 = 6.3 V. duo-diode RF pentode fitted with side-contact base. Originally the system covered only side-contact tubes but after 1938, following the introduction of octal-based tubes, it was modified by adding a second numeral which, when read in conjunction with the first, indicated a particular grouping. Following World War II, when the number of tubes within a particular sequence increased to more than nine, it was necessary use three figures, e.g., EF183. Similarly when the number of different groups increased to more than ten it became necessary to use three numerals, e.g., EL500.

Philips Group Coding

1–10 = side-contact*	80–89 = noval
11–19 = German 8-pin	90–99 = U.S. 7-pin min.
20–29 = U.S. loctal†	180–189 = noval
30–39 = U.S. octal	500–509 = 9-pin magnoval
50–59 = various	800–809 = noval
65–79 = sub-min	900–909 = U.S. 7-pin miniature

*Exceptions are types ECH3G, ECH4G, EK2G, EL3G, KK2G which were fitted with American type octal bases.
†Exceptions were types DAC21, DF21, DF22, DL21, DLL21 which were fitted with American-type octal bases having European style pin connection sequence.

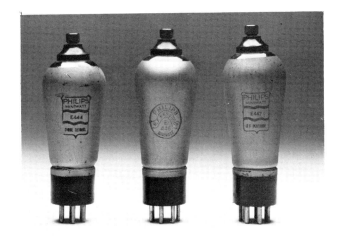

Philips tubes using gold coloured metallised coating 1933.

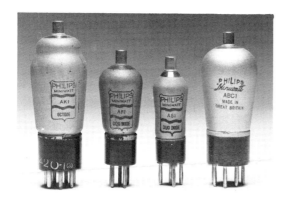

A group of Philips 'Golden' tubes with pin-type bases c. 1936.

A group of Philips 'Golden' tubes with side-contact bases c. 1937.

In 1936, following the American lead, the first range of 6.3-V tubes was introduced and, as in the U.S., this voltage became the standard for AC-operated types. To serve as an introduction and to distinguish them from the earlier 4-volt types the new tubes were known as the 'Red E' series, the name being derived from the red colour of the metallic coating used. Even output tubes and rectifiers had small bands of the same coating, presumably to justify the use of the term 'Red' for the whole range. The Red E series marked a turning point in European tube design because of the greatly reduced physical sizes of all types except output tubes and rectifiers.

In addition to the Red E series of side-contact tubes another range known as the 'E30' series was introduced some three years later. These were identical to the former but were fitted with American-style octal bases. This series was first marketed by Mullard in the U.K. and other British countries in 1939. Although Philips also marketed the E30 series outside Europe in the early post-war years they were largely unknown on the continent itself.

By 1939 Philips had joined Telefunken and Tungsram in producing a range of the German-style metal tubes known as the E11, 12, 13 series.[7] This same year also saw the introduction of the famous E50 'all-glass' tube as well as the EE50 secondary-emission amplifier.[8] A series of tubes using the American-style 8-pin loctal base was

Philips 2.5-volt American replicas 1930.

planned for release in 1940–41 but the war intervened with the result that these tubes did not appear until 1947 and even then only a very few types were produced.

The first miniature tubes produced by Philips were American type 1.4-volt battery types, known as the D90 series, which appeared in 1947. These were followed by 6.3-volt AC and 300-mA AC/DC types, known as the E90 and H90 series respectively. In 1951 the first of the Philips-designed miniatures, based on the American noval series, appeared and these became the post-war European standard for both AC-operated and transformerless radio and television receivers. As in the U.S., no battery-operated types were produced in the noval range, the existing 7-pin miniatures being adequate for the purpose.

A group of Philips 'Red E' side-contact tubes c. 1936–1937.

Although Philips' activities on an international scale were greatly expanded in the years following World War II the first steps in this direction had been taken in the early 1920s. Prior to the war RCA had been able to keep all foreign tubes out of the North American market but following the end of World War II Philips moved into this market with the acquisition of Canadian Radio Corp. Ltd. (makers of Rogers tubes). Production of tubes under the Rogers name was carried on though it is known that some types at least were also produced under Philips' own name. Penetration of the U.S. market was achieved by the setting up of North American Philips Inc. (Norelco) in 1942 and later, about 1955, by the purchase of Amperex Electronic Products Inc., then of Brooklyn, N.Y. Amperex was a well-known maker of transmitting and industrial-type tubes and the same business was carried on under Philips' ownership. Later, however, production of receiving tubes was commenced in addition, and by 1955 a range of European type noval-based types was being advertised.

Details of Philips' Australian valve-making activities will be found elsewhere in this book.

Information on Pope and Condor tubes is included here as both companies were eventually merged with Philips.

The origins of the Pope and Condor brandnames go back to 1885 when an Englishman by the name of Pope established a factory near London for the purpose of making electric lamps. Because of patent difficulties the business was transferred to Venlo in the south of Holland shortly afterwards, thus making Pope the first Dutch lamp manufacturers. In 1920 Philips gained control of the Pope lamp works and in 1921, after the patent difficulties had been resolved, Mr. Pope returned to England where he set up a new factory at Willesden, London, and recommenced making lamps under the name 'Pope Elasta'.[9]

The brandname Pope continued to be used in Holland

Pope tubes. Made in Holland c. 1939.

and first appeared on radio tubes early in 1918, that is shortly before the end of World War I. Holland, as a neutral country, naturally did not have access to the Allied wartime developments and, it may be assumed, had no pressing need of tubes for military purposes.

One of the earliest-known Dutch tubes was produced at the Pope factory to the design of a radio engineer L.J. Bal of Breda. These tubes were quite similar to the better-known Philips-Idzerda design. They carried the dual markings 'Pope' and 'Bal, Breda'. It seems that the Bal-Pope tube was little more than an experimental production which, after its debut in 1919, quickly disappeared from the scene.

Many years later the name Pope reappeared on Philips-designed tubes made by N.V. Pope Draad en Lampen-fabrieken of The Hague. Incidentally, it may be inferred from the juxtaposition of the words in the company title that wire and cable manufacture was the more important side of the business, but, be that as it may, the name Pope on radio tubes was never as well known as Philips. During the 1950s, and possibly earlier, Pope and Philips tubes were sold side-by-side in certain countries but in later years the name Pope was allowed to lapse, though it remained in use on electric lamps.

Another brandname, 'Condor', was also used for both lamps and tubes made at the Pope factory. Tubes bearing the name Condor are known to have been marketed in certain British Empire countries between the years 1924 and 1930. Such tubes were, to all intents and purposes, identical to those made in Philips' Eindhoven factory though a different system of type numbering was used. As in the case of Pope, the name Condor appears to have been used solely as an export brandname and the tubes themselves were similarly sold alongside Philips in some countries during the period mentioned. Similarly, too, the use of the Condor name was eventually discontinued

PR11   PR12   PR16
A group of early Condor tubes 1924.

A group of Condor tubes c. 1924–26.

Pioneers in lamps (since 1889)
Electronic tubes (since 1924)
and Radio components (since 1925)

though it remained in use on lamps for many years afterwards.

The following is a listing of all known tubes carrying the Condor name though it is quite possible that there may have been others. Information on Condor tubes is surprisingly meagre, probably because of their limited production lifetime coupled with their limited distribution.

Condor Tubes c. 1924–1930

PR2	PR33	PR54
PR5	PR41	PR55
PR11	PR48	PR60
PR12	PR50	PR61
PR16	PR51	PR63
PR21	PR52	PR64

REFERENCES

1. H.A. Leighton Lord, *Philips in New Zealand*, pub. 1961, p. 1.
2. Information supplied by Ir. Franz Driesens, of Philips, Eindhoven to the author.
3. Ibid.
4. Ibid.
5. See Philips valve catalogue dated 15 Jan. 1924, p. 6.
6. *The Story of the Pentode*, pub. Philips Radio, undated, p. 1.
7. See *The Bridge to High · Radio Entertainment*, pub. Philips Eindhoven, 1939, p. 1 8.
8. Ibid.
9. Information supplied to the author by Ir. Franz Driesens of Philips, Eindhover Jan. 1978.

Chapter Twenty-Six

U.S.A. After World War II

Because, of necessity, new tube development during World War II had been restricted to the design and production of specialised types intended for military applications, little of this development was of significance in the entertainment field after the war. The one wartime development which did alter the course of subsequent peacetime tube production was the introduction of the first indirectly-heated 7-pin miniature tubes in 1942. It was this development which set the pace in the post-war years and eventually resulted in the abandonment of standard sized tubes in all areas where it was possible to substitute miniature types.

Although most, if not all, receiving tube manufacturers had gained experience in the production of the RCA-designed miniatures during the war this did not mean that no further development of the older series took place once the war was over. For example, Sylvania continued development of their Lock-in tubes and introduced several new types such as 1LG6, 7AG7, FM1000 in the early post-war years. Throughout the 1950s and 1960s many octal-based types were developed by various manufacturers for television applications.

However, as far as standard sized radio tubes were concerned the writing was on the wall as by the end of 1945 no less than 14 miniature types, designed to replace existing tubes, had become available. By 1947 RCA listed a range of 40 different miniatures, though many of these were specialised types unsuited to use in domestic receivers.

Whilst most of the independent tube makers survived the war, two exceptions being Arcturus and Champion, the post-war years were to witness a steady diminution in their ranks. One of the first casualties was Ken-Rad, though in this case it was a change in the identity of the company rather than the closure of a plant which resulted in the loss of a respected name in the industry.

In 1946 Ken-Rad was taken over by the General Electric Co. in order to facilitate their re-entry into the field of receiving tube manufacture after an absence of 16 years. GE, who had originally made receiving tubes for RCA prior to 1930, had in the interim continued to make in-

dustrial and special purpose tubes as well as engaging in the production of receivers. During this period tubes required to equip these receivers had been provided by RCA, but after 1946 GE became self-sufficient in this respect.

A somewhat similar situation occurred in the case of Westinghouse who had also been making receivers but their re-entry into the field of receiving tube manufacture was delayed until 1952 and no takeover of an existing

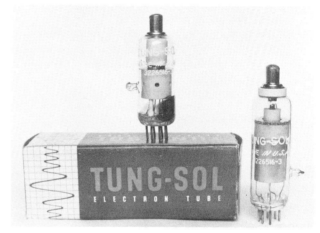

Two Tung-Sol high-voltage rectifiers c. 1960.

Two post-war GE metal tubes in the Red 'computer' range c. 1950.

234

manufacturer was involved. At this time Westinghouse established two new plants, one of which was devoted solely to the manufacture of receiving tubes which were marketed under the name 'Reliatron' (that inevitable 'tron').

Whilst two of the giants re-entered the field most of the remaining independent manufacturers gradually retired from receiving tube production. These included Hytron, National Union, Raytheon, and Tung Sol. Raytheon continued to make non-receiving types whilst relying on foreign manufacturers for the supply of receiving types, which were marketed during the 1960s under the Raytheon label.

Notable among the changes on the American scene was the invasion of the domestic market by, firstly, European manufacturers and then by Japanese. Whereas in pre-war days the American tube industry had played a dominant role on the world scene, both in research and development and in exporting, this situation was now affected by international considerations following the recovery of European countries after the war.

Prior to World War II cartel agreements and patents had effectively prevented the penetration of the American market by foreign tube producers but following the end of the war American political decisions aimed at assisting the recovery of war-torn European countries by encouraging exports to the U.S. resulted in a steady trickle of tubes

from these countries appearing on the American market. Although the appearance of such tubes was initially a result of the need to provide servicing replacements for imported equipment, eventually imported tubes even came to be used by some American receiver manufacturers. Following the rapid post-war growth of the Japanese electronics industry large numbers of Japanese television receivers were imported into the U.S. commencing in the 1960s and this likewise created a large demand for Japanese tubes for subsequent servicing requirements.

Apart from the importation of tubes an unprecedented event was the actual entry of a foreign manufacturer into the United States itself. This occurred when Philips of Holland took over an old-established manufacturer of transmitting tubes, Amperex Electronics Corp. of New York. Philips had first become established in the New World some years prior to World War II when they commenced to manufacture receivers in South America. One of their first post-war moves in the western hemisphere was to establish the firm of North American Philips Inc. in the U.S. to distribute certain Philips products under the name 'Norelco'. Following this came the acquisition of Rogers Majestic Electronics Ltd. in Canada.

By 1957 Amperex was advertising 14 different European type tubes, just over half of which were in the entertainment category. Some seven years later no less than 23

235

variations of one single Philips-designed type, the frame-grid pentode, were being offered.

Yet another post-war development was RCA's establishment tube-making plants outside the U.S., one of the first of these being in Chile. Other factories were located in Brazil (RCA Electronica Ltda), Italy (A.T.E.S.), and Mexico. In addition to this for a short period during the late 1950s RCA arranged with a British valve maker, Ediswan, to have certain noval-type valves branded RCA for marketing by RCA outside Great Britain.

So although the radio tube was invented at almost the same time as the semi-conductor was discovered (the crystal detector was known and used in 1906) and although it reigned supreme for nearly half a century in the end it was the semi-conductor that was the winner. Well almost! By a quirk of fate the one indispensable 'receiving' tube, for which no solid-state counterpart yet exists, remains a device pre-dating both vacuum tube and crystal detector—the cathode ray tube invented by Braun in 1897.

RCA 17JZ8 'Duodecar' (Compactron) 1969.

RCA Victor 6SQ7GT and 6V6 GT. Made in Chile c. 1960.

Some post-war tube cartons.

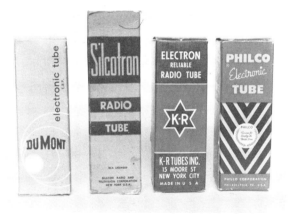

Some post-war tube cartons.

RCA 5U4GB. Made in Brazil c. 1975. Note the address—David Sarnoff Avenue.

Chapter Twenty-Seven

Audio Output

Following the initial use of the triode as a detector of radio signals, which additionally provided some degree of amplification in the process, its ability as an audio amplifier was soon put to good use to increase receiver gain. In Britain such amplifiers were known as 'note magnifiers', the word note referring to the sound of a morse signal as heard in the headphones. The term audio frequency did not come into use until the transmission of speech and music occurred following the advent of broadcasting from about 1921.

Although it was early realized that pre-detector signal-frequency amplification was desirable, it was difficult to obtain in practice and was perforce omitted from the earliest sets. However, once a workable and worthwhile degree of RF amplification became available, attention was again turned to the audio frequency side. Because headphones (which required a minuscule amount of driving power) were in universal use, any general purpose tube could provide ample output for their operation. Not until loudspeakers came on the scene after about 1922 did

the need for tubes having an appreciable 'power' output arise. Even so, it was for transmitting use that the first power tubes were developed.

In March, 1921 RCA announced the first of such tubes, the UV-202, UV-203 and UV-204. By September of the same year the smallest of the three, the UV-202, had developed into the UX-210 and it was in this form that it was put to use as an audio power amplifier where it could provide an output of 1.6 watts at a plate voltage of 425 volts. In November, 1925 RCA proudly advertised the UX-210 as "Probably the most powerful receiving tube in existence."

Because of its high plate voltage requirement this tube was not intended for battery operation and was used mainly in early electric phonographs such as the Brunswick 'Panatrope' and combinations such as the Victor 10-70 where it was used in conjunction with RCA's model 104 Rice-Kellogg dynamic speaker.

The first battery operated power output tube, type UX-112, became available in 1925, but not until an improved

Radiotron UV-202 (1921)

Triad T-10 (= UX-210)

version, the UX-112A was produced in 1927 did it come into general use. At a plate voltage of 135 this tube could provide an output of 135 milliwatts, and because the filament rating was the same as that of the 201A it was frequently used in other stages of a receiver. Not until the arrival of the UX-171 in mid 1926 was there a tube capable of providing more than 200 milliwatts output. By November, 1926 this tube had developed into the UX-171A which could provide 285 milliwatts at a plate voltage of 180. However, as its arrival coincided with the advent of AC operated receivers, the 71A was more commonly used in such sets.

Towards the end of 1928 in the U.S., the subject of audio frequency amplification was beginning to assume some degree of importance amongst 'radio' men, evidence of which is provided in the wording of an advertisement appearing in the December 1928 issue of *Radio News* magazine. Here, an advertisement by the American Transformer Co. (Amertran) contained the following words: "Every year the importance of radio reproduction has advanced until now the question amongst radio enthusiasts has changed from 'How much distance can you get?' to 'How good is your tone quality?'" From this time on, the pages of radio magazines of the day increasingly carried articles on audio amplifiers, and some radio manufacturers were turning to the production of amplifiers in addition to their normal business. At the same time, a few specialist amplifier manufacturers who had not previously made radios were beginning to appear.

Two things which pushed AF power amplifiers into prominence were: the development of AC mains operated radios and the development of moving-coil (dynamic) speakers. Whereas previously the output of battery operated radios had been limited to a few hundred milliwatts, the output of AC radios could be measured in watts. But quite apart from radio, a new field was opening up—public address(PA). An article in the May 1929 issue of *Radio News* contained these words: "The recent development of public address amplification adds still another link in the chain of modern communication..."

But before PA amplifiers with any degree of power could be developed, a new higher power output tube was needed. Such a tube, the UX-250, was developed by Westinghouse and announced by RCA in February 1928. A pair of 50s in push-pull could provide an output of around 11 watts with a plate voltage of 450. As with the earlier UX-210, the high plate voltage requirement restricted its use to large electric phonographs and combinations.

What may be termed the first 'modern' power tube, the UX-245, was released one year after the 50, in March 1929. Due to its greater efficiency and comparatively modest HT requirements it quickly became the most commonly used output tube in AC receivers. Operated in push-pull mode, a pair of 45s could provide an output of

CX-345 (UX-245)   50 (originally UX-250)

about 4 watts. For the next three years the supremacy of the 45 remained unchallenged, but following the introduction of the type 247 pentode in 1931 things were never the same again. (More on this later).

A very short lived American development was the so called Loftin-White direct-coupled system of AF amplification introduced in 1930. In essence it consisted of a type 24 screen grid tetrode direct coupled to an output triode*. Apart from being direct coupled, the other unusual feature was the use of a screen grid tube as an AF voltage amplifier. Many extravagant claims were made for the supposed superiority of the L-W, but only two manufacturers are known to have produced PA amplifiers using the L-W system. It also found limited use in some low priced midget receivers made by a few minor manufacturers. The advent of the L-W was a flash-in-the-pan event which after little more than twelve months quickly faded into obscurity. It was a peculiarly American development, virtually unknown outside the U.S.

Although the L-W lasted for such a short time, its demise was not the end of direct coupling, for a series of direct coupled tubes was developed starting with the Speed type 295 in 1932 and continuing with the production of the 6N6G in 1937; a two-tube circuit using a 6AC5G fed by a direct coupled 76 was the final development in this type of circuitry.

Before that had happened however, there was a short lived move by some radio manufacturers to obtain increased power for their top-of-the-line models by resorting to the use of Class B amplification using a newly developed 'Dual Grid Power Amplifier' tube, the type 46. A pair of 46s when operated under zero bias condition could provide an output of 16 watts at a plate voltage of

300, or 20 watts with 400 volts on their plates, but just how many of the speakers fitted to radio boasting such large outputs could handle this amount of power was another matter. By 1933 it was all over, and the use of Class B audio in AC receivers was gone for good, leaving only the memory of a peculiarly American phenomenon, though its use in battery sets continued for many years.

To obtain a comparable amount of power from a Class A system a new higher power tube was required and this need was fulfilled with RCA's introduction of the 2A3 early in 1933.

In its original form, the construction of the 2A3 followed existing techniques in using a single assembly with planar electrodes, but differed in having a multiple filament consisting of no less than twenty strands of wire connected in series parallel. This revolutionary filament construction provided a copious emitting surface enabling an extremely high mutual conductance of 5250 microhms (5.25 mA/V) to be obtained. However, from a manufacturing point of view such an elaborate type of filament construction was unsuited to mass production and was eventually abandoned. A completely new type of construction was then introduced consisting of two separate assemblies connected in parallel, each section being fitted with a 'M' filament. This type of construction was adopted by other tube manufacturers, including RCA but with the exception of Raytheon, who adopted a completely different approach by producing an indirectly heated version, the 2A3H, some four months after RCA's original had appeared. The fact that the 2A3H was indirectly heated was not in itself significant, but this type of construction avoided using the tricky and difficult to manufacture multiple filament. In 1935 Sylvania brought out a 6.3

Two versions of Raytheon's 2A3H. The one on the right has three cathodes.

volt version, the 6A3, and by 1937 an octal based version, the 6B4G, and an indirectly heated version, the 6A5G, were in production by several other manufacturers.

Although mention of the following matter might be classed as trivia, attention is drawn to a change in the manner of drawing the internal structure of beam tetrodes which occurred in RCA's Tube Manuals from the 1947 edition (RC15) onwards. Prior to this, drawings in the

Original type 2A3 (1933)   Later type 2A3 (1935 onwards)

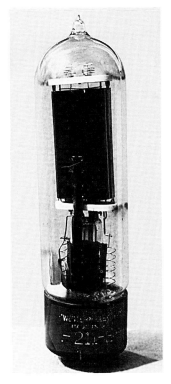

Western Electric 211E (1926), superseded by 242C.

Western Electric 242C (1936), replaced type 211E.

earlier editions correctly showed such tubes as the 6L6 as being without a suppressor grid but having beam forming electrodes. As the drawings of other manufacturers always depicted the same tetrode structure, it may be wondered what caused RCA to change their way of drawing by showing a pentode structure, particularly as the well known sectional drawing entitled—Internal Structure of type 6L6 Beam Power Tube—has remained unchanged ever since it first appeared.

We come now to vacuum tube usage in the area of public entertainment, specifically talking pictures. Although the name of Western Electric has always been closely associated with sound-on-film recording and reproduction, it should be mentioned that one of the earliest workers in this field was none other than Lee de Forest, who as early as 1920 had devised a system of recording and reproduction which he dubbed 'Phonofilm.'

As far as Western Electric was concerned, this firm already possessed tube making facilities and had developed and produced tubes for telephone work as well as for radio transmission and was thus in the position of being able to make any tubes needed for talking picture applications.

It is interesting to note that on entering the talking picture field, W.E. continued their long established practice

first in its power range .. designed specifically for audio service

The Tung-Sol 6550 is a brand new and direct approach to the high power design requirements of high fidelity audio amplifiers. For outputs up to 100 watts, two 6550's in push-pull will provide the same power now attained in most existing designs by the use of four or more tubes. In addition to greater audio output, use of the new 6550 results in simplified electrical balance, reduced maintenance and lower cost. The Tung-Sol 6550 is not directly interchangeable with the 6L6, 5881 or KT66 class of tubes. With proper circuitry, however, the 6550 will provide full power output with approximately the same grid voltage drive as the smaller tubes. The 6550 is produced under laboratory conditions with exhaustive quality control to assure premium performance and long life.

Audio, (December 1954)

240

of renting (hiring) rather than selling equipment so that tubes developed for sound film use were, like all other W.E. tubes, produced on a reliability and long life basis.

A W.E. tube that has achieved an exalted status in the eyes of many present day hi-fi enthusiasts is the type 300B, a filamentary output triode having characteristics similar to those of the 2A3. Originally produced in 1935 as the 300A, the 300B followed three years later and remained in production by W.E. until 1988, thus making it one of the longest lived types ever produced by any manufacturer. And that was not the end, for at the time of writing (1996) the 300B is being manufactured in the U.S. by Cetron as well as being produced 'offshore' by Chinese and Russian tube makers. What a history!

British Developments

Even before the first receiving-type power tubes had been introduced in the U.S., British valve makers appeared to have realized the need to develop valves in this category. For example, as early as 1923 Mullard had produced their first two power valves, types PA1 and PA2 while B.T-H were offering their B2 and B4 in the same year. By 1924, Ediswan and Marconi-Osram had joined the ranks, the former with their 'PV' (Power Valve) series and the latter with their 'LS' (Loud Speaker) series; all were bright emitters, mostly with 6-volt filaments. By 1925, power valves with 2-volt dull emitter filaments were being produced. By comparison, the first American 2-volt battery tube, type 31, did not appear until 1930.

With the coming of mains(AC) operated radios, higher

Marconi-Osram type DA60 later type (1932)

power directly heated output valves were developed by several makers, one of the most widely used and enduring types being M-O.V's PX4. Introduced in 1929, this valve had a 4-volt filament consuming 0.6 amps and had a maximum anode dissipation of 12 watts. Over the years the PX4 underwent several structural changes and improvements in its characteristics resulting in an increase of anode dissipation to 15 watts and an increase in mutual conductance from 2.6 mA/V to 6 mA/V. A pair of PX4s

Ediswan PV2 (1924)

Original PX4 (1929) Note sloping electrode assembly.

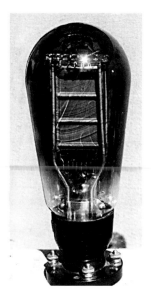

PX25 Original version (1932)

operated in Class A push-pull at an anode voltage of 300 could then provide an output of 13.5 watts compared with 10 watts for 2A3s operating under the same conditions. Such was the production lifespan of the PX4 that it was still being listed as a current type in the *Wireless World* radio valve data, 7th edition, 1961.

An even higher power output triode from the same stable, the PX25, was issued in 1932 and it too shared an equally long lifespan. With a remarkably high mutual conductance figure of 7.5 mA/V it could provide 20 watts output in Class A push-pull at an anode voltage of 500.

Beam tetrodes first appeared on the British market with the introduction of M-O.V's 'KT' series late in 1937. In this connection it is interesting to note that the beam

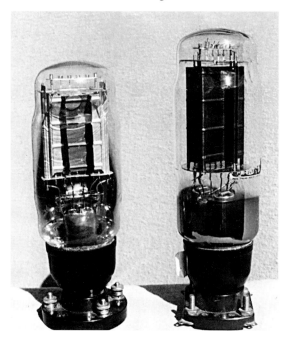

PX4 Final version (c. 1960)   *PX25 Final version (c.1965)*

tetrode was actually invented and patented in England* but was initially thought to be beyond the capability of the M-O.V factory to produce economically. This resulted in the design being handed over to RCA for development in the U.S. and the production of the 6L6 in mid-1936. By the end of 1937 M-O.V had produced a British version, the KT66, which was obviously based on the 6L6, as it had almost identical characteristics. Such was M-O.V's apparent enthusiasm for their 'baby' that they lost no time in re-issuing most of their existing range of pentodes (including RF types) in 'Kinkless Tetrode' form. The only other two valve makers to produce beam tetrodes in pre-war days were Cossor and Mazda; Mullard, understandably remained firmly wedded to pentodes.

The KT66 became and remained the most widely used output valve of its class and in the early post-war years was to be found in such well known hi-fi amplifiers as the Leak and Quad, to name but two. Over the years the KT66 underwent an increase in its maximum plate and screen voltage ratings from 400V and 300V to 500V and 400V respectively, when a maximum power output of 50 watts was obtainable in ultra linear operation.

For outputs in excess of 50 watts a more powerful type of valve was called for and this need was met by the production of the type KT88 in April 1957. Like its smaller brother, this new valve bore very obvious indications of its American ancestry, not the least of which was the entry in the 1957 edition of the GEC Valve Manual which stated that the KT88 was equivalent to the (American) type 6550, a tube released by Tung Sol late in 1954.

The KT88 was the first British valve of its type to make use of what was described as "an all-glass ring seal" in place of the conventional pinch construction. The ratings and characteristics were identical with those of the 6550, a pair in push-pull ultra linear configuration being capable of 100 watts output.

A valve bearing the markings STC 4300A was available at one time in the U.K., but whether it was actually of British manufacture is not known. Its characteristics are listed by Standard Telephone & Cables Ltd. as being identical to W.E.'s 300A/B, but there is an obvious manufacturing difference in that the STC valve has seven ribs visible on each side of the anode, compared with five on the W.E. tube.

Continental Europe

Unlike the situation existing in Britain and the U.S., where the beam tetrode had successfully challenged the pentode's supremacy, the pentode always remained the preferred output tube in most Continental countries. Rather obviously, Phillips as holders of the pentode patents were not unhappy with this state of affairs and continued to further develop pentodes in preference to

* History of the British Radio Valve to 1940, p. 63. Keith R. Thrower, pub. MMA International Ltd. 1992

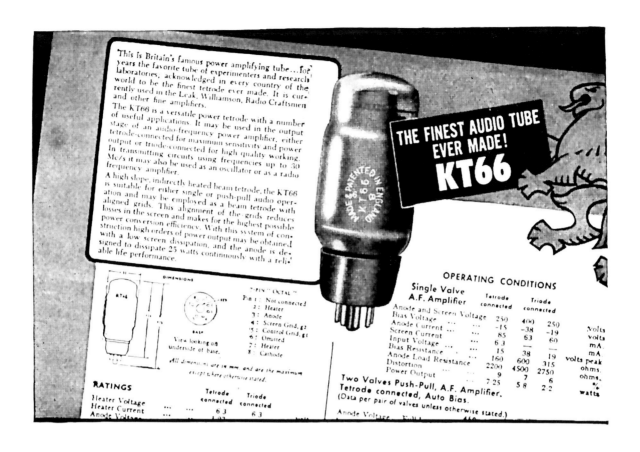

THE FAMOUS **KT66** . . . IN USE ALL OVER

AMERICA AND ACKNOWLEDGED TO BE THE

FINEST BEAM TETRODE EVER MADE

IS AN **Osram** VALVE MADE IN ENGLAND

The photographic reproduction is taken from literature published in America by the British Industries Corporation and gives an entirely unsolicited tribute to this fine valve.

THE GENERAL ELECTRIC CO. LTD., MAGNET HOUSE, KINGSWAY, LONDON, W.C.2

Wireless World, (October 1952)

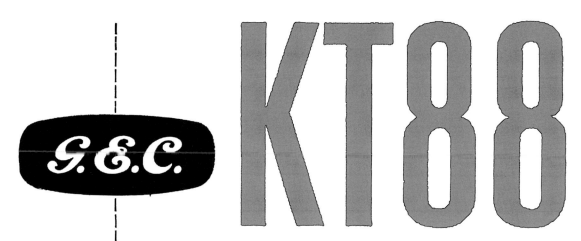

A New Audio Output Valve with an anode dissipation of 35 watts

An addition to the well tried and popular range of G.E.C. Audio Valves, of which the KT66 has set a standard in its class the world over, the new G.E.C. KT88 is now available to meet conditions of use requiring higher power.

POINTS ABOUT THE KT88

1 The KT88 is a beam pentode with aligned grids for maximum efficiency.

2 50 watts output is available from a pair connected in the ultra linear circuit with auto bias and an H.T. line voltage not exceeding 500.

3 100 watts output is available from a pair connected in the ultra linear circuit with fixed bias and an H.T. line voltage not exceeding 560.

4 25 watts output is available from a pair triode connected with auto bias and an H.T. line voltage not exceeding 500.

5 The mutual conductance of the KT88 is 11 mA/V.

6 An all-glass ring seal replaces the conventional pinch seal giving increased strength, higher rating and reduced dimensions.

7 The valve is mounted on an international octal base and has a heater rating of 6.3 volts., 1.8 amps.

Full particulars of these valves can be obtained from the
G.E.C. VALVE & ELECTRONICS DEPT.

THE GENERAL ELECTRIC CO. LTD., MAGNET HOUSE, KINGSWAY, LONDON, W.C.2

beam tetrodes.

Although output triodes were not unknown on the Continent, they ran a very poor second to pentodes in popularity. However, it must be recorded that both Philips and Telefunken manufactured this class of tube, and also receivers incorporating them. The most well known example, the type AD1, a 4-volt 'P' based triode which had characteristics very similar to those of RCA's 2A3, was produced in 1935 by both Philips and Telefunken and was used in a few 1935 receiver models made by both firms. A tube with very similar characteristics to the AD1 but fitted with a German 7-pin base was the type 'Ed' produced by Siemens in 1935.

One effect of the widespread devastation in Europe caused by WW-II was to delay the development of hi-fi amplifiers until the more basic radio requirements had been met. However, by 1950 a new high-power output pentode, the octal-based type EL34, produced by Philips, Mullard and Telefunken, had become available. It was noteworthy for being the first of its type to adopt the relatively new 'ring' seal in place of the conventional stem seal. This new type of construction allowed operation at much higher plate voltages which in turn provided a much greater power output than would otherwise have been obtainable.

A pair of these tubes in Class AB service could provide an output of 35 watts at a plate voltage of 375, or a pair used in ultra linear mode could provide 37 watts at a plate voltage of 430. A highly successful design resulting in a tube which remained in production for over twenty years and was eventually listed by RCA as type 6CA7 in their RC26 (1968) Tube Manual.

(Left to right) STC 4300A. Note 7-ribbed anode compared with W.E.'s 5-ribbed 300B, Northern Electric (Canada) R300A Western Electric 300B

EL34 Mullard and Telefunken

245

Chapter Twenty-Eight

Tube Collecting as a Hobby

In present-day terminology the name given to early factory-made objects which, being less than 100 years old cannot properly be classified as antiques, is 'collectibles'. Such items may include anything from buttons to barbed wire or stamps to steam engines. Of recent years a growing interest has arisen in the collecting of early radio receivers and, as a corollary, the collecting of radio tubes. That tubes are only one of the many individual components that go to make up a complete receiver in no way belittles their importance in the scheme of things as for so long they were the mainspring of receiver development.

Although tube collecting as a hobby is of quite recent origin by comparison with other long-established fields of interest, the idea of assembling a collection of radio tubes goes back almost as far as the origins of the tubes themselves. One of the earliest-known collections was that of Lt. W.A. Eaton of the U.S. Navy. This collection was formed during the early 1920s and although photographs of it remain in existence the collection itself has long since disappeared. Another early collection is illustrated in the U.S. Signal Corps publication *Principles Underlying Radio Communication*, 2nd edit. 1922. Yet another was assembled by a well-known American radio engineer, McMurdo Silver, and is now on display at the Ford Museum in Dearborn, Mich.

In England one of the first valve collectors was R. McVitie Weston who later presented his collection to Standard Telephones & Cables Ltd. More recently this collection has found a permanent resting place at the Science Museum, London. Undeniably the world's oldest and largest collection in private hands was built by Gerald F.J. Tyne of New Jersey. The Tyne collection was begun before World War I and now numbers over 5000 tubes.

What was probably the first published information of specific interest to tube collectors is to be found in a short series of articles entitled *The Tube Collector* which appeared in the American radio periodical *Radio News,* commencing April 1943.

Broadly speaking, interest in a particular tube can be divided into three categories—age, rarity, and historical importance, though these attributes may not necessarily be related. For example, a tube made in 1934 may nowadays be much rarer than one made in 1924. This is because the later tube may have been a type that had a very limited production lifespan or was made by only one company, whereas the earlier tube may have been a type that was made in huge quantities by many different companies, ensuring that a comparatively large number would survive to become collectors' items.

As in other fields of collecting the existence of unusual or 'odd-ball' items provides an added interest to many collectors. In this category are the many American 'non-infringing' tubes made during the early 1920s. These include 'gridless' triodes or those having external control elements. Of similar interest are double-filament and early multiple tubes of the two-in-one or three-in-one variety, as well as tubes having unusual constructional features, and so on.

During the middle 1920s a few American manufacturers produced 201A type tubes having natural or self-coloured bulbs. For example, Supertron and Wards Airline tubes had bulbs made from amber coloured glass while Brightson and Western tubes had blue glass bulbs. The use of coloured bulbs in this manner was solely as a means of brand identification, but presumably due to the higher cost of coloured glass its use did not persist for any length of time. In the case of certain French tubes made at much the same time blue glass bulbs were used, but for a different reason. A dense opaque blue glass was used to conceal a discoloration of the inner bulb surface caused by a particular manufacturing process used at the time.

In the case of certain early thoriated-filament tubes which had bulbs exhibiting a multi-hued or 'rainbow' appearance the colouring came about as a result of the use of a mixed getter containing red phosphorous. For a short period during the late 1920s and early 1930s some American manufacturers used tinted or coloured bulbs as a means of identifying their particular products. The earliest-known examples of such practice were Brightson 'True Blue' tubes which appeared briefly in 1925 and used the same sort of blue glass as used in 'daylight blue' electric lamps. By far the best-known blue glass tubes were those made by the Arcturus Radio Tube Co. during the years 1927–33 when over 70 different types were produced. Of these the Wunderlich detector with its red bakelite base must surely qualify as having the most eye appeal of any tube ever made.

An aspect of any sort of collecting concerns the upper date limit set by individual collectors. In the case of present-day collectors the actual year is likely to be around 1935; on the other hand if a time limit of, say, 40 years or whatever is chosen then of course the actual year will be continuously updated with the passage of time. Whichever method is chosen it is unlikely to be regarded as a hard and fast rule as there are bound to some more recent tubes which will be of interest.

Already the passage of time has made it possible to assemble a quite impressive collection of tubes which are 50 years or more old, that is were made in 1930 or earlier. Such was the pace of development during the early 1930s that if the cut-off date is extended by only five years, until 1935, then a collection can include practically all generic tube types as well as indirectly-heated AC, AC/DC, and automobile types together with many multiple and multifunction tubes.

Tube collectors, like collectors of any sort are naturally interested in the dating of individual items and while it may be difficult or impossible to accurately date a pre-World War I tube such is not the case with many later tubes, particularly those made or sold by RCA which can be accurately dated to within three months of manufacture.

The oldest British valve ever likely to find its way into the hands of a private collector is an example of a commercial form of Fleming diode or as the inventor called it, Oscillation Valve. Such valves were made between ap-

British Army triodes c. 1925.

proximately 1906 and 1916 by the Edison & Swan Electric Light Co. and most, if not all, carried the company's trade-mark—Royal Ediswan—etched on the surface of the bulb. The earliest of these valves used carbon filaments but because Fleming had patented the use of tungsten filaments in 1909–10 it may be assumed that any valves using tungsten filaments would have been made after that time.

In the case of American tubes it is known that there are a considerable number of De Forest Spherical Audions in private hands, most of such tubes being sold between the years 1909–16.

For the benefit of tube collectors it may be mentioned that a useful approximation of the date of manufacture of any early tungsten-filament tube can be obtained by examining the appearance of the lead-out wires where they pass through the press. If short sections of thinner silvery coloured wire can be seen butt-welded to the heavier electrode support rods then the thinner wires will be made of platinum. If, on the other hand, the lead-out wires are of a coppery colour and continue down through the stem in one piece then they are made of an alloy known as 'Dumet'. In both cases the object was to use a material which had the same co-efficient of expansion as glass. Because platinum was expensive only the smallest amount possible was used and after Dumet wire was invented it replaced platinum completely. As Dumet wire came into general use from 1924 onwards it may be assumed that any tube with platinum in the press was made before that date.

As manufactured the bulbs of most tubes using plain tungsten filaments were completely clear due to the absence of any metallic gettering, though certain later British and French productions sometimes exhibited pinkish tinged bulbs due to the use of a red phosphorous getter. Because of the comparatively high operating temperature of pure tungsten filaments they evaporated slightly during

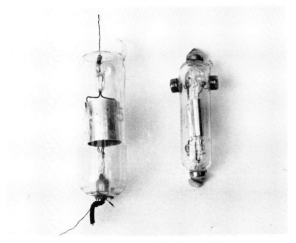

Annaka AAB-5 and QX
Two early Japanese tubes c. 1920. The QX is a copy of the Marconi QX

use, the condensed material then settling on the inner surface of the bulb in the form of silvery patches.

With the introduction of thoriated-filament tubes in the U.S.A. in 1923 the manufacturing process resulted in a silvery deposit completely obscuring the inside of the bulb. This was particularly true of the American types UV/UX201-A and UV/UX199. An exception occurred in the case of the type UX-200A which was not gettered because of the necessary presence of an introduced gas or vapour required by this particular tube's application as a special detector.

Magnesium gettering was likewise not used in European tubes made before 1923 even though one British company—M-O.V.—had used thoriated filaments before that date. The Marconi type L.T.1 dull-emitter valve was marketed in 1921 and in spite of having a thoriated filament it was not magnesium gettered. When an improved version, type D.E.R., was issued during the following year it also originally had a clear bulb though the final issues were magnesium gettered.

A French development of 1926 gave rise to a type of tube employing a barium-coated filament which, during the firing process, resulted in excess barium condensing on the inside of the bulb in the same way as magnesium did in the case of thoriated-filament tubes. The use of barium in this way caused the silvery metallic deposit to exhibit a brownish tinge around the edges and this was particularly noticeable in the case of Philips tubes made up to 1935.

Further dating information can readily be obtained by noting whether any particular tube has a seal-off tip on the surface of the bulb. Originally all tubes, and electric light bulbs too, for that matter, had an external tip seal, or 'pip' as it was known in British parlance, by which evacuation of the bulb was accomplished. Commencing in 1924 in the U.S. a change in production methods enabled evacuation to be carried out via a small-diameter glass tube located inside the hollow part of the mounting stem.

The use of tipless bulbs spread rapidly throughout the industry though it was some years before all manufacturers adopted the new technique. For example, Raytheon gaseous rectifiers and Arcturus 15-volt AC tubes were still being issued in tip-seal form as late as 1927, while Western Electric continued to use tip-sealed bulbs until well into the 1930s. Similarly in the U.K. Marconi-Osram issued their types KL1 and KH1 valves in tip-sealed bulbs during 1927, some two years after the general adoption of tipless construction.

Tipless bulbs remained in use on all standard sized tubes for as long as they were in production but when the first of the so-called 'midget' valves were introduced by Hivac in 1936 their construction made it necessary to revert to the use of tip-sealed bulbs. The same applied to the American Hytron 'Bantam' tubes of 1938. It was the arrival of RCA's 1.4-volt miniature tubes in 1940 which marked the beginning of a new era in tube development and resulted in tip-sealed bulbs once again becoming commonplace.

The introduction of tipless bulbs in the U.S. in 1924 coincided with the introduction of bakelite bases, and although not all manufacturers adopted these two features at the same time it may be said that, in general, the majority of tubes available after 1925 were so constructed. In Europe these two developments occurred a year or so later where Philips of Holland first issued bakelite-based tubes early in 1926. Prior to this the metal shell Franco British base, originally of plain copper or brass, was given a nickel-plated finish by most European manufacturers during 1924–25. The bases used on such tubes as the RE78 and RE83 (shown on page 241) are of black painted aluminum.

Although the use of tip-sealed bulbs in the U.S. was discontinued at much the same time that metal-shell bases became obsolete, certain exceptions occurred during the transitory period. For a short time a few Radiotron bakelite-based tubes were issued which still had tip-sealed bulbs. In addition some independent manufacturers (notably Arcturus) continued using this type of construction up to 1929.

During the time that metal-shell bases were in use on Radiotron tubes these bases were always of plain brass, though certain transmitting types had nickel-plated bases. The bases of Western Electric tubes were always nickel plated except in the case of large transmitting types. A few early De Forest tubes, such as the VT-21 and type 20, were notable for the use of nickel-plated bases.

The first tubes to be fitted with bakelite bases were the Radiotron types UV199 and UV201-A which were released in October 1924. In August 1925 the first long pin tubes, types UX-199 and UX-201-A, were released and by 1926 most other manufacturers had changed to the use of this style of base.

Another readily apparent feature helping to date a given tube is the presence or absence of the so-called 'domed' bulb which originated in the U.S. during 1932. There it was known as the 'ST' style, the designation being derived from the bulb shape which was a combination of the 'S' (sign lamp) shape with the 'T' (tubular) shape. ST bulbs are characterised by the top section being of a smaller diameter than the lower portion. They were introduced on the types 57 and 58 RF pentodes which were released in mid-1932.

With the introduction of bakelite-based tubes in the U.S. came the method of marking the manufacturer's name and the tube's type number on the base by a process known as 'hot-branding'. Any such tubes may be instantly recognised by the depressed lettering appearing on their bases; a case where the word 'brandname' may be taken literally! In the case of RCA Radiotron and most other American tubes this process was used between 1925 and 1936.

Hot-branded markings were rarely encountered outside the U.S., Brimar, for example, being the only British valve

248

maker to use them. However, hot-branded markings have been sighted on some Australian, Canadian, and Japanese tubes.

The only accurate means of determining the date of manufacture of a particular tube is by an examination of coded date markings, if these were used and assuming that the 'key' is available. Whilst it is likely that most American manufacturers in existence after about 1924 would have used some form of date coding the keys would have disappeared when the firms went out of business. Fortunately, however, in the case of RCA Radiotron the factory records were saved from destruction by the enterprise of one individual at the time of the closure of RCA's receiving tube plant in 1977. This action has allowed the compilation of detailed data of much interest to tube collectors though it is much too extensive to be included in this work.

In the case of early British valves a clue to their age is provided by the presence or absence of the so-called 'B.B.C. Trade Mark'. This marking consists of the letters B.B.C. enclosed within a circle which is surrounded by the words 'Type Approved by the Post Master General' inkstamped on the bulb. As this particular marking was used only between the end of 1922 and the end of 1926 it can thus provide some indication of the period in which a particular valve was made. However, because not all valves carried the B.B.C. marking its absence cannot be taken as proof that a given valve was made outside the two dates mentioned.

The BBC trade-mark used on British valves made between 1922 and 1926.

An aspect of tube collecting about which very little information exists concerns the identification of the manufacturer of a particular tube sold under a brandname of other than that of its actual maker. Although authoritative records exist in the case of early Radiotrons which were made by either GE or Westinghouse it is a different matter when it comes to the products of independent manufacturers.

For the purpose of this discussion it is convenient to divide American tubes into two date groupings—those made prior to the licensing of independent manufacturers by RCA in 1929, and those made subsequently. Leaving aside those few independents in existence before the inception of broadcasting during 1921–22 the remainder who sprang up during the 1920s became known as 'bootleg-

BC18   BC9   BD9
Three Fotos battery valves c. 1934. Made in England by a French company.

gers' due to their unlicensed activities. Where such manufacturers issued tubes under different names it was done primarily to conceal their identity rather than to supply 'private brand' tubes to distributors. At that time there was little demand by receiver manufacturers for tubes to be marked with their own brandnames because most sets were shipped from the factory 'less tubes'. In those days tubes were regarded as accessories, like loudspeakers or batteries, and were supplied by the dealer at the time of sale.

It should be realised that prior to licensing the American tube industry was quite disorganised but afterwards acquired a measure of stability, due in part to the establishment of a Tube Committee of the Radio Manufacturers Association in 1933. One effect of licensing was to allow those independents, who desired to do so, the opportunity to expand the scale of their operations secure in their newly-acquired licensed status. The other effect was to reduce dramatically the number of small independents. In 1926 there were over 150 tube brandnames on the market but by 1930 the number had dropped to only twenty. Although most of what were to become the largest independents had been established prior to licensing several new companies entered the field during the next year or so. Of these only two—National Union and Tung Sol—remained in existence for any length of time, in both cases until after World War II.

With the rise in the number of large receiver manufacturers which took place following the introduction of 'all-electric' radios during 1927–28, a demand arose for tubes to be marked with the brandnames of some of the set makers. One of the earliest examples of this practice is to be found in the case of tubes made by Arcturus for the Sonora Phonograph Co. in 1929. Similarly Arcturus tubes were used by Crosley during 1931–31, while later still Crosley used tubes made by Ken-Rad. In all cases these tubes carried the names of the two companies concerned and thus left no doubt as to the identity of the actual manufacturer.

Some other large receiver manufacturers who used tubes marked with their own brandnames were—Delco, Fada, Philco, and Zenith. As a guide it may be mentioned that National Union was a large supplier to Delco; Tung Sol was the main supplier to Fada; Sylvania was the main supplier to Philco; and Raytheon was the main supplier to Zenith. Even far-off New Zealand can provide an example of this practice when in 1933 Ken-Rad supplied tubes to one of that country's largest receiver manufacturers, the Radio Corporation of New Zealand, which bore the markings R.N.Z. Made by Ken-Rad hot-branded on their bases.

Two Japanese tubes of the early 1930s period with hot-branded base markings.

In the U.S. certain large radio distributors also used their own brandnames on tubes fitted to their 'private brand' receivers. Examples are: Airline (Montgomery Ward), Coronado (Gamble Skogmo), Silvertone (Sears Roebuck). Following World War II tubes were marketed by various distributors under such names as ADA, Calvertron, Hudson, K-R, and Silcotron. The only way to positively identify the actual manufacturer of a given tube is to carefully compare it with samples of the same type carrying the names of known tube makers.

Whilst RCA did not normally supply private brand tubes to receiver manufacturers in the same way as did the independents it is known that some RCA tubes were sold under other brandnames. For example, during the middle 1930s unbranded tubes were supplied to Philips in Australia and New Zealand who subsequently added their

own markings before selling them. Such tubes consisted mainly of certain 2.5-volt AC types needed at the time to fill gaps in the existing Philips range. Another example occurred during the 1950s when RCA tubes were sold by an old-established distributor, Ad Auriema Inc. of New York under their ADA brandname.

By comparison the position in Europe has always been more stable though in certain countries, notably England and Holland, various short-lived manufacturers came and went during the 1920s and 1930s. The practice of supplying private brand tubes or valves was almost unknown though a few British examples can be cited. At one time or another Mullard made valves for Six-Sixty, S.T., and Ever Ready. Marconi valves, apart from the earliest Fleming-type diodes made by Ediswan, were made first at the Osram Lamp Works and later by M-O.V. after the formation of that company in 1919. As Marconi's held a 50% interest in M-O.V. it could thus be said that they made their own valves at that time. After Marconi's interest was acquired by E.M.I. in 1931 some M-O.V. valves used in H.M.V. receivers for a short period carried the His Master's Voice name and the well-known 'Listening Dog' trade-mark.

From a collector's point of view an occurrence which causes some confusion was a practice which arose in the late 1930s whereby one tube maker would 'help out' another by supplying unbranded tubes which were then sold under the latter's brandname. As time went by the reduced demand for older type tubes made it increasingly uneconomical for each manufacturer to continue producing a full range of types. This led to individual manufacturers electing to produce runs of certain types which were then shared round amongst the others. During World War II this practice was accelerated when wartime controls severely restricted the manufacture of tubes for civilian use.

A similar state of affairs prevailed in the U.K. and was particularly noticeable after the war when 'label swapping'

RE78   RE11   RE83
Three Telefunken battery tubes. The open date coding is a collector's delight.

Telefunken RE134 battery triode c. 1929.

REN914   RENS1204   REN804
Telefunken AC tubes c. 1931.

card tube-operated equipment, with the consequent need to continue tube manufacture for a longer period.

There is an aspect of tube collecting which may assume greater importance with the passing of time and that is the possibility of encountering either reproductions or even fakes. While there can be no quarrel with the idea of reproducing at a later period any earlier man-made articles, be it works of art or whatever, there always remains the possibility of their being passed off as originals. The existence of faked paintings is a well-known example of this sort of thing. Human nature being what it is, there is no reason to believe that the same cannot happen in the case of radio tubes, even if it may seem unlikely.

The earliest-known reproductions were originally made

A fake tube, made in USA in 1965.

became the norm in the case of many pre-war types. Finally at least one B.V.A. member turned to foreign manufacturers for the supply of certain types of miniature valves. Rather ironically such valves were branded 'B.V.A. Foreign' which was a sad commentary on the state of the British valve industry when it is recalled that one of the original aims of the B.V.A. was to prevent the importation of foreign valves! By this time, however, the British were in good company because the same sort of thing was going on in the U.S. where some tube makers were relying on foreign sources for their supplies of receiving tubes. The final phase in the declining years of the British valve industry occurred during the 1970s when such firms as Tronix, Trigon, and Zaerix purchased valves from any source where they were still procurable and added their own brandnames. By this time it was almost impossible to determine the identity of the maker or even the country of origin. It is known that some of these valves were imported from eastern European countries such as Poland whilst others were obtained from the U.S.S.R.. Communist countries, it seems, had either stock-piled large quantities of tubes or else were not in such a hurry to dis-

Examples of 'Private Brand' tubes c. 1936.

58   2B7
Made by Ken-Rad for the Radio Corporation of New Zealand (1934).

UX227. There ain't no such animal! Believed to be made in Japan c. 1930.

as a hobby interest by a Californian ham radio operator back in 1965. Due to requests the person concerned decided to offer for sale limited quantities on a made-to-order basis at a price of $20 each. To avoid the possibility of these excellent reproductions ever being mistaken for originals the maker wisely decided to identify them by stamping his ham call-sign on the anode of each tube thus: REPLICA Made by W6IS.

Also in 1965 another American ham produced home-made copies of certain early tubes in his basement workshop. He published details of his activities in QST magazine for April 1965 in an article entitled: 'Vacuum Tubes the Hard Way by Sam Diaz Pumara'. Unfortunately, as it turned out, these particular tubes carried no markings and some of them fell into the hands of an unscrupulous dealer who passed them off as originals.

Because Pumara publicised his work it seems obvious that there was no intention to deceive and in any case the Pumara reproductions were extremely crude and could not be mistaken for the real thing by anybody who had any knowledge of the subject. Even so it emphasises the desirability of indelibly marking any reproductions in order to prevent the same thing happening in the future.

Although, at the time of writing, it has apparently not been worthwhile for anyone to undertake the manufacture of reproduction tubes on a commercial basis the steadily increasing prices being paid for originals may eventually lead to this. Apart from the needs of tube collectors there are also the many thousands of owners of antique battery sets who would be only too happy to obtain workable tubes for their old radios. Failing actual manufacture then there exists a need for tube repairers—people who can fit new filaments as was done commercially during the 1920s.

Sooner or later any tube collector will be faced with the problem of how best to display his collection in an attractive and permanent manner. While there may be some who are forced to, and some who are content to, house their collections in cardboard boxes most collectors will wish to have at least a few choice specimens on permanent display.

The simplest, cheapest, and least effective method of displaying tubes is to mount them flat against a display board by means of a thin wire passing around each tube and through the board. This method has the disadvantage that tubes cannot readily be removed for cleaning or inspection. Furthermore where tubes are collected in groups or 'sets' it is not possible to make additions without rearranging the entire group. An alternative means of attaching tubes to display boards is by means of small spring clips, this method being almost essential in the case of tubes having spherical bulbs.

Probably the most satisfactory method of display is to place the tubes in rows on narrow glass shelves but where insufficient wall space is available it may be necessary to use wider shelves which will allow two or three rows to be placed on each shelf. To reduce the amount of unnecessary handling caused by the need for frequent cleaning it is desirable that the shelves be contained within glass-fronted cabinets.

The use of shelves will of course require some means of mounting the tubes and while suitable tube sockets may be used for this purpose it is frequently difficult or impossible to obtain enough of them. In place of actual sockets small circular wood blocks drilled with the appropriate holes can form a very effective means of mounting. Such blocks are readily turned up on a lathe and have the advantage of uniformity of appearance. A diameter of 2″ (50 mm) is suitable for all but large transmitting tubes. Even tubes having short pins (UV bases) can be held firmly if the holes are made slightly undersize. Unbased tubes are best mounted by one or two small spring clips attached to a suitable backing which will allow them to be placed in either a vertical or horizontal position.

Where it is desired to identify particular tubes or to record dates or other details small self-adhesive labels may be attached to the tube base or bulb or else to the mount. It is also possible to apply markings direct to the bulb surface by means of a fine felt-tipped pen.

Within the confines of these pages the author has tried to present a coherent account of the rise and fall of the radio tube. Of necessity much interesting material has had to be left out, partly through lack of space and partly because the main emphasis of the book is concerned with developments taking place during the decade 1930–1940. It is hoped that such omissions as occur will be accepted for those reasons.

Although the year 1977 marked the end of the road for receiving tube production by most of the world's leading manufacturers, the receiving tube is not yet dead. At the time this book goes to press, late in 1982, tube manufacture continues in such places as Brazil and Mexico as well as in some European countries. Furthermore, the production of the famous KT66 and KT88 output tetrodes has recently recommenced by GEC-AEI Ltd in the U.K. It would be a rash person indeed who would dare to prophesy and predict the day when the last tube factory finally closes down.

6Q7G   56   58
Crosley tubes made by Ken-Rad c. 1936.

6H8C   6P3C
Two Russian octal-based tubes (1954).

35L6GT   6K7GT
Two Italian FIVRE tubes c. 1939.

Glossary

'A' BATTERY: American term for a filament-heating battery.

ANODE: Fundamental positively-charged electrode in any tube.

AUDION: An early American term for a vacuum tube

AUDION: Trade-mark used by various De Forest cos.

'B' BATTERY: American term for plate supply battery.

BASE: That portion of a tube carrying the base pins.

BASE SHELL: Cylindrical metal sleeve forming part of base.

BRIGHT EMITTER: Any tube with a plain tungsten filament.

BULB: The glass envelope of any tube.

'C' BATTERY: American term for grid bias battery.

CAP: British and Dutch term for base (q.v.).

CATHODE: The electron-emitting electrode (emitter).

CONTROL GRID: See grid.

DETECTOR: Any tube used to detect radio frequency signals.

DIODE: Any two-electrode tube.

DOUBLE-GRID TUBE: An early form of four-electrode (tetrode) tube.

ELECTRODE: Any internal functioning part of a tube.

ELECTRONS: Negatively-charged particles forming the space current in any tube.

ELECTRON STREAM: The current passing through any tube.

ELECTRON TUBE: Term which superseded the older 'radio' tube.

ELEMENT: American term for electrode.

EMISSION: The production of electrons at the surface of a hot cathode.

FILAMENT: The cathode in all directly-heated tubes.

FILAMENTARY CATHODE: See above.

GAS: Gas present inside the bulb which may be there by design or which may occur due to a fault.

GASEOUS RECTIFIER: A rectifier tube dependent for its operation on the presence of an inert gas.

GETTER: A substance used during manufacture to assist in maintaining a high degree of vacuum in a tube.

GRID: The fundamental control electrode in any tube.

HEATER: Heating element used in tubes having indirectly-heated cathodes.

HEPTODE: A seven-electrode tube.

HEXODE: A six-electrode tube.

KENOTRON. A tradename used for early high voltage rectifiers made by the General Electric Co.

OCTAL BASE: The eight-pin base originally developed for use on American metal tubes in 1935.

OCTODE: An eight-electrode tube.

OSCILLATION VALVE: An archaic British term for a two-electrode detector valve.

OSCILLATOR: Any tube used to produce electrical oscillations.

OXIDE-COATED FILAMENT: A filament coated with a metallic oxide during manufacture.

PENTODE: A five-electrode tube.

PIP: A colloquial British term for the external seal-off tip on any valve.

PLATE: American term for anode, also used in other countries.

RADIOTRON: Tradename used on tubes made or sold by Radio Corporation of America (RCA).

RECTIGON: Westinghouse tradename for an argon-filled low voltage rectifier.

RECTRON: An out-dated name for high voltage rectifiers sold by RCA.

SECONDARY EMISSION: A normally unwanted emission occurring at some point other than the cathode of a tube.

SCREEN-GRID: A second grid used in tetrode RF amplifying tubes.

SOCKET: American term for the receptacle into which a tube is inserted.

SPACE CHARGE: The 'cloud' of electrons adjacent to the surface of any tube's cathode.

SPACE CURRENT: See electron stream.

SUPPRESSOR GRID: The third grid in a pentode tube.

TETRODE: A four-electrode tube.

THERMIONIC TUBE: Any tube having a hot cathode.

THORIATED FILAMENT: Tungsten filament having improved emission obtained by processing during manufacture.

TIP: The external seal-off point on the surface of a bulb.

TIT: Colloquial American term for above.

VACUUM TUBE: The original American term for radio tube.

VALVE: British term, contraction of thermionic valve.

VALVEHOLDER: British term equivalent to the American tube socket.

WING: Archaic American term for plate.

Index

Index by Tube Number

UV201   16, 17, 21, 146, 183
UV201A   17, 18, 20, 36, 148, 188, 248
UV202   18, 127, 128, 237
UV203   128, 237
UV203A   129
UV204   237
UV210   18
UV216   110
UV217   112
UX12 (Jap), 250
UX112   18, 21, 22, 237
UX112A   21, 237
UX120   18, 22, 166
UX121B   184
UX171   22, 238
UX171A   238
UX199   17, 18, 42, 188, 248
UX200   17, 18
UX200A   17, 18, 239
UX201A   18, 19, 188, 248
UX210   18, 22, 42, 237
UX213   18, 110, 111, 113
UX216B   18, 110, 113
UX222   39, 40, 65, 151, 166, 223
UX225   45
UX227 (Jap), 243
UX240   18, 32
UX245   238
UX250   21, 22, 238
UX280   111
UX281   110, 111
UX852   128
UY56 (Jap), 250
UY224   45, 65, 66, 165, 223
UY224A   45, 65
UY227   45, 46, 47, 152, 162, 177
UY227A   184
UY235   45

V24   11, 12, 36, 38, 133, 143, 200
V99   18
V453   194
V914   84
VCL11   73, 229
VEL11   73, 229
VHT4   89, 90, 214
VMP4K   97
VMS4   96, 97, 151, 152
V04   91
VP4   63
VP4A   151
VP4B   151
VP41   194, 215
VP61   194
VPU1   215
VR53   186
VR55   186
VR91   107
VR92   141
VS24   97
VS24K   97
VSG1   205
VT (Moorhead), 27
VT1   13, 14
VT2   14, 128, 162
VT5   133
VT11   121
VT12   121

VT13C   131
VT32   13, 27
V190   189
VT126   77
VT139   77, 124
VT269   33, 173

W1   217, 218
W2   217, 218
W3   217, 218
W30   96, 97
W81   158
WD11   18, 20, 23, 148, 162, 197, 235
WD12   18, 20, 23, 148, 147, 162
WD40   87
Wecovalve A&B   223
WR1   217
WR2   217
WR3   217
WR21   11, 20, 21, 147, 148
WR21A   20
WR21D   20
Wunderlich   83, 170, 171
WX12   18, 21

X41   93
X65M   188
X78   93
X79   93, 188
X81   95, 158
X99   18
X199   176

Y61   124, 125
Y63   124, 125
Y64   125
Y65   124, 125

Z1   131, 132
Z2A & ZIIA   131, 132
Z2B & ZIIB   131, 132
Z3   132
Z77   140

Numerical

0Z3   114
0Z4   114, 115, 206
0Z4G   114, 115
01B   184
01C   184
054V (Mullard), 51
071 (Arcturus), 168
071A   "   171
071H   "   171
099   "   170
1A4   40
1A4P   40
1A4T   40
1A5G   103, 104
1A6   61, 89
1A7G   103
1AC5   138
1AD6   138
1B4   61
1B4/951   40, 61
1C5G   103
1C6   89

1D5   205
1E7G   61
1E8   138
1F4   61, 102
1F5G   102
1F6   84
1G6G   78
1H5G   103, 104
1K6   189
1LA6   107
1LG6   234
1N5G   103
1Q5GT   72
1R5   92, 138
1S2   141
1T4   138
1T5GT   72
1T6   138
1V   118, 171
1X2B   141
2A3   21, 202, 239
2A3H   53, 239
2A5   59, 63, 188
2A6   171
2A7   88, 89, 153
2B6   79, 153, 171
2B7   84, 243
2D2   84
2D4A   84, 215
2D4B   84, 164
2D13   84
2D41   215
2E5   124
2G5   124
2HF   76
3D-HH13   142
3NF   76
3NFB   75, 76
3Q5GT   72, 74, 75
5E225   55, 192
5E415   192
5U4G   111, 120
5U4GB   104, 111, 236
5V4G   116
5VCX   33
5X4G   111
5Y3G   111, 120
5Y3GT   111
5Y4G   111
5Z4   97, 98
6A3   239
6A4/LA   171
6A5G   53, 239
6A6   78, 153
6A7   89, 101
6A7S   186
6A8   89, 98
6A8G   89
6A8GT   89
6A8MG   99
6AB5   123
6AB6G   81
6AB7   98
6AC5   137
6AC5G   238
6AC6G   81
6AC7   98
6AD4   138

6AD6G	124, 125	6P3C	253	25A7G	81
6AD7G	81	6P8G	106	25L6G	72
6AE8	93, 188	6P6	188	25N6G	81
6AF6	124, 125	6Q7	153	25Z5	118
6AK5	139, 154	6Q7G	253	25Z6	118
6AL5	84, 86	6SA7	92, 98	25Z6G	118
6AL7GT	124	6SB7	92	26	171
6AQ5	72, 138	6SC7 6SF5	98, 153	27	100, 170, 174
6AR7GT	189	6SH7	98	29	84, 85
6AT6	138, 139	6SJ7	98	30	77
6AY3	154	6SK7	98	31	59
6B4G	239	6SL7GT	104	32	61
6B5	79, 81	6SN7GT	78, 104, 153	32L7GT	81
6B6M	186	6SN7GTB	104	33	56, 59, 78
6B7	84, 153	6SQ7	98	34	61, 63
6BA6	138	6SQ7GT	236	35	174
6BA7	92	6T5	124, 170	35/51	67
6BC7	87	6U5	123, 124, 125	35L6GT	253
6BE6	138	6U5G	124	35Z3	119
6BF5	138	6U7G	102	35Z4GT	119
6BQ6	152	6V6	71, 72	35Z5GT	119
6C4	137, 154	6V6G	71, 72, 73	36A	170
6C5	98	6V6GT	71, 236	37	118
6C8G	78	6X4	117, 138	37A	170
6C9	95	6X5	117, 118	38	57, 59, 153
6C10	95	6X5G	118	38A	170
6CW4	142	6Z4	118	39	57
6D2	215	7A3	63	39/44	57, 153
6D5	98	7A8	91	39A	170
6D6	102	7AG7	234	41STH	93
6DS4	142	7B8	89	42	57, 59, 63, 79, 153
6E5	123	7C5	72	42/42E	206
6F5	123, 124	7D3	205	42MP/Pen	63
6E8	100	7D6	205	42S	186
6EB6	92	7F8	78	43	63
6F32	194	7J7	95	44	57
6F5	98, 153	7S7	95	45	78, 170, 175
6F6	97, 98	7Y4	116	45Z5GT	119
6F6G	72	8A1	63, 205	46	69, 70, 170, 173, 238
6F7	81, 89, 91	8D2	205	47	59, 69, 78, 174
6FG6	72	8D3	207	47/47E	206
6G5	123, 124	8D5	207	49	70
6G6G	71	9A1	63, 205	50L6GT	105
6H5	123	9D2	205	50Y6GT	119
6H6	82, 98, 99	9D6	207	51	100
6H6G	82	11D3	205	52	70
6H8C	244	12A5	59	53	78, 153
6J6	137, 154	12A6	206	55	83, 170
6J7	98, 153	12A7	81	56	170, 173, 253
6J8G	93	12AT7	78	56S	185
6K3	101	12AU7	78, 139, 154	57	57, 170, 173, 188, 189, 248
6K4	138	12AX7	78, 139, 154	58	57, 153, 170, 173, 189, 248
6K7	98, 101	12B8GT	81	58AS	185
6K7GT	189, 253	12CJ5	154	58S	180
6K7M	186	12K5	139	59	57, 59, 61, 153, 170, 175
6K7MG	99	12SJ7	206	70	85
6K8	91, 93	12SK7	206	71A	59, 175, 178
6K8GT	189	12SR7	206	75M	186
6L6	71, 72, 240, 242	12Z3	118	78/78E	206
6L6G	71, 73	14	174	79	78
6L6GC	71, 104	15	61, 88, 89	80	111, 115, 116, 117, 120, 188, 189
6L7	91, 98	17	174	80S	117
6M1	124	18	171	81	111, 116, 171
6ME10	126	19	19, 77, 78	82	115, 171, 173
6N5	123	20	165, 239	83	115, 116, 170
6N6G	79, 81, 238	22	171	83V	116
6N6MG	81	24	66, 100, 174	84	118, 171
6N7	78	24A	65, 66, 67	84S	185

263